REGIONS OF THE BRITISH ISLES
EDITED BY W. G. EAST M.A.

THE EAST MIDLANDS
AND THE PEAK

LIST OF TITLES

SOUTHEAST ENGLAND	S. W. Wooldridge, C.B.E. D.Sc. F.R.S.
WESSEX	R. A. Pelham, M.A. Ph.D.
SOUTHWEST ENGLAND	A. H. Shorter, M.A. Ph.D. F.S.A. W. L. D. Ravenhill, M.A. Ph.D.
THE BRISTOL REGION	F. Walker, M.A.
THE EASTERN LOWLANDS OF ENGLAND	B. T. Bunting, M.A. P. G. Hall, M.A. Ph.D.
THE EAST MIDLANDS AND THE PEAK	G. Dury, M.A. Ph.D. F.G.S.
THE WEST MIDLANDS	R. H. Kinvig, M.A. M. J. Wise, M.C. B.A. Ph.D.
LANCASHIRE, CHESHIRE, AND THE ISLE OF MAN	T. W. Freeman, M.A. H. B. Rodgers, M.A.
YORKSHIRE	W. G. East, M.A. H. C. K. Henderson, M.A. B.Sc. Ph.D.
NORTH ENGLAND	A. E. Smailes, M.A.
WALES	E. G. Bowen, M.A.
SOUTHERN SCOTLAND	A. C. O'Dell, M.Sc.
THE HIGHLANDS AND ISLANDS OF SCOTLAND	A. C. O'Dell, M.Sc. K. Walton, M.A. Ph.D.
IRELAND	J. P. Haughton, M.A. M.Sc.

REGIONS OF THE BRITISH ISLES

EDITED BY W. G. EAST M.A.

The East Midlands
and the Peak

G. H. DURY M.A., Ph.D., F.G.S.

Professor of Geography, University of Sydney

THOMAS NELSON AND SONS LTD

LONDON AND EDINBURGH

THOMAS NELSON AND SONS LTD
Parkside Works Edinburgh 9
36 Park Street London W1
117 Latrobe Street Melbourne C1

THOMAS NELSON AND SONS (AFRICA) (Pty) LTD
P.O. Box 9881 Johannesburg

THOMAS NELSON AND SONS (CANADA) LTD
91–93 Wellington Street West   Toronto 1

THOMAS NELSON AND SONS
18 East 41st Street New York 17, N.Y.

SOCIÉTÉ FRANÇAISE D'ÉDITIONS NELSON
97 rue Monge Paris 5

Printed in Great Britain by Thomas Nelson and Sons Ltd, Edinburgh

CONTENTS

1 Introduction   1

PART I   THE PHYSICAL SETTING

2 Geological Basis   4
3 Form of the Ground   18
4 Climate, Weather, and Water Supply   43
5 Soils and Vegetation   62

PART II   DEVELOPMENTS UP TO 1800

6 Peopling, Settlement, and Economy   74
7 Fabric and Form of Rural Settlement   101
8 Agriculture and Industry in 1800   124

PART III   THE NINETEENTH AND TWENTIETH CENTURIES

9   Farming, Hosiery, Leather   144
10 Transport, Extractive Industries, Engineering   166
11 Regional Population and Growth of Towns   187
12 Conclusion   224
    Tables   230
    References   279
    Index   293

TABLES

1	Stratigraphical succession of the Carboniferous Limestone	230
2	Grits of the Millstone Grit Series	231
3	Lithological subdivisions of the Permo-Trias	231
4	Charnian rocks of Charnwood Forest	231
5	Summary of the Jurassic succession	232
6	Succession in the Northamptonshire Ironstone Field	233
7	Succession in the Inferior and Great Oolite Series	233
8	Correlation of Pleistocene sequences	234-5
9	Temperature data ; length of growing season	236
10	Temperature/height gradients	237
11	Absolute maximum and minimum temperatures	237
12	Ground frost	237
13	Bright sunshine	238
14	Rain-days	238
15	Lying snow	238
16	Thunder	238
17	Stations supplying data on precipitation ; percentages falling in summer half-year	239
18	Standardised and other values of precipitation	240
19	Standardised monthly means of precipitation	241
20	Precipitation and runoff	241
21	Precipitation, runoff, water loss, and soil-moisture	242
22	Potential evapotranspiration	241
23	Soils in the southwest of the region	243
24	Soils near Ivinghoe	244-5
25	Estimated populations of counties 1086–1570	246
26	Estimated populations of towns 1086–ca. 1700	247
27	First known appearance of selected place-name elements	248
28	Frequency distribution of selected place-name elements	249
29	Medieval religious houses	249
30	Estimated ratio of urban to rural populations 1086 and 1377	250
31	Prosperity indices 1341–1693	250
32	Rates of population increase 1377–1801	251
33	Cropping ratios 1363–1588	251
34	Estimated populations of counties 1570–1781 and census totals for 1801	252

35 Comparative growths of agricultural and industrial populations
      1674–1801   252
36 Examples of rural domestic architecture   253-4
37 Land use for six counties in the early nineteenth century   254
38 Totals of knitting frames 1660–1845   255
39 Iron furnaces in Derbyshire in 1806   255
40 Land use (all land) by counties 1866–1958   256-7
41 Land use (farmland) by counties 1866–1958   258-9
42 Distribution of region among categories of land use 1866–1958   262
43 Cattle and sheep 1866–1958   260-1
44 Land-use data for Bedfordshire in the 1940s   262
45 Land-use and livestock changes in the southeast 1931–1951   263
46 Land-use data for sample areas 1870, 1913, 1932, 1958   264-5
47 Parishes used as sample areas in Table 46   266
48 Footwear manufacturers in Northamptonshire 1847–1877   266
49 Coal production 1808–1959   267
50 Output of pig iron 1720–1916   268
51 Output of pig iron 1913–1960   269
52 Blast furnaces existing in selected years   269
53 Opening and closing dates of blast-furnace plants   270
54 Extraction of iron ore 1855–1960   271
55 Output of crude steel 1937–1960   272
56 Reserves and prospects of the Jurassic orefields   272
57 Distribution of population among categories of density 1801   272
58 Distribution of population among categories of density 1851   273
59 Distribution of population among categories of density 1901   273
60 Distribution of population among categories of density 1951   273
61 Percentage distribution of population among categories of density 274
62 Distribution of workers among categories of employment   276-7
63 Populations of selected towns 1801–1961   275

LIST OF ILLUSTRATIONS

FIGURES

1	Solid geology	5
2	Geological profiles	6
3	Correlation of coal seams	8
4	Bouguer anomalies	10
5	Possible correlation of the permo-Trias	11
6	Geological profile along the Jurassic cuesta	14
7	Geological profile east of Oxford	16
8	Relief	20
9	Drainage	21
10	Morphology	22
11	Subdivisions of terrain	23
12	Elements in landform evolution	24
13	Erosional facets	33
14	Glacial advances in the Trent and Avon basins	35
15	Glacial and associated deposits	39
16	Mean monthly temperatures	44
17	Régime of temperature range	44
18	Dispersion diagram of temperatures at Northampton	46
19	Isohyets	49
20	Graphs of standardised mean monthly rainfall	52
21	Dispersion diagrams for standardised rainfall	53–5
22	Precipitation and runoff for the River Derwent	56
23	Precipitation and runoff for the upper Nene	56
24	Precipitation and runoff for the Nene at Orton	56
25	Precipitation and evapotranspiration for Buxton	57
26	Water balances for the upper Nene	57
27	The Derwent Valley Water Scheme	58
28	Water supply in the Ouse valley	60
29	Land-use in the late eighteenth century	68
30	Comparison of solid geology with parent material of soils	71
31	Geography of Roman times	77
32	Domesday settlements	82
33	Recorded Domesday population	83
34	Sites of depopulation	92
35	Distribution of elements in rural domestic architecture	103

36 Location map, form, and pattern of rural settlement   112

37 Forms of rural settlement   114

38 Form of the village of Hellidon   116-17

39 Pattern of settlement in the eighteenth century—an example from
    Northamptonshire   119

40 Pattern of settlement in the eighteenth century—an example from
    the Peak District   120

41 Pattern of settlement in the eighteenth century—an example from
    Leicestershire   121

42 The same part of Leicestershire in the mid-nineteenth century   122

43 Mining in the north of the region in the early 1800s   138

44 Ferrous metal-working in the north of the region in the early
    1800s   139

45 Trends in land-use 1866–1958   147

46 Land-use in selected years, by counties   148

47 Trends in livestock totals   149

48 Farming combinations of the late 1930s   151

49 Distribution of cattle in 1958   154

50 Distribution of sheep in 1958   155

51 Land-use in 1958, by advisory areas   156

52 Land-use trends for blocks of parishes   158

53 Distribution of knitting frames, mid-nineteenth century   160

54 Elements of industrial geography about 1850   162

55 Graph of trends in coal output   170

56 Collieries active in 1829   172

57 Collieries active 1869–1905   172

58 Collieries active in 1925   172

59 Collieries active in 1939   173

60 Collieries active in 1959, classed by numbers of employees   173

61 Collieries active in 1959, classed by output   173

62 Comparison of coalfields, by tonnage   176

63 Comparison of coalfields, by percentages of national output   177

64 Elements of industrial geography 1960   178

65 Graph of trends in pig-iron production   179

66 Graph of trends in iron-ore production   181

67 Distribution of population 1801   188

68 Distribution of population 1851   189

69 Distribution of population 1901   190

70 Distribution of population 1951   191

71 Density of population 1801   192

72 Density of population 1851   193

73	Density of population 1901	194
74	Density of population 1951	195
75	Population change 1801–1851	196
76	Population change 1851–1901	197
77	Population change 1901–1951	198
78	Population change 1851–1951	199
79	Population change 1801–1951	200
80	Population change 1951–1961 (numbers)	201
81	Population change 1951–1961 (density)	202
82	Percentage changes in rural populations	205
83	Employment, by counties	208
84	Growth of selected towns	210
85	The railway net	212
86	Accessibility of towns by bus	213
87	Ranking of towns by population total	214
88	Possible regrouping of urban hinterlands	215
89	Buckingham in the eighteenth century	217
90	Buckingham in the mid-twentieth century	217
91	Morphology of Chesterfield	219
92	Extension of Nottingham	220
93	Administrative subdivision	226

PLATES

The Plates will be found at the end of the book.

1   Kinderscout in winter
2   Upper Derwent valley
3   Deepdale
4   Abbey Bank
5   Charnwood Forest
6   River Trent
7   Scarp near Long Clawson
8   View from Sharpenhoe Clapper
9   Dry valley south of Barton in the Clay
10 Trent in flood
11 Olney mill
12 Ladybower Reservoir
13 Hill fort, Burrough Hill
14 The Fosse Way

15 Buckworth, Hunts.

16 Warden Abbey

17 Ridge and furrow, Byfield

18 Alconbury, Hunts.

19 Cottages at Bakewell

20 Pantiles and brick at Lound

21 Houses at Wansford

22 Houses at Sharnbrook

23 Stonework at Filkins

24 Thatch at Ramsey

25 House at Everton

26 Houses at Winwick

27 Farm at Stagsden

28 Green at Caddington

29 Haddon Hall

30 Aynho

31 Blenheim

32 Belvoir

33 Panorama near Burrough on the Hill

34 Market gardening near Melbourne

35 Combine harvester near Newnham

36 Spray irrigation near Cucksey

37 Ollerton colliery

38 Opencast working near Kerby Hall

39 Limestone quarrying near Buxton

40 Thame

41 Speed's Chart of Huntingdon

42 Oxford

43 Bedford

44 Centre of Nottingham

45 Terrace housing, Nottingham

46 Nottingham housing estate

47 Staythorpe power station

48 London-Birmingham motorway

COLOUR MAP

A full-colour map of the East Midlands and the Peak District will
be found at the end of the book, arranged to open out so that it
can be consulted simultaneously with the text.

xi

ACKNOWLEDGMENTS

The author wishes to record a manifold debt to many individuals and to many organisations for informed criticism, for helpful counsel, and for the generous supply of material both printed and manuscript. Certain public bodies have been especially helpful : among these, the Ministry of Agriculture provided statistics of land-use, and the Trent River Board through its Chief Engineer, Mr Marshall Nixon, supplied the rainfall data analysed in Chapter 4. Professor H. C. Darby and Dr J. T. Coppock gave access to certain texts in advance of publication, while Mr B. T. Bunting kindly made available the results of his studies in the Peak District. The work of the Nottingham school of Geography, especially that published in the *East Midland Geographer*, has proved most useful in numerous contexts, as also has the advice of Dr T. J. Chandler on the Leicester area. Among the several libraries used, that of the Institute of Historical Research, University of London, was particularly valuable.

The author also wishes to acknowledge the kindness of the following in giving permission for the reproduction of illustrations :

Aerofilms Ltd. (Plates 10, 17, 30, 31, 39, 40, 42, 43, 44, 45, 46, 47, 48) ; Ashley, Hallam Ltd. (Plates 3, 19, 29) ; the Derwent Valley Water Board (Plate 12) ; Eric G. Meadows (Plates 8, 11, 27) ; Dr St Joseph (Plates 5, 7, 9, 13, 14, 15, 16, 18, 32, 33, 34, 38) ; the Southern Literary Agency (Plate 35) ; W. Woods (Plates 1, 4).

Figures 8, 9, 30, 31, 37, 38, 86, 90, 91, 93 are based upon Ordnance Survey maps, and Figures 1 and 15 on Geological Survey maps. In all cases this is by permission of the Controller of H.M. Stationery Office, and Crown Copyright is reserved.

INTRODUCTION

THE area described in this book does not constitute a geographical region. No discussion of the unsatisfactory topic of regional grouping and regional boundaries is required to demonstrate lack of regional cohesiveness. On the other hand, since the series to which this book belongs is meant to deal with the whole of Britain, some kind of partition is necessary. An arguable case exists for placing Derby, Nottingham, Leicester, and Northampton in a single group ; when the counties go with the towns, the region comes to include the Peak District. There can be no point in detaching Rutland from Leicestershire, or the Soke of Peterborough from Northamptonshire ; and once Northamptonshire is included, Huntingdonshire and Bedfordshire introduce themselves, if merely in contrast to the fens adjacent on the east. By a reasonable process of extension, much of Buckinghamshire and most of Oxfordshire are also added, but the chosen boundary excludes the Chilterns. Because the boundary runs along the Chiltern crest, two Hertfordshire parishes have been included immediately northwest of Tring. Oxfordshire, possessing in its Cotswold portion strong affinities with Gloucestershire, cannot well be styled East Midland ; but a title designed to be fully descriptive, and responsive to the local consciousness of dwellers in all parts of the area, would be impossibly cumbrous.

County boundaries offer high convenience in statistical description, although they have naturally been replaced by closer networks for particular purposes. It is not proposed to compare the area here described with areas, for example, of census groupings, of planning, or of public-utility service : exercises of this type seem to lead no great distance and in no clear direction. But it would be a sad omission not to mention that estimable journal the *East Midland Geographer*, founded and published by the Department of Geography at the University of Nottingham, and drawing heavily on that Department for contributions. The following text and its bibliography signalise numerous debts to writers in the *East Midland Geographer*, without whom the present author's task would have been far longer and far more arduous than it has proved. Now, although K. C. Edwards observes in that very journal that the East Midlands possesses little regional consciousness, the East Midland concept indubitably has some kind of force. The coverage of papers in *E.M.G.* inevitably reflects in part the range of field study performed with Nottingham as a university base. The journal is not only published in the East Midlands; it is explicitly concerned with them. Its scope suggests that Nottinghamshire, southern Derbyshire, Leicestershire, Rutland, Northamptonshire, and parts of Lincolnshire seem East Midland when regarded from Nottingham.

As in the present book, so in the *E.M.G.*, the whole of the exposed coalfield in Derbyshire forcibly associates itself with the concealed coalfield of Nottinghamshire, bringing the practical limits of regional discussion within sight of Sheffield. Little difficulty arises here, however. Chesterfield is fortunately distinct from Sheffield in a number of respects, and a regional boundary may pass between the two. The High Peak belongs with upland Derbyshire generally, if only for the sake of its contribution to denudation chronology; but the small industrial towns and the patchy little outcrops of Coal Measures in the northwest of the county belong geographically with Lancashire.

It is in the southeast that arise some of the most stimulating problems of boundary drawing. Luton, Bedford, and Aylesbury are in some senses metropolitan—large and fast-growing outer satellites of London; and now that metropolitan England is spreading well beyond the London Basin the convenient physical boundary of the Chiltern crest promises to lose much of its relevance to subdivision.

Because the mechanism of geographical influence is little understood, the following chapters offer statement rather than explanation. For example, the east of the region is drier than the west, and persistently records the higher fraction of land in tillage; but responses of farming to climate have been anything but direct and uncomplicated for at least two hundred years, and much of the region's farmland is in fact readily convertible. It seems pointless to inquire what might have happened if industries had taken other lines; but the industrial scene at any given time, including the present, represents in fact the outcome not only of trial and error but also of individual or corporate success through inspiration or failure through unwisdom. What actually happened in many a crisis of decision must remain unsaid.

In respect of tabulation and analysis of data, this book falls into the class of description by inventory. If justification for the chosen form is required, surely it is provided by such works as Farey's account of Derbyshire and by the Domesday survey. Arrangement varies little from the traditional: a statement of the physical background precedes a sequential account of the developments which have produced the distributions of the present day. Breaks occur in the running story from time to time, to permit conditions at a particular time to be synoptically reviewed. Since few references to source material appear in the main text, the bibliography must stand as the principal acknowledgment to previous writers ; all works drawn upon are there included.

CHAPTER 2

GEOLOGICAL BASIS

OUTCROPS of crystalline and pyroclastic rocks are very limited in the East Midland region, being confined to the lavas, tuffs, agglomerates, and mineral veins of the Peak District, and to the petrologically varied rocks of Charnwood Forest, Mountsorrel, and the Croft-Enderby neighbourhood. Sedimentary units range from Carboniferous upwards; Pleistocene and Recent deposits are very widespread, but the youngest solid formations belong to the Cretaceous (Fig. 1).

Although the upraised South Pennines can be regarded as an oldland, with the Permo-Trias excavated to form an inner vale, and with successive Jurassic and Cretaceous formations producing a series of vales and cuestas, this is emphatically not a region of simple uniclinal structure. Throughout the sedimentary succession, lateral variations in thickness and in lithology are pronounced. Sedimentation occurred on shelves, on slopes, in fault angles, and in dimpling basins separated by positive areas of thin deposition, no deposition, or actual erosion. Topographical prominences correspond generally to sites where arenaceous or calcareous sediments accumulated in bulk, and became more or less firmly cemented, although certain thin bands of resistant rock are feature-forming where they occur amid thick clays and marls. Because of lateral change, detailed lateral correlation is possible only with the aid of classifications beyond the scope of the present account. Attention will here be limited to changes which strongly influence relief or are significant in economic geology. Sedimentation was subject to the control of movements in the basement rocks; but much in this connection remains obscure. The exposed parts of the basement, and the results of geophysical survey, give but a sketchy indication of the tectonic activity which undoubtedly occurred during the deposition of the rocks now exposed.

In Carboniferous times the Pennine division of the region was the site of thick sedimentation in a subsiding cuvette. A rigid block, composed at least in part of pre-Cambrian rocks and underlying the Derbyshire Dome, strongly affected the local mode of sedimentation. Limestones which formed in the clear, rather shallow water above the block are those of the massif or standard facies—finely fragmental, thickly bedded or massive, and with minimal shale partings. Round the margins of the block appear limestones of the reef facies, for example in the Castleton District and in the Manifold Valley and west

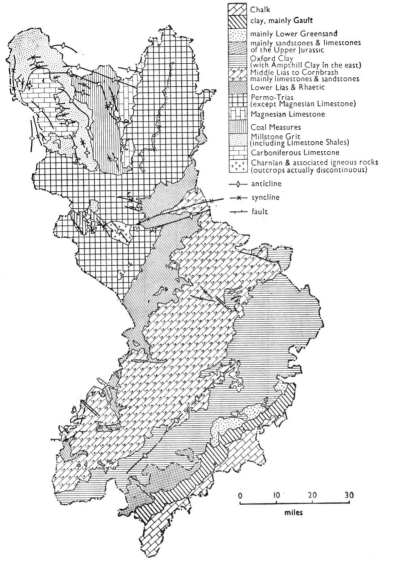

0   10   20   30
miles

Fig. 1   SUMMARY DISTRIBUTIONS OF SOLID GEOLOGY.

Derbyshire, where thick shelly lenses withstand erosion and form hills. In the north of Staffordshire, and north of Castleton, the rocks belong to the basin facies. The sequence here is much thicker than above the block, for considerable bulks of shale lie interbedded with the generally thin limestones. The very sharp borders of the massif indicate faulting, as in the Craven District of Yorkshire.

Contemporary earth movements are expressed in erosion and

5

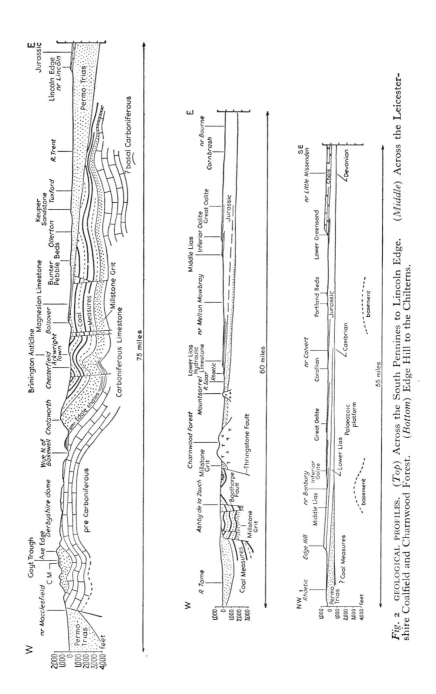

Fig. 2 GEOLOGICAL PROFILES. (Top) Across the South Pennines to Lincoln Edge. (Middle) Across the Leicester-shire Coalfield and Charnwood Forest. (Bottom) Edge Hill to the Chilterns.

6

unconformity (Table 1). They were accompanied by igneous activity, producing lavas, tuffs, and agglomerates ; olivine-basalts (toadstones) occur on many horizons. Exposures of lavas and tuffs are concentrated in two roughly triangular districts, marked respectively by Castleton, Buxton, and Bakewell, and by Wirksworth, Winster, and Matlock. Tuff and agglomerate lie in old vents at Grangemill and Calton Hill. Contemporary volcanics occur in a similar tectonic setting, in Carboniferous Limestone of the massif facies, beneath Eakring. The age of the Derbyshire ore veins is still in doubt. Except at Millclose Mine in the Stanton syncline, the ores are concentrated in anticlines, and even at Millclose the only rich deposits are concentrated on the up-dip side. The chief ores are those of lead and zinc : galena, cerrusite, blende, and calamine. Some of the deposits are locally argentiferous, silver having been recoverable as a by-product. Locally, too, the ores are associated with ochre and with black oxide of manganese. Veins run westward from the eastern outcrop boundary of the Carboniferous Limestone. Gangue minerals consist of fluorite in the east, barytes and fluorite farther west, and calcite alone in the extreme west.

The total thickness of the Millstone Grit Series (Table 2) is about 1,600 feet. Precise thicknesses are difficult to give since the Series varies rapidly in thickness and also in facies. On the east flank of the Pennines it thins away towards the south and east (Fig. 2). The black carbonaceous Edale Shales at the base are 700 feet thick at Mam Tor, where they overlap unconformably on to the Carboniferous Limestone ; it is in the Peak District, too, that the arkosic Kinderscout Grit Group attains its maximum thickness of about 1,500 feet, including up to 500 feet of thick-bedded coarse sandstone. The Chatsworth Grit is mainly fine-grained and massive, but thickens and becomes pebbly around Chatsworth itself. The coarse and distinctly arkosic Rough Rock Grit is conventionally taken as the uppermost member of the Millstone Grit Series, but is not distinguished lithologically from the conformably following rocks at the bottom of the Coal Measure succession.

Originating as deltaic sediments, the Millstone Grit is disposed in lenses or leaves. It displays repeated sedimentary rhythms, lateral variations notwithstanding. Rhythmic sedimentation is also well developed in the Coal Measures. A full rhythm of coal, mudstone, siltstone/sandstone/grit, and fireclay/ganister may be 100 feet thick, although 30 feet is a rough average for the Derby and Nottinghamshire coalfield. The Productive (Lower and Middle) Measures reach a thickness of 3,000 or even 4,000 feet on the east of the Pennines, while the unproductive Upper Coal Measures consisting largely of red beds, may be as thick as 600 feet. Twenty-five seams of coal occur in the full sequence beneath the Permo-Trias (Fig. 3), although those above the Top Hard are mostly thin and impersistent. The chief working seams are those from the Top Hard downwards, the best-developed of all being the Main Coal of Leicestershire and the Deep Soft and Deep Hard coals of Derby and Nottinghamshire. The close-set seams from

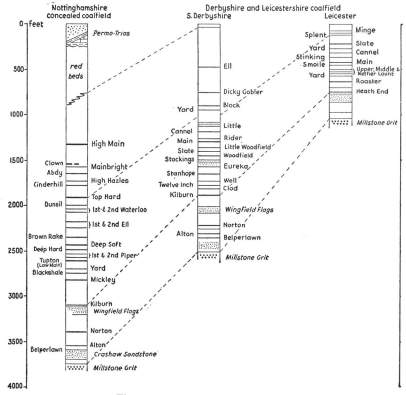

Fig. 3 CORRELATION OF COAL SEAMS.

the Deep Soft downwards outcrop, or lie at modest depths, along the faulted and eroded Erewash valley anticline, enabling the valley to be a working coalfield within a coalfield.

Coal-Measure sedimentation in the South Pennine area was thickest at a basin centre which lay between the sites of Sheffield and Manchester. Southwards and eastwards from this centre the total thickness of the Coal Measures lessens, quite independently of the effects of later erosion. Round the margins of the basin, contemporaneous movements were strong enough to condense the sequence or even to provoke removal. A thickness of 3,000 feet in the concealed coalfield of Derby and Nottinghamshire is reduced to 2,500 feet in south Derbyshire, and a further rapid reduction to about 1,250 feet occurs between the south Derbyshire and the Leicestershire parts of the southern coalfield (Fig. 3). Subsidence of the Coal-Measure basin (probably a main cuvette with marginal extensions) was accompanied in places by elevation of parts of the rim, perhaps mainly along lines of faulting. The Permo-Trias rests unconformably on the Coal Measures, testifying to deformation and erosion in Carbo-Permian times (Fig. 2). The attitudes of flanking Jurassic and Cretaceous rocks indicate renewed uplift in Secondary, and doubtless also in early Tertiary, times. Since no Tertiary outcrops occur close at hand, uplift continuing well into the Tertiary cannot be proved, although it can be suspected. Occasional slight earthquakes show that certain structures in the basement are still active. However, the main folding of the Carboniferous rocks, inevitably accompanied by erosion, preceded the deposition of the basal Permo-Trias.

Doming of the Carboniferous rocks in the South Pennines involved wholesale uplift—the general rise, with little or no tilt, of the rigid block. Since the ore bodies of Derbyshire fail to penetrate the Millstone Grit, they cannot be directly related to late Carboniferous or Carbo-Permian events ; but since the upper limits of the ores appear to be set by sealing cover-rocks rather than by unconformity, it is at least possible that the bodies were emplaced at the end of Carboniferous times. If so, they are likely to be associated with some large igneous mass beneath the rigid block. It is not easy to explain the association of the uplifted block with concentric folds round the margins (Fig. 1). These folds are either offset or variable in amplitude along their lengths. Upfolding is best exemplified in the inliers of Ashover and Crich, which are rather complexly interrelated by structural saddles and by faults. The long sinuous concentric fold-axes run southeastwards into the south of the exposed coalfield. Around Matlock, and again along the northwest rim of the coalfield, they are associated with, or superseded by, pitching folds running roughly west–east. Folds of this second group are responsible for preserving down-bent rocks of the Millstone Grit Series on the west side of the Derwent valley, and for scalloping the northwest boundary of the exposed coalfield. Farther east, the concealed Carboniferous rocks of the Eakring district are raised in a group of domes (Fig. 2).

No such structural complexities affect the Permo-Trias, which is however far less simple than the usual lithological subdivision implies (Table 3). R. L. Sherlock has convincingly shown that many lateral changes are due to alteration of facies rather than to wedging. Two main cuvettes were the sites of thick deposition, one centred beneath the Vale of Belvoir, the other beneath the Trent valley from Newark

9

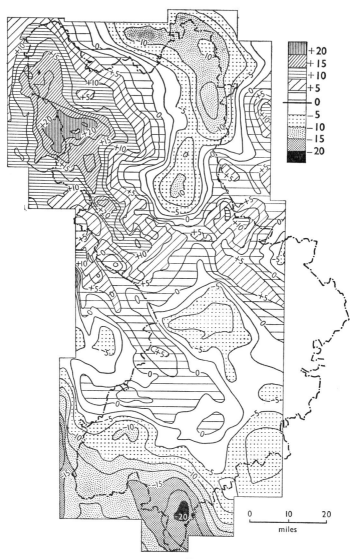

Fig. 4 RESULTS OF GEOPHYSICAL SURVEY : Bouguer anomalies, interval 2·5 milligals.

downstream. Both are well brought out by low Bouguer values on the
map of gravity anomalies (Fig. 4). Sedimentation opened with the
spreading of piedmont breccia and gravel on a desert plain, continued
with marls and limestones of the Zechstein Sea, and was completed
with pebbles, sands, and evaporites thickly laid down on a land surface.
In the absence of fossils, classification by facies is as valid as classification by apparent vertical succession. A somewhat extreme view of
correlation in the main cuvette is presented in Figure 5, where the

datum plane is the present land surface. Except on the east of the Pennines, where the customary lithological sequence can be traced down-dip, the Permo-Trias is represented at the surface mainly by Keuper Marl, in which lenses of sandstone occur at various horizons.

Permo-Triassic outliers occur in ancient sinkholes in the Carboniferous Limestone of Derbyshire and North Staffordshire. Some of the holes are 600 feet across, and unbottomed at depths of 500 feet. As the fills are considerably disturbed by slumping it is impossible to gauge their original height relative to the enclosing limestone. P. E. Kent takes dolomitisation of the limestone in mid-Derbyshire as possible

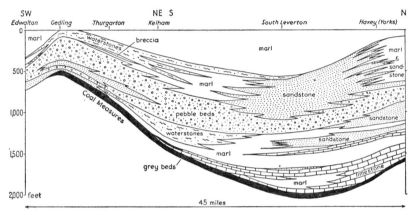

Fig. 5 A POSSIBLE CORRELATION OF THE PERMO-TRIAS beneath the Lower Trent, based on facies change.

evidence for transgression by Zechstein Sea on to the margins of the rigid block, west of the present limit of the Magnesian Limestone. In and around Charnwood Forest a group of former inselbergs located near the margins of the south Nottinghamshire cuvette is being exhumed. The exposed Charnian rocks consist of volcanics and pyroclastics, accompanied by some ordinary sediments, and traversed by intrusions (Table 4). They are raised in an elliptical dome much broken by faults. Natural sand-blasts have pitted the rock on the outlying inselberg of Mountsorrel, where the granodiorite is coarse-grained and homogeneous ; wadi sections occur in Charnwood Forest and at Enderby. The folded and eroded Coal Measures west of Charnwood Forest are cut by a powerful fault, or series of faults, which formed one of the scarped edges of the ramifying cuvette of Lancashire-Cheshire.

The south and southeast margins of the Permo-Triassic cuvettes developed desert landscapes appropriate to range-and-basin structure, for earth movements continued during sedimentation. In some places previously deposited Coal Measures were eroded. Deposits formed in late Coal-Measure times were mainly red beds thinning across the margins of a stable or gently rising massif. This massif has been variously called the London-Ardennes Island, the London Platform, and the Oxfordshire Shallows. In part it is mantled with Lower Palaeozoic sediments, which in places reach aggregate thicknesses far greater than those of overlying Carboniferous, Permo-Triassic, Jurassic, and Cretaceous rocks (Fig. 2). In some districts, however, the surface of the basement rises : at Bletchley it is only 160 feet below sea level. Early assumptions that the eroded surface of Lower Palaeozoic and older rocks is gently and uniformly down-warped to the northwest, or that the pre-Cambrian basement is uplifted along continuous axes striking northwest–southeast, are falsified by recent geophysical survey (Fig. 4). The pattern of gravity anomalies suggests rising blocks and subsiding basins rather than the repeated movement of long Charnoid folds. The belt of high Bouguer which includes the Derbyshire Dome and Charnwood Forest is followed on the southeast by a roughly rectangular patch of low Bouguer ; the belt of high Bouguer which bounds this low on the northeast points directly at the depressed cuvette of south Nottinghamshire. The tectonic conditions indicated for Jurassic times resemble those of the Carboniferous and the Permo-Trias—that is, uneven subsidence of quite small basins, and irregular relative uplift of the areas intervening.

The concealed Trias wedges out quite rapidly towards the southeast. It is absent beneath Wyboston (Bedfordshire), where Lias overlies Old Red Sandstone, Devonian, and Cambrian ; at Calvert, Lower Lias rests directly on Cambrian. In the Banbury area the pre-Cambrian basement probably approaches within 3,000 feet of the surface. Farther west, beneath the North Cotswolds and towards the lower Severn, the deep floor plunges sharply downwards ; the boring at Stowell Park, near Coln St Denis (Gloucestershire), proved the thickest Liassic succession yet known in Britain—nearly 1,700 feet. Keuper Marl sets in here at 1,534 feet below sea level, and Trias is still unbottomed at $-3,943$ feet. This particular cuvette continued to subside from Triassic into Jurassic times. Equally persistent subsidence affected the basin which extends from Oxford southwards, forming an extension of, or at least connecting with, the Hampshire Basin. It is in the Oxford area, where gravity survey records markedly low Bouguer anomalies, that prospects of concealed productive Coal Measures appear best ; seams were proved by borings near Witney in 1960.

The Permo-Trias thickens off the Pennines, but also thickens off the London Platform ; it is somewhere between the Banbury district and the Malverns that signs of deep and persistent (although irregular) subsidence are strongest. The question of relationship of place between Permo-Triassic and Jurassic sedimentation is complicated by the Rhaetic transgression, which brought thin but very widespread marine and lagoonal marls and limestones, and by the later dimpling of the floor of the Jurassic sea ; the main Jurassic sequence is distinctly lenticular. Both in the down-dip direction, and along the strike across the whole region, most Jurassic formations are liable to wedging and to facies change. Data of thickness are meaningless unless they are referred to specific localities (Table 5). Moreover, although in the broad view it is easy to contrast deep infilling of Jurassic basins in Gloucestershire and Lincolnshire with shallower sedimentation through-out the intervening area, individual basins occupied by individual minor formations often fail to accord with the major pattern of relative subsidence.

The Rhaetic consists of black shales below and white limestones above. The limestone member is a potential scarp-former, but is rarely prominent in relief because of heavy dissection and thick overspreading by drift. The succeeding Lower Lias comprises thick clays or shales, with which argillaceous limestones alternate towards the base. The limestones combine with their intercalated shales in the Hydraulic Limestone Series. Cement-works quarries in this Series provide almost all the exposures of Lower Lias within the region ; very little is known of the structure of the whole formation. The outcrop, seven to ten miles wide, swings across the axes of west–east folds in Leicester-shire ; faults are known outside the region, west of Southam in Warwickshire, but elsewhere movement has not been demonstrated. Underground thinning of the Lower Lias towards the southeast is clearly shown by Table 6, which also indicates the effects of thickening across the regional boundaries towards the west and towards the north ; the total thickness at Grantham is 750 feet.

The Middle Lias includes clays and silts in the lower part, and sandy limestones in the upper. The strong upper division, a powerful feature-former, is usually known as the Marlstone ; in some contexts, however, the term Marlstone is used to indicate the iron-bearing rock at the top of the division. Where the Marlstone (in the wider sense) is thickest, it can include more than one bed of limestone ; in west Northamptonshire, for instance, it commonly gives rise to four lines of springs. It is especially massive at Edge Hill, where it is 25 feet thick ; it thins to some 10 feet across the Cherwell valley, and almost vanishes near Market Harborough, but wedges in again towards the Melton Mowbray district, reaching a thickness of 35 feet or more near the Lincolnshire border. The thickening in the Banbury Ironstone

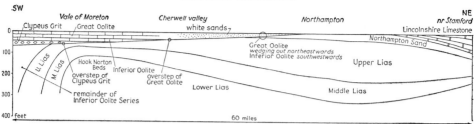

Fig. 6 GEOLOGICAL PROFILE ALONG THE MAIN JURASSIC CUESTA.

Field is due to subsidence of an elliptical basin during deposition ; the northeastward thinning is due partly to non-deposition and partly to erosion. Thick sedimentation around Melton Mowbray results partly from the sagging of the Lincolnshire basin and partly from the development, during sedimentation, of the Melton Mowbray syncline (Fig. 1).

Superficial structures developed during the Pleistocene make the total thickness of undisturbed Upper Lias hard to assess ; however, the formation thins markedly from the Cotswolds towards the Vale of Moreton, where uplift relative to the western basin accompanied, or shortly followed, deposition. Towards the northeast the Upper Lias comes in once again in force (Fig. 6), thickening into the Lincolnshire basin, where 180 feet have been proved at Grantham. The reduction from Northampton to Stamford shown in the diagram is probably the combined effect of irregular subsidence, subsequent erosion, and the general tendency to wedge out down-dip.

In the North Cotswold area, beyond the Vale of Moreton and thus outside the limits of the region, there is a very thick development of the Inferior Oolite, consisting mainly of limestone. At Cleeve Hill the total thickness is about 365 feet, but the base of the formation rises sharply towards the Vale of Moreton, and the lower members are overstepped by the Trigonia and Clypeus Grits, at the base of which the main local unconformity occurs (Fig. 6). The Clypeus Grit and Hook Norton Beds (Inferior Oolite) thin towards the northeast, while the non-sequential Chipping Norton Limestone (Great Oolite) passes in the same direction into the Swerford Beds of the Cherwell Valley and the White Sands of Northamptonshire. The Inferior Oolite succession is reintroduced by the Northampton Sand and the Lincolnshire Limestone. The chief development of the ironstones in the Northampton Sand is concentrated in a basin comparable to that which includes the older ore of Banbury, but the Lincolnshire Limestone thickens away to the north, reaching 75–100 feet in south Lincolnshire.

Variations along the dip allow some lower parts of the Inferior Oolite to be represented in the north of Oxfordshire, where a transition occurs from the dominant limestones of the Cotswolds to the dominant sandstones of Northamptonshire; but since the Inferior Oolite in this area is everywhere thin, and everywhere underlain by Upper Lias, it has been heavily dissected. Beds of the sandstone facies are preserved as far west as the down-faulted Dassett Hills and the parallel northwest-trending Epwell Rift. In the southern part of the Northamptonshire Ironstone Field, along the margins of the Lincolnshire basin, the Lower Estuarine Series appears between the Northampton Sand and the Lincolnshire Limestone; in this Series, as in the Northampton Sand below and the Lincolnshire Limestone above, non-sequence and penecontemporaneous erosion are well demonstrated.

Throughout the combined outcrop of the two Oolite Series, lime-stones at or near the base of the Great Oolite lie very close to limestone or sandstones at the top of the Inferior Oolite; along much of the boundary, strong formations actually adjoin. The two series can be treated as one for most geographical purposes. Summaries of the successions in the northeast and the southwest are given in Tables 6 and 7. Rocks of both Series have been much used for building; in the northeast and in the southwest there occurs a lens of highly fissile limestone which has supplied roofing-slabs—Stonesfield Slate in the middle of the Great Oolite, and Collyweston Slate near the base of the Lincolnshire Limestone. These particular formations serve to re-emphasise the lenticular character, and the liability to lateral change, which typify the whole of the two Series.

The succeeding Cornbrash is as persistent as the Rhaetic. It results from a general transgression, or rather from a double trans-gression, for the upper and lower divisions contrast strongly in fauna. Located chiefly along the base of the main backslope, the thin Corn-brash can scarcely be expected to produce well-marked surface features. Its outcrop pattern, however, reveals a long axis of uplift striking northeastwards in the Ouse and Ray valleys (Fig. 1).

Like the Lower Lias, the Oxford Clay outcrops in a broad belt of low ground. Its full thickness has rarely been penetrated by boreholes, and estimates based on dip and outcrop alone are likely to be mis-leading. There is little to suggest that the maximum greatly exceeds 400 feet anywhere in the region; the widening of the outcrop towards the northeast is a function of lessening dip.

Rocks of Corallian age cross the Thames to enter the region on the outskirts of Oxford. Their basal part is sandy, except where in the re-entrant outcrop southeast of Otmoor they include Arngrove Stone, a sponge reef. The upper part consists of coral-reef limestone, the Coral Rag, at Cowley, but this wedges laterally into bedded limestones, which in turn thin and change towards the northeast, where they are overlain by Ampthill Clay. The boldness of features carved in

Corallian rocks thus decreases away from the Thames, until northeast of Aylesbury the Oxford, Ampthill, and Kimmeridge Clays merge in a broad expanse of weak rocks.

The Kimmeridge Clay, coming in near Wing, is 180 feet thick beneath younger rocks at Cuddesdon. Like the succeeding Portland and Purbeck Beds, it results from deposition near the northern margin of an enlarged Dorset-Hampshire basin. The Portland Beds, composed mainly of sandstone in the lower part and limestone in the upper, cap a scatter of little hills. Three groups of hills are aligned on synclinal axes which run northwestward respectively through Stone,

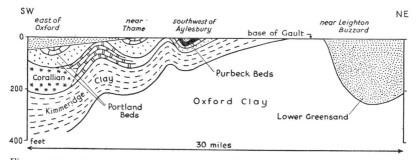

Fig. 7 GEOLOGICAL PROFILE EAST OF OXFORD, illustrating wedging and facies change.

just east of Thame, and between Oxford and Otmoor. West of Thame, between the last two of the three synclines, the Portland Beds are overstepped by Lower Greensand, which rests directly on the Gault, and Lower Greensand overlies Kimmeridge Clay immediately southwest of Oxford. As might be expected of an area of marginal sedimentation, the combination of local earth movements with changes of sea level has produced a varied pattern of outcrops, with signs of erosion following not long after deposition (Fig. 7). The Lower Greensand is itself discontinuous in the extreme south. Its principal development begins on the margin of Bedfordshire, where it rapidly thickens to a total of some 250 feet before thinning more gradually to half that value at Sandy. In this district the formation is composed of sands, mainly ferruginous but of glass-making quality at Leighton Buzzard, which although loosely cemented are resistant by comparison with the Oxford Clay below and the Gault above.

A representative total thickness for the Gault/Upper Greensand in Buckinghamshire is 250 feet. The adjoining Chalk is 700 feet thick or more, but its marly lower part usually merges topographically with the upper part of the Gault in gentle footslopes below the main scarp. Potential formers of sub-scarps occur within the Chalk—Marl Rock about 65 feet above the base, Totternhoe Stone at about 100 feet, ragstone (a rough grey Chalk) at about 130 feet, Melbourn Rock at the bottom of the Middle Chalk and some 180 feet above the base of the Chalk formation, and Chalk Rock at the bottom of the Upper Chalk, about 400 feet above the base of the formation. Chalk Rock caps most of the highest scarp-tops, the succeeding 230 feet of Upper Chalk coming in down-dip on the Chiltern backslope. Eminences based on the resistant beds of Chalk are discontinuous, just as the beds themselves are impersistent or at least variable. The Chalk generally, however, is boldly transgressive, passing across the London Platform from the south. How far it once extended to the northwest is one of the crucial problems of local geomorphology. Extrapolation of the sub-Eocene floor suggests that the eroded Chalk feathered out beneath Tertiary rocks some twenty miles beyond its present outcrop—a value sufficient to extend it as far as Buckingham and to call for severe erosion in the locally unrecorded beginnings of Tertiary time.

CHAPTER 3

FORM OF THE GROUND

RELIEF is strong only in the northwest, where heights exceed 2,000 feet. The remainder of the region consists of far lower ground, where well-dissected broad divides separate the main rivers (Figs. 8, 9). There is little in a small-scale map to show that the drainage of almost the whole region is incised, however shallowly, or that sharp contrasts in the form of the ground can be seen in the field. In any event the casual impression given by most of the region is of small irregular hills, soft in outline and partly obscured by hedges and trees ; there is little really flat land, apart from narrow bands of floodplain, terrace, or scarp crest. Lack of definition is emphasised by the smooth forms developed on glacial deposits, and by the cambering of cap-rocks.

At the same time, close study permits a subdivision of the region according to character of terrain (Figs. 10, 11). The criteria used in constructing these maps are height, amplitude of relief, and surface texture as expressed in assemblages of landforms. Figure 10 itself, and the following account, are intended to be merely descriptive.

Although the scheme presented in Figures 10 and 11 is supported by detailed mapping of parts, and by a thorough ground-check of the whole, it involves the usual difficulties of subdivision of a continuous surface. Furthermore, because the region is poor in area names, the following list is highly artificial. It does not purport to be strictly hierarchical, for some of the units are intermediate in status between *tract* and *stow*.

TERRAINS OF THE EAST MIDLANDS AND THE PEAK

1. The Derbyshire Dome
    1a. The Carboniferous Limestone Plateau
    1b. The Shale and Grit Rim
    1c. The Flanking Belt of Coal-Measure Country
2. Cuestas on the Pennine Flanks
    2a. The Magnesian Limestone Cuesta
    2b. The Bunter Cuesta
    2c. The Keuper Cuesta

3. Fringes of the South Pennines
    3a. Foothills of Carboniferous Rocks
    3b. Fringing Permo-Trias Country
       (i) Well-dissected low hills
       (ii) Subdued hills and broad valleys

4. The Trent Floodplain and Associated Terraces

5. The Smite Basin

6. The Swadlincote Hill Country

7. Charnwood Forest

8. Low Hill Country of the Soar Valley

9. The Main Jurassic Cuesta
    9a. The Marlstone Shelves
       (i) West of the Cherwell
       (ii) East of the Cherwell
       (iii) of Belvoir
    9b. Highly Dissected Hill Country
       (i) In the Nene and Tove Basins
       (ii) North of the Welland
       (iii) North of the Wreake
    9c. Dissected Plateau Country
       (i) The Oxfordshire Cotswolds
       (ii) The Brackley Plateau
       (iii) The Nene Plateau
       (iv) The Ermine Street Plateau

10. The Fenland Margins

11. The Main Strike Vale
    11a. Vale Floors of the Thames System
       (i) Vale Floors of the Thames, Cherwell, and Ray
       (ii) Vale Floor of the Thame
    11b. Hills East of Oxford
    11c. Low Hills of the Winslow Area
    11d. Vale Floor of the Ouzel
    11e. The Lower Greensand Cuesta
    11f. Low Hills between Newport Pagnell and Bedford
    11g. Vale Floors of the Great Ouse and Ivel

12. The Chalk Scarp
    12a. The Crestal Belt and Main Scarp
    12b. The Sub-Scarps

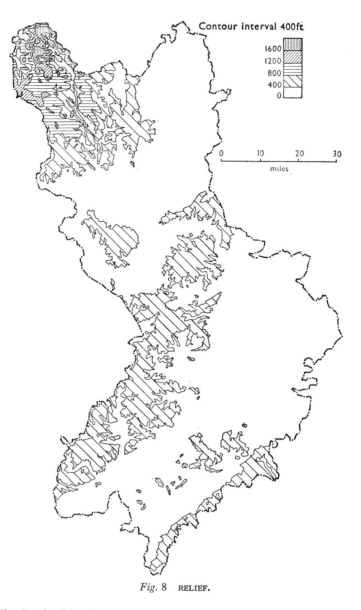

Contour interval 400ft

1600	
1200	
800	
400	
0	

0   10   20   30
miles

Fig. 8   RELIEF.

The Derbyshire Dome is quite distinct from the remainder of the region. Carboniferous Limestone exposed in the core forms wide stretches of open plateau, ranging generally in height from 1,000 to 1,500 feet. The largest single patch of unbroken plateau lies on the long subdued crest of the Derwent-Dove interfluve, carrying the old Roman road south from Buxton and the modern main road from Buxton to Matlock through Cromford. Between Buxton and Bakewell,

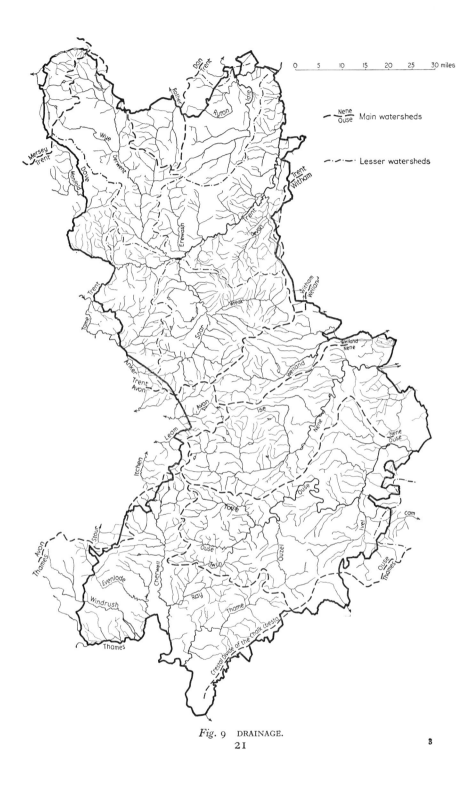

Scale: 0 5 10 15 20 25 30 miles

Nene / Ouse — Main watersheds

— Lesser watersheds

Fig. 9 DRAINAGE.

21

3

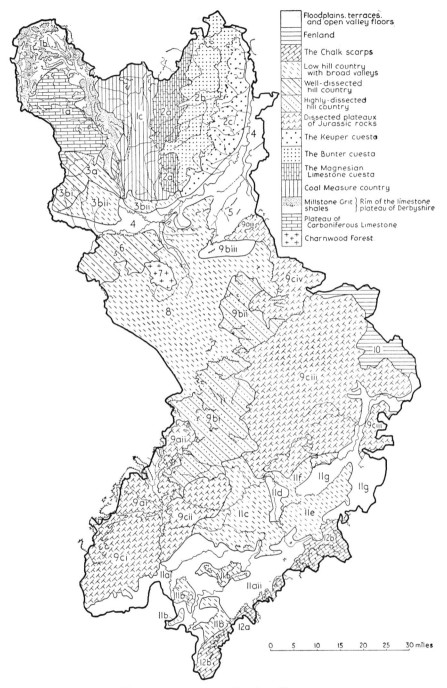

Fig. 10 MORPHOLOGY. See also adjacent map.

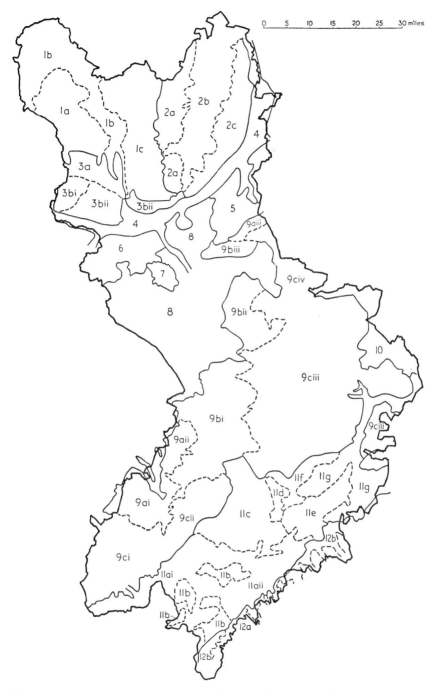

Fig. 11   KEY TO SUBDIVISIONS OF TERRAIN.   See also adjacent map and accompanying text.

23

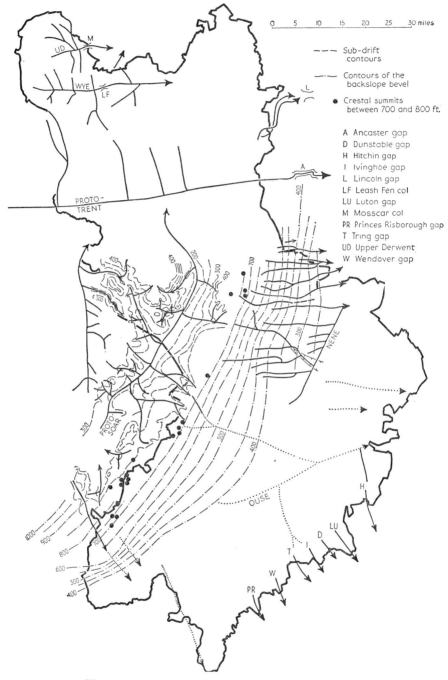

Fig. 12   SOME ELEMENTS IN MORPHOLOGICAL DEVELOPMENT.

24

and again between Bakewell and Castleton, a stiffening of basic lava enables the ground to rise to higher steps.

Summits in this central part of the Dome are undulating rather than flat, but the openness of the terrain is enhanced by the scarcity of timber, by sparseness of settlement, and by the location of villages below the general level. Valleys are narrow and gorge-like, many of them streamless. The Dove for seven miles below Hartington, and a large part of the Wye system, are very sharply incised. Both streams traverse winding trenches where soft creamy-grey exposures of limestone are hung with decorative ashwood (Pl. 3).

Upstream of Matlock, patches of rock belonging to the Millstone Grit formation occur on the west side of the Derwent, forming blocks of hills with hanging woods on their flanks. As the Edale Shales thicken towards the north, and as summits rise above 1,200 feet, woodland gives way to moor. In Hope Dale and in Edale the shales have been deeply eroded, valley basins lying 1,000 feet or more below the flat summits. On Kinderscout the very subdued peat-mantled capping of grit rises slightly above 2,000 feet, giving way on the northern side to abrupt edges and shelves below which long smooth slopes descend steeply to the incised Ashop. The unstable valley walls diminish in height as the valley shallows headwards, until nothing remains but a small depression at the edge of the peat of Featherbed Top. In this reach, as along the Derwent, blocks of conifers planted by the Forestry Commission clothe the valley walls; not all of them are recorded on the Seventh Series of the O.S. 1:63,360 map (Pl. 4).

Grit-based and peat-covered moorland north of the Ashop again exceeds 2,000 feet on Bleaklow, with the deeply cut and reservoir-lined valley of the Etherow on the far side. A strip of high but subdued summit encircles the head of the Derwent, declining fairly steadily in height towards the south until it attains only 1,000 feet in the vicinity of Matlock. In this belt, immediately east of and overlooking the Derwent, occurs the finest development of gritstone scarps, reduplicated, it is true, on the west side of the dome, where the Goyt has however not cut so deeply as the Derwent. On the west, in addition, dips are steeper than on the east. The western side brilliantly displays whole cuestas in perspective, while the east is distinguished by vistas of gritstone edges. The dark blocky outcrops of bare Grit scowl upon the bright limestone pastures below. Each Grit is a potential scarp-former, but topographical expression varies; two of the most prominent edges are Stanage Edge north of Hathersadge, which continues in Burbage Rocks, and Froggatt Edge-Curbar Edge farther south (Pls. 1, 2).

On the backslope of the Grits lies a narrow belt of intact plateau, largely devoid of roads and settlement, and covered mainly with

25

moorland, siliceous grassland, or heath. This district, extending south into the tongue of high ground between Matlock and Ashover, is well exemplified by the bleak expanse of Hallam Moors, where a few miserable hawthorns mark the remnantal persistence of scrub. The moorland strip is, however, too narrow to be truly dismal, particularly when fine weather reveals the woody Derwent valley through notches in the Grits, and opens great sweeping views across the lower ground to the east. On a smaller scale, the gutted anticline of Ashover is clearly seen from points on the brink ; surprisingly abrupt scarps here face one another across the Amber.

Roughly midway between Bakewell and Chesterfield the crestal plateau is, exceptionally, cut in Coal Measures ; but most of the Coal-Measures outcrop is well dissected. West of the Rother it descends from 1,000 to 400 feet in long, rather uneven, spurs between close-set east-flowing streams. Numerous minor roads, scattered hamlets, and single dwellings built of Coal-Measure sandstone combine with small woods to contrast with the overtopping plateau. Similar terrain stretches eastward beyond the upper Rother, and runs southward through the middle Amber valley into the basin of the Erewash. In these areas, however, the landscape is raised to a high level of complexity by industry, which superimposes on irregular relief a patchy distribution of collieries and settlements. Sandstones in the Coal Measures largely fail to impose order on the pattern of relief, even though the upper Rother, the Doe Lea, the middle Amber, and the Erewash suggest a development of subsequent drainage.

In direct contrast, the Magnesian Limestone forms a prominent scarp, rising at Bolsover 300 feet above the Doe Lea. The summit, at about 600 feet, is wholly tabular, widely in arable cultivation, and pocked by quarries. In places the scarp is deeply cleft by the narrow valleys known locally as grips. The edge of the Magnesian Limestone is, as would be expected, ill developed in the headwater district west of Mansfield, and fails to re-express itself fully in the lowish ground between Nottingham and the Erewash.

Streams draining the backslopes of the Magnesian Limestone occupy shallow valleys, which in the south carry water to the Leen. This river, pursuing a southerly course beneath the Bunter scarp, has no counterpart in the north, where the Rainworth Water, Maun, Mede, and Poulter cut through the Bunter scarp on their way to the Idle. The Ryton also transects the Bunter scarp, but is still short of the Keuper belt when it turns abruptly northward.

The line marked in Figure 10 does not coincide precisely with the edge of the Bunter outcrop, for the scarp-forming rocks occur slightly above the junction with the underlying Magnesian Limestone. The line swings westward north of the head of the Leen, where rather weak rocks have survived denudation in a central area of watershed. Nothing comparable to the intact crest of the Magnesian Limestone occurs on the Bunter outcrop, for the terrain is one of ragged hills and integrated gentle slopes. More than one sandstone is capable of sustaining a recognisable edge : a minor scarp, for instance, looks west across Rainworth Water between Blidworth and Ollerton, running north to attain a length of 7 miles without exceeding 50 feet in height. Elsewhere small hill masses bespeak the foundation of weak sandstone. Wide shallow valleys contain rivers with modest floodplains. Surface runoff is very low, and the régime of the streams is too even for flooding to happen frequently. In this division the abundant woodland, scrub, heath, and parkland distract attention from the patternless relief.

The Keuper Sandstone, also occurring above the formational boundary, rises sharply in another line of broken scarp to heights of 300 to 500 feet. Hillside slopes in the Keuper country are distinctly steeper than on the Bunter Beds, the low range of height notwithstanding. At the same time, parts of the Keuper backslope appear to be very softly moulded, as for example near Tuxford, where valleys descend smoothly from the almost treeless ploughland of flattish divides. Much of the Sandstone crest forms a watershed between drainage to the Idle and drainage direct to the Trent. In the south, however, streams break through the scarp.

The main belt of foothills on the southern margin of the Derbyshire Dome is composed, for the most part, of Carboniferous rocks. Ranging from sandstones through shales to limestones, these have been well denuded. A fringe of Permo-Trias broadens westward from the lowermost Leen to the lower Dove ; the pattern of outcrops, itself complex, is further complicated by facies changes, and the well-defined subdivisions of the Pennine flank are not repeated. The chief contrast is between the area where streams, having made no great progress in the present cycle, flow in narrow dumbles, and the area of much weaker relief north of the Dove-Derwent confluence. Heights in the foothill district range from 800 feet beneath the plateau edge to 250 feet near the lower Dove.

The extraordinary trench of the Trent is an old meander trough, patched by low rises of gravel, edged by bluffs, and adjoined by terraces. Minor cuestas rise on the right-hand side. In the Smite basin, where little asymmetrical lines of hill are capped by Keuper Sandstones, Rhaetic Limestone, or resistant members of the Lower Lias, the terrain is reminiscent of the Somerset Plain.

The coalfield and its surroundings west of the Soar form quite hilly country, rising in irregular slopes to some 600 feet, and being sharply dissected by the feeders of encircling main streams. Lack of clear pattern in relief is matched by uneven formlessness of settlement. The most noticeable single feature is the outfacing edge of downflexed Keuper Sandstone north of Ashby de la Zouch. Charnwood Forest, although only slightly exceeding 900 feet, is clearly distinguishable from the Swadlincote Hill Country by its whole texture and colour. The Charnian trend of structures, and the alignment of antique volcanoes, from northwest to southeast, is not easy to see on the ground, mainly because the pre-Cambrian rocks were already severely dissected before their burial under the Trias. The main impression is of small rocky outcrops, confused hills, patchy wood, disused quarries, and little reservoirs; both in detail and as a whole, the Forest differs strongly from its surroundings (Pl. 5).

A wide stretch of low and generally undulating hills runs from the basin of the Soar into the heads of the Avon and Welland valleys. Summits in the triangle marked by Hinckley, Wigston Magna, and Watling Street rise little above 400 feet. Their accordance results from the infilling of Glacier Lake Harrison. The tendency for summits to be wide and flat is strongest near Lutterworth; but as the thick outwash has been dissected into hills where summits merge roundly into flanks, the terrain is undulating rather than tabular. For this reason, and because a mantle of boulder-clay links the watershed with low hills cut in Lower Lias, a single subdivision in Figure 10 is made to include not only the edges of the former lake-basin but also the subdued country which runs north from the Sence and into the Wreake valley. An almost intact cover of drift masks any topographical break which may once have distinguished the Leicestershire Wolds, north of the Wreake valley, from the Nottinghamshire Wolds; these enclose the heads of the Devon in a drift-capped little cuesta of Keuper rocks.

In the Leicestershire Wolds, if anywhere, the lines drawn in Figure 11 are belied by the ground. Boulder-clay draped on the sides of the main valleys runs far down the spurs between lateral streams. Nevertheless, the highest ground of all has a sure structural and lithological basis in Middle Lias and Inferior Oolite, which form scarps wherever the drift has gone.

In detail the scarped ascent to the Main Jurassic Cuesta is modified by variations in the drift cover, by variations in the thickness of scarp-formers, and by facies change. Matters are simplest where there is no drift, and where a crest forms a main watershed. They are most complex where drift is thick and abundant, where more than one well-defined scarp is present, and where the main watershed lies down-dip of a prominent edge. But for all the apparent confusion in places,

28

three types of terrain can be recognised : well-marked shelves on the Marlstone, severely dissected hill country, and plateaux where broad expanses of summit are little broken (Pl. 7).

The Marlstone shelves are developed on the stony members of the Middle Lias at their thickest. Edge Hill, west of the Cherwell, rises just above 700 feet, and stands more than 300 feet higher than the sub-edge country of the Avon basin. The backslope is remarkably smooth, sloping flatly down-dip between the gashes of valleys draining to the Cherwell. Outliers of younger rocks first appear in rounded hills along the Epwell Rift. The corresponding shelf east of the Cherwell carries numerous outliers of Upper Lias with thin sandy cappings of Inferior Oolite. A third shelf, near Belvoir, is far smaller in extent than the other two.

The belt of highly dissected hill country is in some degree alternative to the Marlstone shelves ; but it includes rocks below the Marlstone in the Avon valley, where little-known bands of limestone have been etched into relief, and rocks younger than Middle Lias in the upper valleys of the Nene and Tove. Here the capping has been widely removed and the Upper Lias widely exposed, but little of the Marlstone is revealed. Drift lies on the hilltops around the northern heads of the Nene, occurs farther west as gravelly outwash, and generally prevents or obscures the development of scarps. The Marlstone edge appears with difficulty through glacial deposits north of the upper Welland and west of Oakham, where Upper Lias is again widespread under the drift. Strong dissection north of the Wreake marks the effect of the northward bend of the trunk stream and the deep incision of feeders.

The northern limit of dissected plateau, as opposed to highly irregular hill country, is drawn where cappings of Inferior Oolite appear in large number. Although both the Inferior and the Great Oolite Limestones are mechanically capable of forming edges, the older formation alone appears in relief. It forms a clean scarp in northeast Leicestershire, overlooks the Welland below Market Harborough, and is the main basis of the broken scarps which terminate the Marlstone shelves about the Cherwell. The backslope has been eroded into a surface where change of outcrop makes little difference to the aspect of the plateaux.

Broad flat divides in the Oxfordshire Cotswolds separate sharply cut well-incised meandering valleys ; many side-valleys are streamless. The Windrush, Evenlode, Glyme, and Dorn have cut more deeply into the Oxfordshire Cotswolds than have the Ouse and Twin into the Brackley Plateau. Glacial drift appears near and beyond the Twin, slightly weakening the austere forms of the plateau near

Buckingham, and concealing on the far side of the Tove the passage from Great Oolite Limestone and Cornbrash to the feather-edge of Oxford Clay. The Ise and its tributaries upstream of Kettering, and the Gwash and Chater systems in Rutland, slit the Nene and Ermine Street plateaux in sub-parallel valleys between divides rising above 500 feet. Valleys become shallower as the ground sinks eastward, until the maximum height in Huntingdonshire is little above 250 feet. The eastern limit of the plateau at the edge of the Fenland is, however, distinct on the ground. Terrain with some amplitude of relief abuts on terrain with none.

Subdivisions of the Main Strike Vale accord closely with geological distributions. The vale floors correspond to outcrops of the solid clays, from which glacial drift, if formerly present, has been cleared away. East of Oxford, in the basins of the Thames and Ray, broken hills and tiny cuestas mark the outcrops of Corallian rocks, Portland Beds, Purbeck Beds, and Lower Greensand, offering fine views across the low ground. The drift mantle has been carved into low undulating hills in the Winslow area; the Ouzel, working in Oxford Clay, has cut a vale floor of its own. The thick development of Lower Greensand about Woburn is reflected in a bold cuesta which, declining uncertainly in height and degenerating in form towards the northeast, is boldly resumed beyond Sandy. Both the Hiz-Ivel and the Ouse near Bedford have excavated vales lined by wide terraces, and little space remains for the indeterminate hilly terrain which forms a minor watershed east of Newport Pagnell.

Strikingly level summits slightly above 800 feet enhance the apparent continuity of the Chiltern scarp. Even more than the main Jurassic scarp, the face of the Chalk is remarkably straight, despite notching by cols. Notwithstanding its wall-like aspect in oblique views, it is however multiple, for strong sub-scarps are developed in places, mainly upon the Melbourn Rock at the base of the Middle Chalk. At Wendover and Tring, and near Edlesborough, flat triangular benches appear on the sides of gaps, their points uniting in the gaps themselves; in front of the Luton gap lies a bench 7 miles long and up to 5 miles across, standing 100 or 200 feet higher than the adjacent vale country to the north, and presenting an arc of bold scarp, scalloped by dry re-entrant valleys, along most of its outer edge. In this district, Chalk country protrudes from the Chilterns into the East Midland region (Pls. 8, 48).

Parts of the region were formerly drained by streams running from west to east. Such streams are referable in the long view to Tertiary warping. D. L. Linton holds that east-flowing consequent rivers first developed on the emergent floor of the Chalk sea. The scheme allows for the westerly thinning, if not indeed the wedging-out, of Chalk across the high ground, and provides a reasonable explanation of the reconstructed courses of early streams in the Peak District (Fig. 12). Some explanation is required, for instances of superimposition abound : the drainage of the Peak is far less well adjusted than might be suspected from small-scale maps where fold-axes are not shown. Linton suggests that the converging upper Derwent, Westend, Alport, Ashop, and Noe united, with now-disrupted streams coming from the south, into a trunk river which discharged through the Moscar col (1,182 ft.) along the line of the Rivelin, supporting his views by the arrangement of residual slopes on the flanks of the postulated trunk valley. The height of the Moscar col means that the reconstructed sheaf of streams must be referred to a landscape of high antiquity—the Upland Surface at 1,000 feet and above. The high hills encircling the reconstructed basin belong to the still higher Summit Surface, with remnants between 1,650 and 1,800 feet ; since the hills are devoid of water-gaps, it follows that the reconstructed drainage of the upper Derwent basin was inherited from the Summit Surface itself. Thus for this district two episodes of advanced but incomplete planation are postulated before the Moscar outlet was abandoned.

A similarly reconstructed early Wye, again draining part of the Upland Surface, passed eastward through the Leash Fen col (930 ft.). This second reconstruction accords with the restored histories both of the Derwent to the north and of the Trent to the south. Moreover, the mechanism of certain captures can be inferred : for instance, rejuvenation on the invading Matlock Derwent passed rapidly along the shale outcrop on the Upland Surface, intercepting a right-bank tributary of the Wye in Deep Dale.

Apart from the fact that the Summit and Upland Surfaces belong somewhere in the Tertiary era, satisfactory evidence for their age is completely lacking. On the ground that the 600-foot level relates to the base of the Pleistocene, the Upland Surface may seem to belong in Pliocene times, emphasising, if so, the great break in the record since west–east drainage was initiated. Assuming that streams were superimposed from the emergent Chalk, it is still difficult to perceive the character of the undermass into which they cut. The Permo-Trias in all probability thinned westwards across the Dome, but may not have been altogether removed. P. E. Kent interprets the Triassic relics of the South Pennines as pocket-deposits contained in large sinkholes, considering the sinks to have originated at the edge of Carboniferous shales at levels of about 1,250 feet. Thus the Trias appears to have lapped on to the centre of the Derbyshire Dome, at no great height above the Upland Surface, and eminences rising to some 1,250 feet may be relics of the sub-Triassic floor. What effects the structures and facies of the Trias may have had on streams penetrating a Chalk cover cannot, at present, be imagined.

The southern boundary of the early east-flowing Wye cannot be accurately defined. This boundary was in any event subject to migration and to displacement by capture ; the Wye basin could easily be invaded by streams draining towards the south, particularly if it were underlain by Triassic rocks. The Manifold, Dove, Amber, lower Derwent, and others may well represent left-bank tributaries of the early Trent. Even when all possible allowance is made for local adjustments of these streams to specific outcrops and structures, their sub-parallelism is impressive.

Some individual derangements can have been due to the development of underground drainage. Although exposures of bare rock on flat tops are uncommon, the limestone generally is freely permeable, and surface water is rare except in deep valleys ; and although the fills of Trias in old sinks indicate karstic sculpture of very early date, there is no reason to think that underground cavities have ceased altogether to grow. Caverns naturally accessible from the surface are concentrated chiefly in the reef-limestones ; those penetrated by mine workings extend in places at least to 600 feet below sea level, with their maximum depth still unknown. Hence in Derbyshire, as in other limestone regions, any full explanation of underground cavities must allow for very lengthy, albeit probably spasmodic, extension of the systems.

On the interfluves of the Pennine foothills, and on the crests and backslopes of the east flank of the Pennines, are preserved remnants of erosional benches. For the most part these remnants are scattered and small. The recent fashion in British geomorphology has been to interpret such erosional facets as survivals from broad platforms, referring them to high but horizontal base-levels ; the topic mainly debated has been that of origin, whether subaerial or marine. Taken as a whole, the evidence indicates repeated rejuvenation, which at high levels is recorded on benched spurs, while lower levels provide valley-side benches, river terraces, and knickpoints on long-profiles. The ranges of height quoted in the accompanying diagram (Fig. 13) mean that partial levelling in a given epicycle has affected a considerable reach of a given main valley. There is no reason for corresponding sets of gentle slopes to lie in a given range of height today, even if rejuvenation has been controlled exclusively by an intermittently falling base-level. In view of the known difficulties of interpreting, and of restoring, long-profiles it is not possible to correlate by extrapolation. Until physical continuity has been demonstrated in the field, it is therefore impossible to equate the various sequences with one another.

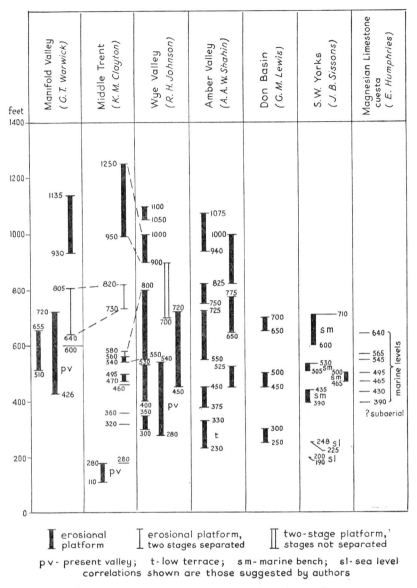

Fig. 13 EROSIONAL FACETS, according to various authors.

The Coal-Measure belt is drained by streams of diverse origin.
The Rother, Doe Lea, Amber, and Erewash, like the Leen on the
Permo-Trias, all possess large elements which, aligned on strikes, can
be classed as subsequent. Any early east-flowing streams have been
dismembered or reversed. A strong contrasted array of drainage
appears on the Permo-Trias outcrop, where southwest–northeast

courses are numerous. Breaching of the scarps by streams in this division has already been noticed. Although the scarps have been developed and pressed down-dip, dip-streams seem not to have been correspondingly reduced. Three obvious possibilities are that drainage was superimposed on the Permo-Trias from a vanished cover, that it was superimposed from an erosion platform, and that it developed by the extension of consequents across a sea-floor revealed by marine regression. No choice among these possibilities can yet be made. Bevelling of the Magnesian Limestone at about 600 feet suggests, however, the control of the early Pleistocene sea, and marine levels have in fact been claimed in the range 710–190 feet (Fig. 13).

The trunk Trent is the result of piecemeal development no less complex than the development of the Thames or of the Severn-Avon system. The proto-Trent, rising in North Wales, was outstandingly large among the postulated east-flowing master-consequents of Tertiary time. Very little of its original course remains. Reaches within and upstream of the Dee Gap have no direct bearing on the origin of the East Midland landscape. If the ancient river once flowed fairly directly along the line from the Dee Gap in the west to the Ancaster Gap in the east, its middle section has migrated southwards off the flanks of the Derbyshire hills into the weak marls of the adjoining Triassic basin. A powerful trunk stream is certainly required to receive the drainage of the South Pennines, and to collect the waters of the ancestral Soar (Fig. 12).

F. W. Shotton has traced a proto-Soar rising at least as far south-west as Bredon Hill. Much of it was reversed during the Pleistocene. Ice approaching from the west, northwest, north, and northeast impounded a glacier lake (Lake Harrison) in a basin bounded on the southeast by the face of the main Jurassic cuesta (Fig. 14). At its maximum extent the lake attained an area of 750 square miles ; the ice-front rested against the North Cotswolds, blocked the broad corridor which intervenes between the Cotswolds and the Black Country Plateau, covered the outer flanks of the Plateau itself, and looped round Charnwood Forest to turn south across the Northamptonshire hills. A wave-cut bench at about 410 feet O.D. marks the rim of the lake from the Vale of Moreton to the upper Leam. The main outlet, and possibly the sole outlet, at the 410-foot level was the Fenny Compton Gap, which leads into the Chernwell valley. W. W. Bishop, making detailed studies in the valley of the Warwickshire Itchen, has shown that the lake surface earlier stood at 435 feet, high enough to permit overspill through the Vale of Moreton, the gaps on both sides of the Dassett Hills, and probably also through the Watford (Kilsby or Daventry) Gap into the Nene valley. This last gap, however, is thickly encumbered with drift, and its rôle as spillway is uncertainly known.

Sub-drift contours, determined by Shotton in the valley of the proto-Soar, make it possible to reconstruct not only the main stream but also a number of tributaries (Fig. 12). The trunk Soar, working in the Keuper Marl, had thrown out extensive systems of feeders, both on the left side into the flanks of the Black Country plateau and Charnwood Forest and on the right side into the Lower Lias belt. Although fine detail cannot be expected from the contours of the

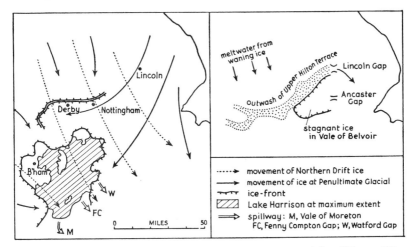

Fig. 14   GLACIAL ADVANCES IN THE TRENT AND AVON BASINS ;   origin of Upper Hilton Terrace according to Poznansky.

sub-drift surface, there is enough to show that the Hydraulic Limestone of the Lower Lias did not form a divide between drainage to the Trent and drainage towards the Thames or the Wash. Then, as now, feeders of the Soar broke through and ran round discontinuous cuestas of Rhaetic and Lower Liassic Limestones, biting deeply and widely into the Lower Lias Clay. The gaps listed previously, and the gap of the Welland, show that the Soar was pressing back the divide on the southeast ; the scarps were receding, leaving some headstreams rising beyond the crestal line. Very little scarp-recession has taken place since Lake Harrison was formed, so that captures and divide-migration must be referred to mid-Pleistocene and earlier times.

The inflection of the sub-drift contours near Leicester suggests that the Soar, before the invasion of its valley by ice, swung round Charnwood Forest along the Keuper outcrop before joining the Trent, that is, that it then followed the line which it still pursues. The Trent valley from Nottingham downstream has been so deeply and widely cut that there seems little prospect of tracing the valley bottom on which the two rivers formerly united. Reconstructions of this part of the Trent at higher levels are bound to be speculative. Nevertheless, much of the lower Trent seems to represent a subsequent, developing headwards from the Humber drainage, forcing back the divide of an opposed subsequent which drained to the proto-Trent, and finally breaking into the channel of the trunk river. This general hypothesis is entirely compatible with the highly complex sequence of capture, diversion, and glacial damming which is required by gaps in Lincoln Edge, by the late entry of ice, and by the former presence of proglacial lakes in the lower Trent valley.

The Ancaster Gap, with its present sill-level little above 150 feet, seems to have acted as a spillway of some kind : well-washed drift lies thickly at its eastern end. Location of the gap on the possible line of a proto-Trent draining across the whole of England from a source in North Wales is not conclusive ; on the other hand, the swinging bend in the gap itself, east of Ancaster, is of the same order of size as the identifiable valley meanders of the nearby Trent. This meagre evidence, so far as it goes, accords with the view that the Trent passed along the Ancaster line late enough to erode the sill below the 200-foot level. Indeed, it is physically possible for the combined drainage of the Trent and the reconstructed Soar to have escaped by the Ancaster route, for the river from Leicester to Ancaster would have been some 45 miles long, and the difference in height could have been as great as 45 feet. If the gap in something like its present form was ever so used, the Trent had been diverted from it by the time that the 100-foot terrace was formed ; for K. M. Clayton's map shows the Hilton Terrace, here some 90 feet above the alluvium, diverging from the present line of the Trent, curving round north of the present Witham, and making for the gap at Lincoln. The Beeston Terrace, at about 35 feet, follows a similar but lower route. Here seems to be part of the record of successive northward displacements of the lower Trent.

M. Posnansky distinguishes the effects of three glacial advances in the valley of the middle Trent. The first of these, which brought Pennine Drift, he associates with an advance of ice from the north, correlatable with the Lowestoft stage of the East Anglian sequence of R. G. West and J. J. Donner. Presumably this advance correlates also with the lower of the two boulder-clays in Northamptonshire, and with the Northern Drift of the Northants-Oxfordshire area (Table 8). Little remains by way of deposits to mark the subsequent deglacial interval, but the next succeeding glacial is well documented by erratics from two directions—from the north, extending about as far as the southern extremities of the Pennine foothills, and from the northeast, projecting boldly far up the valley of the Trent (Fig. 14). This second glacial was that in which Lake Harrison formed in the Avon basin. Posnansky regards the Hilton terrace as fluvioglacial material, deposited early in the subsequent deglaciation, when he considers the Vale of Belvoir to have been occupied by stagnant ice directing the Trent through the Lincoln gap. He places the Beeston terrace rather dubiously in the Last Glacial, when he infers that the present course of the Trent to the Humber was established. As he indicates, much remains to be done before the existence and extent of Glacier Lake Humber, postulated by A. Raistrick to occupy the Trent valley about as far upstream as Nottingham, can be taken as proven.

G. A. Kellaway and J. H. Taylor use the records of numerous boreholes to reconstruct former drainage on the northeastern part of the main Jurassic cuesta. By means of crestal cols, now plugged by drift, they demonstrate former eastward-flowing streams which had been somewhat modified by capture before the onset of glaciation. Since ice overspread this part of the region at two glacial maxima, and since little is known of the lower boulder-clay, it is hard to ascertain how far capture had gone before the first entry of ice. Most of the plugged valleys are thought to be either buried wind-gaps or buried upper portions of previously beheaded valleys.

The boulder-clay rests upon a remarkably plane surface bevelled across the backslope of the main Jurassic cuesta. By projecting outcrops on to the restored surface of this bevel, Kellaway and Taylor show that preglacial subsequents were accurately located on weak outcrops, and that the pattern of consequents had been slightly modified by adjustment to belts of faulting or localised warping. The picture is of an extensive erosional surface with drainage incised to no great depth, and with much of an undoubtedly consequent system of rivers surviving. The backslope bevel can be traced throughout the whole length of the main Jurassic cuesta, running eventually across the regional boundary in the Cotswolds (Fig. 12). There is little to show that streams once coursed directly down the bevelled surface in the centre and southwest, as would be expected from the tilting claimed by Kellaway and Taylor for the east.

If the present attitude of the bevel is due to tilting, movement has occurred very widely indeed; the swing of the reconstructed contours would suggest an up-doming involving the Derbyshire block, Charnwood Forest, and the Black Country Plateau, if not indeed a still wider movement affecting parts still farther west; the close parallelism between the reconstructed contours and the run of the Jurassic and Cretaceous scarps would then be an astonishing coincidence. Again, in view of the relationship between the bevel and the preglacial drainage, the tilting would have to be referred to the very late Tertiary. The bevel can scarcely be wave-cut, since it descends very smoothly through a vertical range of at least 500 feet. Since, moreover, it terminates in the outcrop of Oxford Clay, it cannot be an exhumed unconformity. Again, the sloping bevel seems itself to be truncated by a summit surface which lies in the range 700–750 feet (Fig. 12). All these observations make the bevel very difficult to explain, unless it be a late-Tertiary pediplain; but whatever the correct interpretation, the feature exists. It is the bevel which imparts a tabular character to so much of the backslope.

Further difficulties arise in explaining the courses of the Welland, Nene, and Great Ouse. All three streams traverse solid outcrops obliquely. The Welland is thought to have been developed by the piecemeal modification of west–east consequents. For 25 miles upstream of Sharnbrook the Great Ouse follows the extension of the Islip axis, and thus seems to have become adjusted to an outcrop of Oxford Clay on the crest of a long upfold; when this adjustment is discounted, the Great Ouse, like the Nene, flows at an angle across the strike. No reason for these circumstances can at present be suggested.

Near the time of glacial maximum, proglacial lakes must certainly have formed in some of the valleys which feed the Welland, Nene, and Ouse. Kellaway and Taylor suggest that a straight dry valley east of Southorpe may have been a spillway connecting the Welland and the Nene, and that a col northeast of Dingley may have carried spillwater from the Welland or one of its feeders. Outwash between Daventry and Weedon, now somewhat dissected, forms a flat spread occupying extreme head-valleys of the Nene system, and other valley heads to the south are also choked with gravel. There is, however, little evidence here for major glacial derangement of drainage. The Chalky Boulder-Clay and its associated outwash seem not to have penetrated the Cherwell valley except to a very slight extent. Gravel trains running into the Cherwell have been identified at two places. One, in the valley of the little Eydon Brook near Chipping Warden, may perhaps be no more than outwash reworked by a postglacial stream; but the bulky train which crosses the divide from Fawsley to Charwelton occupies a distinct channel, and was probably deposited by meltwater.

The total extent of surviving glacial deposits is considerable (Fig. 15). All too little, however, is known of the boulder-clay fabric, of the distribution of far-travelled erratics, and of the detailed sequence of advance and retreat. Perhaps because they are largely formless, the drift spreads have as yet attracted little careful attention. The Northern Drift of Northamptonshire and Oxfordshire—the lower of the two series—is referable to the Antepenultimate (=Elster) Glacial, while the

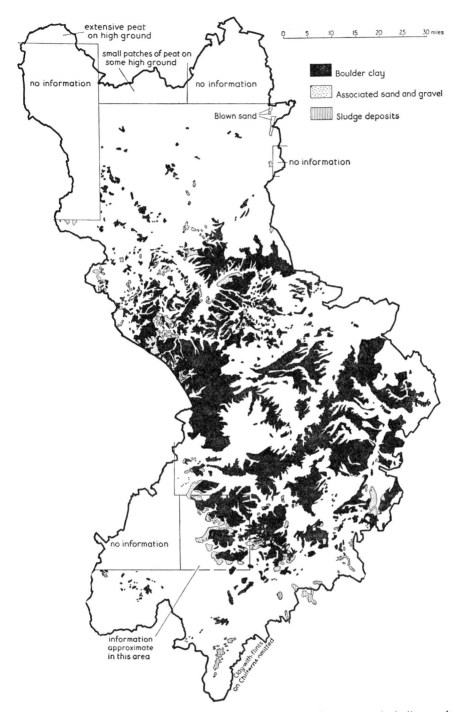

extensive peat
on high ground

small patches of peat on
some high ground

no information

no information

Blown sand

no information

no information

information
approximate
in this area

Clay with flints
on Chilterns omitted

	Boulder clay
	Associated sand and gravel
	Sludge deposits

0   5   10   15   20   25   30 miles

Fig. 15   GLACIAL AND ASSOCIATED DEPOSITS.   Compiled from various sources, including results of field reconnaissance.

upper, much bulkier, Chalky Boulder-Clay belongs to the Penultimate (=Saale) Glacial. The Northern Drift contains very few flints, but much Bunter material. Where exposed, it is usually thin and severely weathered. Patches of superficial deposit in the Oxford area, formerly mapped as Plateau Gravel, have been reclassified as weathered boulder-clay and assigned to the Northern Drift; a tongue of ice probably extended as far south as Oxford during the Antepenultimate Glacial, when the Ouse valley was perhaps occupied by an ice-lobe. If so, the ice of the Antepenultimate advance went somewhat beyond the limits of the Penultimate ice. Unfortunately for the record, the critical clay-based area has been much lowered by post-glacial erosion, so that hopes of defining the extreme limits of ice during the earlier glacial appear small.

During the interval between the two Glacials, that is, in the Penultimate Interglacial, the backslope streams from the Cherwell westwards were strongly rejuvenated and became deeply incised. The Freeland and Coombe Terraces, of direct outwash or of re-worked outwash in originally shallow valleys, were cut through. The formation of terraces firmly contained in trenches began with the deposition of the Hanborough Terrace material. According to Bishop, the record of the Wolvercote Channel, the Wolvercote Terrace, and the base of the Summertown-Radley Terrace extends through the late part of the Penultimate Interglacial and the whole of the succeeding Penultimate Glacial (Table 8). Where broad troughs have been carved in weak clays, they are usually occupied by continuous belts of terrace, as on the Soar near Leicester. Where, on the other hand, meandering valleys are incised into strong rocks, terraces are restricted to crescentic patches on spurs, as on the middle Nene.

Periglacial conditions were responsible for much sludging of rock-waste, especially on the sides of deep valleys and in combes cut into scarps. Sludging occurred during the Penultimate Glacial, as can be seen from deposits in the Oxford district, but the main surviving spreads of sludge-gravel belong to the Last (=Weichsel) Glacial. The largest spreads within the region lie beneath the Chiltern scarp (Fig. 15), but additional sludge-fans are known beneath the scarp of the Cotswolds. Some of the backslope valleys are thickly encumbered with sludge-gravel—for instance that of the Evenlode above the so-called gorge, where limestone gravel underlies alluvium. Some of the outwash gravels are contorted and festooned by thaw-freeze, while W. J. Arkell records cracks produced by wedges of ground-ice.

Frozen ground is held to account also for the widely developed superficial structures of the Jurassic belt. These include cambering, whereby cap-rocks are gently arched over; valley bulging, whereby weak rocks in the floors of valleys are pushed up ; and various fissurings and disturbances of strong rocks on hill brows. The effects of cambering are particularly noticeable in the field, for they soften the transition from hilltop to hillside. The whole series of superficial structures was first described for the Northamptonshire Ironstone Field, but identical disturbances have been proved in North Oxfordshire and the Cotswolds, in the Cornbrash outcrop, and in the Millstone Grit of the Pennine division.

Deep downcutting by feeders of the Thames during the Penultimate Interglacial was presumably controlled by the rejuvenation of the trunk stream itself. Although slight shifts of line have been demonstrated for the Thames at and above Oxford, the present course of the river seems to be a fair representation of its course at a considerably earlier time. Now the Thames above Oxford, the Thame, and the Ray, are all well adjusted to weak strikes. The Cherwell and the Evenlode, on the other hand, flow down the backslope from the deep gaps in which they rise. These two rivers seem to be the descendants of quite early drainage, while the adjusted rivers are subsequents. Gaps in the crest of the Chilterns may result from the beheading of streams on the Chiltern backslope, in which case there is evidence for the wholesale disruption of streams flowing roughly down-dip. However, it is quite possible for dry gaps to be formed by the recession of a scarp across valley heads, without any capture, so that firm indications of capture become reduced to those cases in which a stream rises beyond the crestal line, or in which capture is proved by the distribution of river deposits. The Evenlode is known to have been beheaded during the Pleistocene, losing to the Stour that portion which rose in the Campden Tunnel Gap ; one of the heads of the Cherwell still rises on the Lower Lias outcrop, at Priors Marston ; and the head of the Lea extends beyond the main Chalk scarp north of Luton. Capture is dubious in some degree, although the deep gap of the Thames at Goring seems to demand former south-flowing drainage across the southern part of the region. The erosion platform at about 800 feet, recorded in the subdued crests and residual deposits of the Chilterns, presumably extended well to the northwest of its surviving remnants. The Cherwell-Thames must surely be regarded as a development of one of the master-streams which reduced the land to about the 800-foot level. It is likely to have been a principal feeder of the proto-Thames, comparable to the proto-Soar which fed the proto-Trent.

The straightness of the Cherwell-Thames is nevertheless difficult to explain. Recent gravitational and magnetic surveys reveal the probable form of the basement rocks under much of the Mesozoic outcrop, while detailed re-surveys of the surface geology show the importance of posthumous movement. The geophysical surveys fail to provide evidence for the long, continuous Charnoid axes once thought to extend from the Midland Triangle into the London Basin, or for structures which, by posthumous movement, could guide the development of backslope streams. The origins of trunk drainage and of principal feeder streams in and south of the main Jurassic cuesta thus remain obscure.

Main streams are underfit throughout the region. Underfitness is best displayed south of the Trent, but can also be perceived in the Pennine division and on the Trent itself. The Trent near Nottingham occupies an alluvial trough, swept out by large meanders which can still be traced. Similar troughs occur on the upper Nene, Cherwell, and Evenlode. The change from open trough to incised meandering valley is a response to change in rock-type. Some meandering valleys are known to contain large meandering channels beneath the alluvium of their floodplains. All streams in the region have undergone a reduction in volume at the bankfull stage in response to change of climate. The latest major episode of channel-cutting occurred in very late glacial times, or shortly thereafter. The forms of some terraces in plan, and the forms of the Oxford terraces in cross-section, record previous channelling. The high rates of surface runoff demanded by meandering valleys and large meandering channels are quite adequate to explain the cutting of now-dry valleys in the limestones both of the Jurassic belt and of the Chilterns; in particular, they can explain the numerous short dry side-valleys which, in North Oxfordshire and the Cotswolds, have discharged fans of rock-waste into the valleys of trunk streams. Rainy conditions in the Atlantic Phase of post-glacial climate probably involved some clearance of the fills of the large channels, but it seems unlikely that these channels were completely re-cleared at that time (Pls. 6, 9, 10).

CHAPTER 4

CLIMATE, WEATHER, AND WATER SUPPLY

QUITE apart from its inclusion of a portion of Highland Britain, the East Midland region does not fail to display spatial variations in climate. Some of these variations reflect the eastward increase in continentality across the low ground, others express the local interplay of climatic and topographic influences. There is a perceptible eastward decrease in precipitation, and an increase in the same direction of the fraction falling in the summer half-year. Topography is in part responsible for the high incidence of fogs and thunderstorms in the Trent valley near Newark, for the strength of the winds on the Cotswold plateau, and for cold-air drainage. Its influences are strongest in the Pennine division, where they have been best studied. Here, also, the ground rises high enough to release the instability in maritime air from the west ; fronts can be checked against the upland, or the stagnant air of high-pressure systems be banked against its eastern side. The change in climate from west to east is quite rapid in the north of the region, whereas it amounts to a steady transition elsewhere.

Contrasts between north and south are apt to be overshadowed by local contrasts, or to be obliterated by the contrasts between east and west. January mean sea-level temperatures, for instance, run at about 40°F in the extreme northwest and in the south ; an eastward decrease towards 39°F marks increasing continentality. The southward increase in July mean sea-level temperatures is but a matter of a degree or so ; annual mean sea-level temperatures are somewhat below 49° in the north and about 50° in the south. Concentration of high annual rainfalls in the north is largely a matter of relief, not of latitude ; similarly, liability to snow increases very sharply with the ascent of the Pennines. Differences among stations on the low ground are delicate, while contrasts between lowland and highland, and contrasts within the highland, can be very abrupt indeed.

Mean monthly actual temperatures are given in Table 9, while graphs are drawn for three stations in Figure 16. Annual régimes and annual ranges vary but slightly across the region. It is true that Buxton has perceptibly the smallest mean annual range, 21·6°F, while Belper, with 23·0°, records the lowest range among the other stations listed. Elsewhere, mean annual ranges are 23·2° or 23·3°, except at Northampton ; but the apparent range of 24·7° at this station is perhaps due to the use of a non-coincident twenty-five-year series of

43

records. Cambridge, beyond the boundary of the region and with a mean annual range of 23·7°, appears to give a fair indication of the influence of increasing continentality towards the east.

In ranges between mean values, for single months, of daily maxima and minima, Buxton again records low values; Mansfield has the next lowest, and Belper the highest when summer values for Cambridge, outside the region, are left out of account. Thus the curves for Mansfield and Belper, in Figure 17, form an envelope which would enclose curves for the four other stations. As with mean annual range,

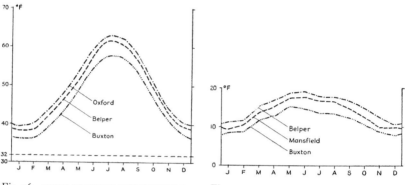

Fig. 16   MEAN MONTHLY TEMPERATURES for selected stations.

Fig. 17   RANGE BETWEEN MEAN MONTHLY MAXIMA AND MEAN MONTHLY MINIMA for selected stations.

the distinctiveness of Buxton is probably due to its frequent exposure to maritime air, which offsets the very low minima recorded during inversions.

Differences in mean annual, mean January, and mean July temperatures from station to station cannot be wholly explained in terms of height. Whereas the mean annual difference between Buxton and Belper corresponds closely to the gradient of 1°F for 300 feet, the contrast in monthly means is greater in July than in January (Table 10). Buxton may well be the more subject, in winter, to maritime winds which reduce extremes, while Belper profits the more from a sheltered position in summer. The difference in mean annual temperatures between Mansfield and Belper is negligible, but Mansfield is perceptibly the colder in winter—allowance being made for altitude—presumably on account of radiation and of the ponding of cold easterly air against the Pennines. The temperature/height gradient between Luton and Cambridge is slighter than the standard value, most markedly so in January, when both stations can be influenced by the chill air of highs. The contrasting high gradient from Luton to Oxford, however, cannot be entirely explained by the more frequent arrival of maritime air at Oxford than at Luton, for the gradient exists both in summer and in winter.

Although the Table of absolute maximum temperatures (Table 11) is not based on records for identical series of years, its general import is clear. Absolute maxima increase southward in all months but December, when Buxton is liable in some years to high temperatures introduced by Atlantic air. In the series of minima, Buxton has recorded temperatures below freezing in every month but August; at Belvoir Castle, July and August alone failed to record screen frost during the period of record, but Oxford, with a considerably longer series of readings, had no frost in June, July, or August. The period April–August inclusive seems distinctly less subject to extreme low temperatures at Oxford than at Belvoir Castle, but there is nothing at Belvoir Castle to compare with the sub-zero temperatures noted for Buxton in December, January, and February.

Differences between absolute maxima and absolute minima are greater in August than in July at Belvoir Castle and at Oxford, where, in addition, August has recorded the highest maximum. The greater variability in August than in July is in accordance with the dispersion diagram of monthly temperatures at Northampton for 1933–57 (Fig. 18). The contrast between July and August is probably due to the high temperatures of clear-sky highs in some Augusts and the free advection of maritime air in others. Other highly variable months at Northampton are December, January, and February. Variable temperatures in December are accompanied by quite reliable rainfall, but those in January and February are associated with rainfall which is also highly variable. However, the interquartile band of December temperatures is narrow enough. The wide scatter of temperatures for January and February results from the low means recorded in about one year in four; the lower quartile for these months is very large indeed. Low recordings represent the effects of high-pressure systems which promote frost; here, as with the variability of August temperatures, the blocking pattern is in question. In direct contrast, November temperatures for Northampton produce a very narrow lower quartile, corresponding to the flow of maritime air which makes November rainy.

Annual averages of days recording minimum temperatures of 32°F or less rise from 50 in the extreme south to nearly 100 in the northwest. Figures for ground frost (Table 12) may be affected by the urban climate of Sheffield, but liability to ground frost on low ground certainly rises eastward. Average dates of first screen frost are about 15 October in much of the region; average dates of last screen frost are about 1 May in the north and the south, but rather later elsewhere. There is thus little variation about 170 days in the length of frost-free period, but topographic effects seriously increase liability to frost in many Pennine valleys.

Graphical determination of the length of growing season, using the mean temperatures cited in Table 9 and the limit of 42·8°F, gives more than 250 days in the southwest (Table 9, last column), and

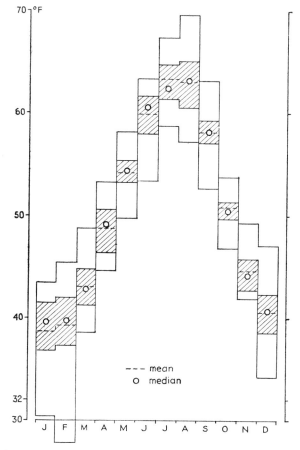

Fig. 18 DISPERSION DIAGRAM FOR MEAN MONTHLY TEMPERATURES at Northampton for 1933–57 inclusive.

between 230 and 250 days in much of the lowland elsewhere. The apparent contrast between Luton and Cambridge may result mainly from difference in height, but the contrast between Luton and Oxford is likely to correspond to a greater influence of maritime air in the winter months at Oxford. Increasing latitude may be responsible for the northward decrease in length of growing season from Oxford, through Northampton and Sutton Bonington, to Mansfield. Belper, enclosed in a coalfield valley, seems to benefit from the temperature effects associated with rain-shadow as markedly as Mansfield perhaps suffers from the effects of radiational cooling. Slight mean annual ranges of temperature mean that the effects of altitude are disproportionately great ; thus the growing season at Buxton, at a height of 1,000 feet, falls to 200 days.

A. Garnett's records for midwinter 1948–9 show air temperatures in the Peak District running below 40–42°F for 85–95% of the time at a height of 2,000 feet, and below 32° for 35–55% of the time. Corresponding figures for valley bottoms 1,000 feet lower are 50–70% of time and 20–30% of time. Scanty though this information is, it provides a useful pointer to the severity of the summit climates, even when no account is taken of the frequency of strong winds at high levels. Furthermore, the contrast between summit and valley would be even greater without the effects of cold-air drainage.

Temperatures published in the *Journal of the Northamptonshire Natural History Society* suggest that stations in incised valleys in the Northamptonshire Uplands experience marked cold-air drainage during highs in winter ; similar effects are to be expected in the Cotswolds, and scarp-slopes probably develop their own local climates in calm weather at all seasons : some of them promote strong thermals during sunny weather in summer. A. B. Tinn and T. J. Chandler supply evidence for the development of urban climates in Nottingham and Leicester.

Garnett has taken continuous temperature records which reveal striking inversions in the Pennine valleys of the upper Derwent system. During high-pressure conditions in summer, valley floors may experience air temperatures at night 16° lower than the air temperatures on summits 1,000 feet above. Summer inversions, however, do not persist throughout the day : temperatures between floor and summit are equalised by 8 or 9 a.m., after which the valley temperatures rise several degrees above those of the summits, remaining the higher until 8 or 9 p.m., when the inversion is re-established. Cold-air drainage is naturally more powerful in winter than in summer : many hillsides receive little or no sun in the winter season, so that winter inversions can be both severe and persistent. In Edale, and in the Hope and Ashop valleys, killing frost in the bottoms can be associated with continuous temperatures of 40°F or more on the higher ground. The inversion is likely to be steepest at low levels, where noonday temperatures commonly run 12° below those of high stations ; in extreme cases the noonday difference may be 20°F.

No station records as much as 35% of possible bright sunshine, and the percentage falls below 30% in a northwestern belt wide enough to include Charnwood Forest. The average daily bright sunshine is less than 3½ hours in the Pennine division, rising to more than 4 hours in the south and east. Table 13 illustrates the contrast, in hours of sunshine, between the low ground and the cloudy highland.

Much of the foggiest district of the British Isles is included in the East Midland region, where an annual average of more than 50 occasions of fog (visibility less than 1,100 yards at 9 a.m.) extends from the Trent, through Sherwood Forest and the coalfield, and into the industrialised West Riding of Yorkshire. A rather larger area, embracing the whole Pennine division and reaching across the Middle Trent, experiences an annual average of 10 or more thick fogs (visibility less than 220 yards at 9 a.m.), the average rising a little above 20 on the Trent itself east of Nottingham.

Mean annual precipitation ranges from below 22·5 inches along the eastern border of the region to above 60 inches on Kinderscout and Bleaklow. There is a very close relationship between altitude and total precipitation (Fig. 19), which does not, however, entirely conceal the tendency for totals to decrease eastward. The Chiltern summits receive an average total of more than 30 inches; the Cotswolds have 27·5 inches or more throughout their high parts, and the isohyet of 27·5 inches encloses Charnwood Forest. Values below 25 inches occur on some of the low ground in the basins of the Thames and its tributaries near Oxford, in much of the basins of the Ouse, Nene, Welland, and Soar, and in the trunk valley of the Trent. The East Moor of Derbyshire is faithfully indicated by a closed isohyet of 35 inches. Mean annual precipitation in the Peak District tends to increase westwards at any given altitude, but, at the same time, maximal isohyets are eccentrically located with respect to summits. The highest closed isohyet associated with Kinderscout, that of 63 inches, encircles as much hillside as top, and the 60-inch line runs right down to the valley floor.

The average daily maximum fall in a single year increases from less than 1·25 inches in the southern half of the region to 1·5 inches in the Pennines, but the disparity in average fall per rain-day is much greater than this. The annual average of rain-days exceeds 200 in the Pennine division, falling below 175 in an irregular belt which stretches southwestward from the direction of the Wash into the valley of the Warwickshire Avon. At Buxton, with 211 rain-days a year (Table 14), the average fall per rain-day is 0·23 inches; at Belvoir Castle, with only 6 rain-days fewer, the average fall per rain-day is only 0·12 inches —less, that is, than the 0·15 inches of Oxford.

Mornings with lying snow average 20 a year on the Chiltern summits and exceed 10 on the Cotswolds. Up the Pennine slopes the prospect

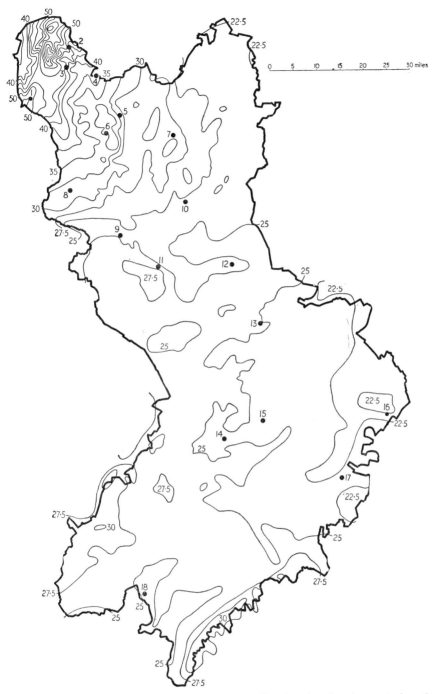

Fig. 19 ISOHYETS OF MEAN ANNUAL PRECIPITATION. Numbered points locate stations for which graphs of régime and dispersion are given.

49

of snow increases abruptly, producing at the most an average of 40 mornings with snow lying (cf. Table 15).

Thunderstorms are just as clearly concentrated as are liability to snow and to fog. Most of the region records an average of between 10 and 15 days with thunder, that is, with a thunderstorm within ten miles; but the total rises above 15 in the Pennine foothills, in the Trias belt west of the Trent, in the Trent valley below Nottingham, and in the Leicestershire Wolds. Here, straddling the Trent near Newark, is the most thundery part of the whole of the British Isles, with more than 20 days with thunder in the average year (Table 16).

As S. Gregory demonstrates, trends of annual rainfall vary spatially. The Pennine division of the East Midlands lies in the area where mean annual totals increased from about 1900 to 1925, with a subsequent fall, followed in turn by a steadying or by a renewed rise. Parts of the south of the region recorded a falling trend in the late nineteenth century as great as 3 inches in range, with an equivalent rise up to 1925 and then a slight decline. At intermediate stations the trends were less clearly defined.

Quite apart from secular trends, however, whether cyclic or non-cyclic, series of records of moderate length are likely to include a few unusually large or unusually small totals. For example, a number of stations in the Trent basin received in May 1932 monthly totals to be expected once in a span of 200 years. Irregular variations of this kind can be offset by probability analysis of the sort developed by E. J. Gumbel for application to rivers but valid also for the treatment of rainfall records. In accordance with the techniques designed by Gumbel, data for selected stations (Table 17) are here standardised to a period of 25 years (Table 18). Standardised monthly means differ little from crude means, but still tend to simplify graphs of annual régime. Standardised values greatly simplify dispersion diagrams, in addition to making them strictly comparable from station to station, and to supplying values of most probable monthly falls. The graphical analysis from which standardised values are derived can also give likely extreme totals, according to the length of period; thus, a rough extrapolation from Buxton (Portobello Bar) suggests that an annual total of 80 inches can be expected at some time during each century.

Standardised monthly means of precipitation are given for ten stations in Table 19, and graphs for all eighteen stations are drawn in Figure 20, where most probable monthly falls are also marked. These graphs, and the dispersion diagrams which follow, are, of course, drawn for 30-day months. The first four stations, all located on high ground, have their lowest rainfall in late spring and early summer, and their highest in late autumn and early winter. July is rainier than June and August at all four places. At most of the remaining fourteen stations a secondary maximum in summer involves more than one month; it is most clearly displayed by the graphs for Matlock, Stanton, and Northampton, which rise from March or April until August. May is wetter than April or June at Clay Cross, Mansfield, Sneinton, Nanpantan, Wellingborough, St Ives, and Sandy, while the May fall at Oxford constitutes the peak of a secondary maximum. The graph for mid-year months is irregular at these eight stations, as also at Rodsley and Uppingham, where April is wetter than March or May. In part at least, this minor peak of spring rainfall is due to high variability in the month concerned. November is the wettest month at all stations but Uppingham, where however the early series of records is perhaps not wholly satisfactory. December generally is markedly drier than November, and at most stations is also drier than January: graphs running on from December into the following months would reveal an irregularity concealed by the conventional arrangement.

The contrast between upland and lowland stations, both in total and in régime, is well brought out by the graphs for Buxton and Stanton; a further contrast, between oceanic and marginally continental régimes, appears in a comparison between the graphs for Stanton and St Ives. As Table 17 shows, the percentage of annual rainfall which comes in the summer months is well below 50 in much of the Pennine division. Its easterly increase across the low ground is well exemplified by the fractions listed for Rodsley, Stanton, and Sneinton, and by the progression from Oxford through Sandy to St Ives.

The forms of dispersion diagrams (Fig. 21) depend on values of standardised median falls, on determinations of variability for single months, and on the length of period used. These diagrams, drawn for a 25-year period, indicate the distributions to be expected if the highest total for any month were the highest to be expected in 25 years. In actual records, of course, higher values occur. Similarly at the lower ends of the graphs the limits are drawn at the lowest totals which may be expected in a run of 25 years, but lower values appear in actual records. The distance between the upper and lower limits, for any month, is a measure of variability independent of the length of period. Low variability is typical of April, September, and December, so that these months are rarely exceptionally dry or exceptionally wet—exceptionally, that is, by comparison with their means.

Although few river-gauges have been operating in the East Midlands for any length of time, something is known of the régimes of surface runoff—enough to provide a check of actual loss against computed evapotranspiration. Regional flood frequency has previously been

Fig. 20 (*below and facing*) MEAN MONTHLY PRECIPITATION, drawn for 30-day months and standardised to a 25-year period. Circles indicate most probable monthly totals. Stations are located on the isohyetal map.

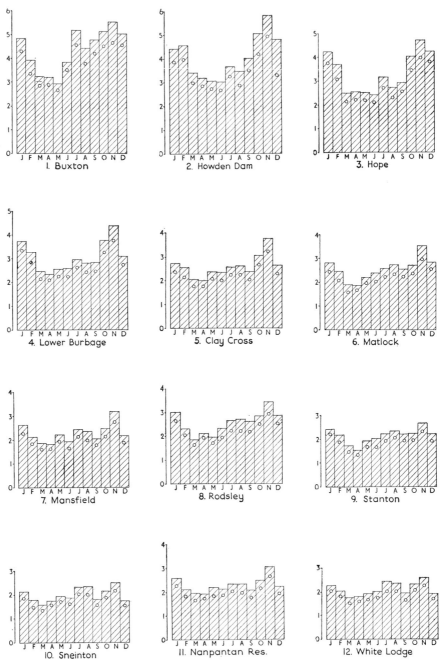

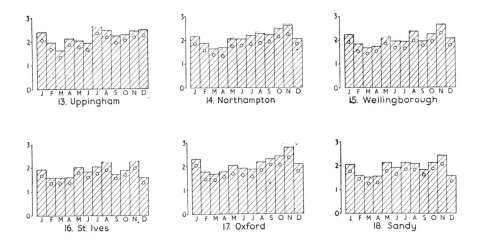

Fig. 21 (*below and overleaf*) DISPERSION DIAGRAMS OF PRECIPITATION, drawn for 30-day months and standardised to a 25-year period. Circles indicate median values. Interquartile bands shaded. Stations are located on the isohyetal map.

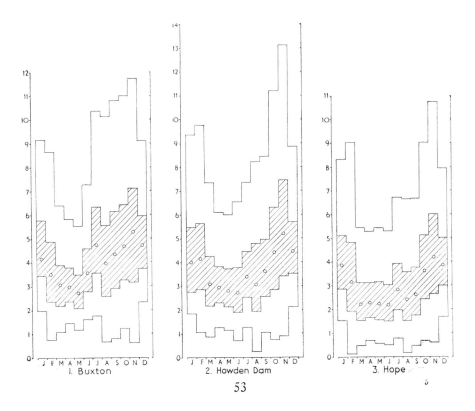

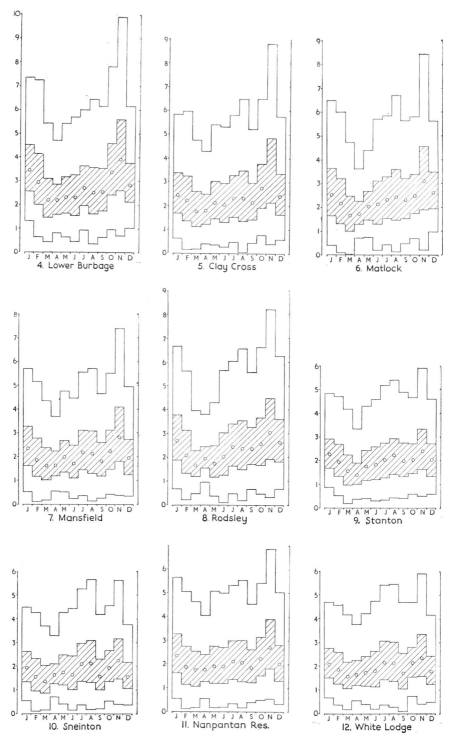

4. Lower Burbage

5. Clay Cross

6. Matlock

7. Mansfield

8. Rodsley

9. Stanton

10. Sneinton

11. Nanpantan Res.

12. White Lodge

54

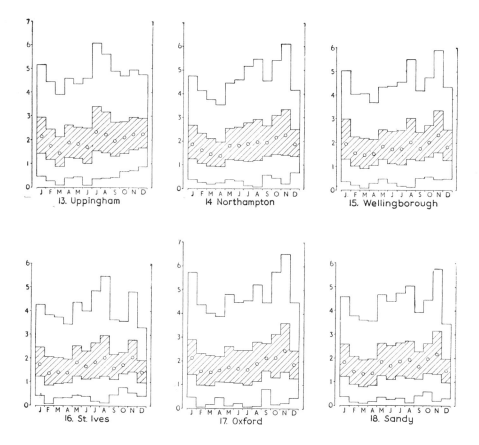

13. Uppingham   14 Northampton   15. Wellingborough

16. St. Ives   17. Oxford   18. Sandy

analysed for the Nene and the Great Ouse, where the annual peak discharge is a linear function of catchment area. Selected types of régime are stated in Table 20 and illustrated in Figures 22, 23, and 24. The means given in the Table are arithmetical means, subject to adjustment by probability analysis; however, they do indicate what actually happened during the years of record. The two stations on the Nene—one above Northampton, and one near the eastern boundary of the region—display closely similar régimes of discharge. Runoff increases sharply from October to November, increases slowly or actually decreases in December, when rainfall decreases, and then rises to a peak in February, after which there is a decline to the lower summer flows which are established in June. On the upper Derwent there is a double peak in winter discharge, reduced rainfall in December being associated with reduced runoff; a steep decline in runoff from February to May/June is followed by an increase into September, and that by a steep increase towards the first winter peak.

Since values of runoff are corrected for abstracted and effluent

55

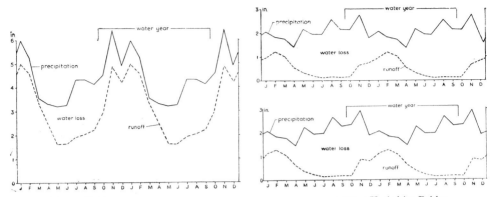

Fig. 22 (*left*) PRECIPITATION AND RUNOFF FOR THE RIVER DERWENT at Yorkshire Bridge (48·9 sq.m.). Means for 30-day months for the water years 1937/8 to 1953/4 inclusive.

Fig. 23 (*top right*) PRECIPITATION AND RUNOFF FOR THE BRAMPTON HEAD OF THE RIVER NENE (89·9 sq.m.). Means for 30-day months for the water years 1940/1 to 1956/7 inclusive.

Fig. 24 (*bottom right*) PRECIPITATION FOR THE RIVER NENE at Orton (631·0 sq.m.). Means for 30-day months for the water years 1940/1 to 1956/7 inclusive.

water, the differences between rainfall and runoff indicate actual loss of water. On the upper Derwent the loss does not vary greatly from year to year, running close to 16 inches (Table 21).[1] This loss is by no means in accordance with the order of loss suggested by calculations of evapotranspiration according to C. W. Thornthwaite (Table 22). Computed potential evapotranspiration at Buxton is plotted in Figure 25 against rainfall, indicating a partial depletion of soil moisture and a subsequent recharge of only 0·33 inches. Considerable additional allowance should probably be made for wind-speed, among other factors.

Calculated losses for the upper Nene are also less than actual losses (Tables 21, 22). The difference may perhaps indicate, however roughly, a soil-moisture recharge of about 2 inches a year on the upper Nene. It may well be significant that the value is highest on the Kislingbury Branch above Dodford, where the catchment is extensively clothed with permeable outwash ; in the other catchments there are extensive outcrops of boulder-clay and of solid Lias clays.

Calculations of the groundwater balance of the Brampton Branch for the water years 1940-1 to 1956-7, allowing for actual runoff as well as for the difference between rainfall and potential evapotranspiration, give a somewhat lower value for soil-moisture depletion/recharge, namely, 1·62 inches ; they also indicate a total recharge of 3·18 inches, the difference of 1·56 inches apparently being recharge of groundwater.

---

[1] Discrepancies between the losses given for the Derwent and the Brampton Branch of the Nene in Table 21, and the apparent losses to be read from Table 20, are due to the use of non-coincident series of records.

Excess groundwater recharge in winter is equalled in the long run by discharge in summer, although there can sometimes be a carry-over from one year to another. The stated value of recharge is, moreover, greater than the 1 inch (approximately) derived from the data of Tables 20 and 21 ; results of all the various calculations are clearly imprecise. At the same time, the actual depletion/recharge of soil moisture cannot fail to be less than the 4 inches allowed by Thornthwaite. The régimes of rainfall, evapotranspiration, depletion/recharge

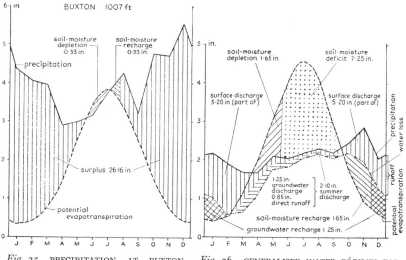

Fig. 25 PRECIPITATION AT BUXTON, with evapotranspiration computed according to C. W. Thornthwaite.

Fig. 26 GENERALISED WATER RÉGIMES FOR THE UPPER NENE.

of soil moisture, discharge/recharge of groundwater, and runoff, possibly combine in the upper Nene basin in the manner illustrated in Figure 26.

This graph is meant to illustrate the several water balances. It does not imply that soil-moisture depletion has been completed by early June. However, graphs of evapotranspiration and rainfall for other stations suggest that, even if certain soils can take in the equivalent of 4 inches of rain, depletion is likely to be effective from midsummer onwards, and that the deficit is widely of the order of 3 inches or more, increasing into the Trent valley and into the east of the region. Depletion is deferred at lowland stations in the west of the region, while stations in the coalfield belt have calculated deficits of 1 inch or less which become apparent in August. As has already been pointed out, the calculated deficit for Buxton is nil. Although the ratio of rain to potential evapotranspiration at Buxton does not help to explain the loss of water which is known to occur in the highland catchments, it does show that heavy falls on the high ground are likely to result in high discharges, except in most exceptional seasons. The heavy falls of May 1932 caused serious flooding on the middle Trent.

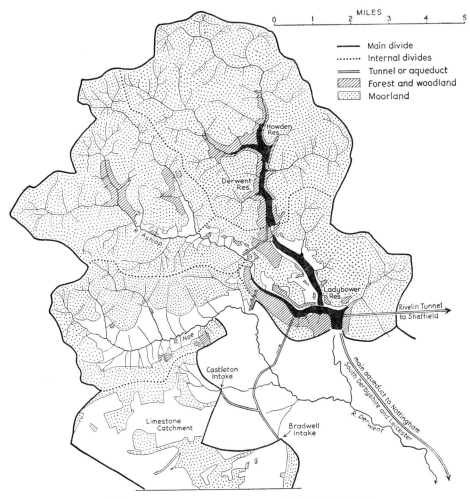

Fig. 27   THE DERWENT VALLEY WATER SUPPLY SCHEME.

Floods of a contrasted kind, nourished in part by snowmelt, affected the Nene and Ouse early in 1947. A third type of flood, the flash flood provoked by thunder-rain of high intensity, has been described by F. A. Barnes and H. R. Potter for some left-bank tributaries of the Dove. Occurring in August 1947, the flash floods of southern Derbyshire led to discharges estimated as high as 1·56 in./hour. Barnes and Potter conclude that liability to flooding has been increased by deforestation and improvement of drainage, and infer changes in régime sufficient to renew, or to intensify, erosion in the narrow dumbles.

Practice and problems of water supply contrast strongly between the north and south of the region, as can readily be seen from a comparison of the Derwent valley with the valley of the Great Ouse upstream of the Fens. The Derwent drains high moorland country cut by deeply incised valleys, where the mean annual rainfall exceeds 50 inches. Here a series of works has been constructed by the Derwent Valley Water Board, constituted in 1899 to include representatives of Sheffield, Derby, Derby County, and Nottingham, that is, of authorities dealing with town supplies on the Pennine flanks and margins, or, as at Leicester, with more distant towns whose local supplies were small. The scheme relies mainly on the impounding reservoirs of Howden, Derwent, and Ladybower, with a total capacity of 10,410 million gallons. The works, completed by instalments in the period 1912–60, comprise mainly the three impounding reservoirs of Howden, Derwent, and Ladybower, but also include a diversion from the Ashop to Derwent Reservoir, a second diversion from the Noe to Ladybower Reservoir, and two intakes from the limestone plateau. Water is carried to Sheffield by the Rivelin Tunnel, and to Derby, Nottingham, Leicester, and South Derbyshire consumers by the main aqueduct along the Derwent valley (Fig. 27).

The catchment area above Ladybower Dam (Plate 12) is nearly 50 square miles; the diversion from the Noe adds 11½ square miles, while the limestone catchment is estimated at 16½ square miles; this catchment is, however, not fully utilised. Nearly 50 million gallons of water per day are distributed. A group of local authorities in Derbyshire is entitled to make a prior claim of some 7½ million gallons a day, after which the remainder is available for distribution in the following proportions.

	%
Leicester	35·72
Sheffield	25
Nottingham	25
South Derbyshire Water Board	14·28

Sheffield's quarter-share currently amounts to more than 10 million gallons per day—about one-third of the total town supply. Apart from additional exploitation of the limestone catchment, possibilities of increasing supplies from the Derbyshire Pennines appear limited ; it is for this reason that proposals exist for taking water for Sheffield from the Yorkshire Derwent.

Afforestation has been going on since 1908, mainly on the steep hillsides by the three reservoirs. The Water Board has planted nearly 2,000 acres [1]—that is, about 5% of the catchment, the limestone plateau section excluded.

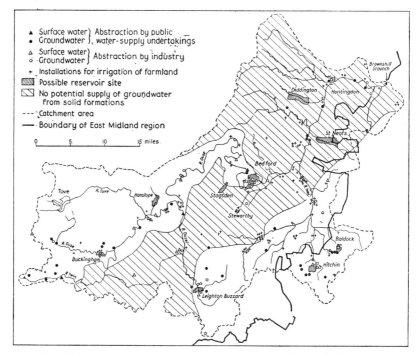

Fig. 28   WATER SUPPLY IN THE OUSE VALLEY above Brownshill in 1960.

Above Brownshill Staunch, where tides make themselves felt, the Great Ouse drains 1,170 square miles. Whereas the problems in the rainy South Pennines are those of supply to large and growing towns, the prospective difficulties in the Ouse valley result from a combination of low rainfall, high evapotranspiration, and rising demand of water for irrigation. Mean annual rainfall varies from about 28 to 22 inches across the catchment ; loss by evapotranspiration is about $17\frac{1}{2}$ inches, so that the equivalent of some $6\frac{1}{2}$ inches of rain is alone available for surface discharge and for consumption. Much re-use of water already occurs : in the dry summer of 1959 the water reaching Bedford had

1961 figure.

been used twice over, even before half the flow was drawn in by the waterworks there.

From Bedford downstream, prospects of groundwater from solid formations are negligible in the trunk valleys and in the valleys of tributaries except the Izel (Fig. 28); above Bedford, parts of the Ouzel and Twin catchments also lack potential groundwater supplies. Undertakings marked as taking groundwater where the solid formations are not water-bearing rely mainly on wells in valley fills or in other superficial deposits, although the Lower Greensand beneath the Gault contains artesian water which yields about 1 million gallons a day at Biggleswade.

Irrigation of crops and grass has greatly increased since the Second World War, principally by means of sprinklers operated by tractor-driven pumps. The demand, concentrated in the period April–October when river discharges are typically low (Fig. 24), ranges from the equivalent of 7 or 8 inches of rainfall in one year in ten, to nil in two or three years in ten. The extent of irrigated land in 1960 was 5,200 acres (less than 1% of the total catchment), requiring some 1,400 million gallons a year on the average, equivalent to about $2\frac{1}{2}$ inches of rainfall. While the annual rate of increase in area irrigated was running in 1960 at about 3·5% in the catchment from Bedford to Brownshill Staunch, it was 15% in the upper basin; the combined rate is alarming, for nearly 40% of the total catchment is potentially irrigable, and capable of exerting a demand equivalent to half the existing supply of the whole country. If the possible reservoirs marked in Figure 28 were impounded, they could serve with the assistance of pumped storage to supply irrigation water to some 70,000 acres. Pending the construction of these or alternative works, however, the outlook is of mounting abstraction from rivers, and of increasingly noticeable reductions of surface discharge at times of low flow.

CHAPTER 5

SOILS AND VEGETATION

EVEN in those parts of the region which are neither farmed nor built over, the plant cover has been greatly modified by people and by domestic animals. Grazing, clearing, and burning may be supposed to begin with the arrival of Neolithic herdsmen, so that a vegetation map for the beginning of Neolithic times would illustrate the region in a wild state. Since then, however, climatic changes have continued to provoke changes both in vegetation and in soils, so that climax communities appropriate to existing conditions would differ strongly, in places, from those of eight thousand years ago. It thus seems pointless to attempt a reconstruction of the once-continuous cover of wild plants.

Although pollen analysis may in time reveal the whole course of clearance, reclamation, drainage, and breaking, it is not yet possible to map the extension of farming in Iron-Age and Romano-British times. Similarly, although some place-names record Dark-Age assessments of the vegetation cover, it is not yet practicable to trace in detail the pressing back of forest by settlement, or the whole slow process of clearing, over-grazing, and over-exploitation which went far to ruin the once-extensive forests of the region, even before the Civil War and the later expansion of smelting with charcoal occasioned reckless felling. For all that, the most resistant blocks of woodland, marsh, and upland bog can be located with some confidence. Detailed information is available about the present status and past history of a number of sites, so that the likely wild state of some least-modified parts of the region can be specified, and the cover of the most cultivated parts, as it survived into the Dark Ages and the early Middle Ages, can be inferred.

With certain exceptions, soils are much more difficult to treat than is vegetation. Lithological character of parent materials and soil texture are quite well known for most parts of the region; soil-profile characteristics are not. Until the work of the Soil Survey is done, information of the greatest relevance to geography must remain wanting. Nevertheless, something can be made of profiles from individual sites, some of which fortunately correspond with the sites occupied by plant communities at their least modified.

Distribution of solid rocks, and slope of the ground, probably constitute the main controls of soil distribution north of the Trent, even though glacially re-worked material may be more extensive there than is usually thought. Soil boundaries do not coincide precisely in detail with outcrop boundaries, especially at the feet of steep slopes, but correspondence is close enough to make the Table of solid formations a useful system of reference in the discussion of soils. Uncultivated vegetation north of the Trent is most widespread on the grits and shales of the Peak District and on the Bunter outcrop, with lesser concentrations on the Carboniferous Limestone. The following review of its chief manifestations draws heavily on the work of C. E. Moss, T. W. Woodhead, J. W. Hopkinson, O. E. Balme, V. M. Conway, and W. H. Pearsall.

The Millstone Grit, rising high into the rainy Atlantic air, weathers into coarse-grained and permeable rock-waste. Except on flushed sites, severe leaching in cool conditions tends strongly to promote podsolisation. Immature humus-iron podsols are thought to occur widely beneath the moors, that is, on the drier heaths, where a shallow layer of sandy raw humus is characteristic. On the summit plateaux, however, profile drainage is poor enough to favour the growth of peat, and organic soils with their exaggerated A horizon are widely distributed on gentle slopes at high levels. Both on the grits and on the shales, soils are highly siliceous, with a lime content ranging from 0·02% to 0·05%.

The principal peat-former at the present day is cotton-grass. Sphagnum, reported by Farey as widespread a hundred and fifty years ago, is now uncommon except in wet soakways. Burning and sheep-grazing seem responsible for the rise to dominance of cotton-grass, which Pearsall estimates to cover some 500 square miles of the southern Pennines; its supersession of sphagnum is well documented from Ringinglow Bog, where very thick peat occupies 400 acres of ground.

Attractive though it be in close view, in the mass and at a distance cotton-grass moss looks bleak; its sombre aspect is intensified by the greyness of the sheep, with fleeces discoloured by a fall of soot reaching eight tons a month on each square mile.

The South Pennine peats today are degenerating at their margins, as can be well seen on Kinderscout and on Bleaklow. Lengthening headstreams gash and drain the edges of the moss, permitting bilberry, cloudberry, and crowberry to come in; but these also vanish as erosion continues, and the peat itself becomes stripped entirely away. Growth, dissection, removal, and re-growth of the mosses seem to constitute a natural cycle responding to the very wet climate of the last 2,500 years; but rotational burning practised to encourage the grouse-sheltering heather, and minor shifts in climate, may have speeded degeneration. During the Boreal Phase, forest ran 200 or 250 feet above its present limits—that is, to about 1,500 feet—as is abundantly shown by the remains of trees exposed by peat erosion. Thickening and spreading in the Atlantic Phase, the peat displaced the pine, oak, elm, alder, and hazel in turn; at lower levels, forest yielded to heather moor or to grass heath. Slightly increased dryness in the sub-Boreal favoured a partial dominance of ling and bilberry on wet sites, without interrupting the forest history, and renewed climatic deterioration later enabled the mosses to reach their present extents, and thicknesses which in places exceed 15 feet.

Natural recession of the forest has been reinforced by felling and grazing, which first became severe about 1100 and reached a maximum of depletion in the seventeenth century. Strings of trees today run up the steep-sided cloughs on all sides of the blocks of hills; birchwood, nowhere extensive, typifies the range between 1,250 and 1,000 feet; oaks are stunted above 800 feet, but grow to full size at lower levels; streams on the shales can be fringed by long thickets of alder, willow, and ash. C. E. Moss may have over-stressed the retrogressive nature of Pennine shrub in tracing various passages from oakwood and birchwood at the one extreme to siliceous grassland or moor at the other. But siliceous grassland, diversified by bracken on sheltered and well-drained sites, is in fact extensive, and the native trees persist at the higher altitudes with obvious difficulty.

Heather moors occupy many intermediate positions between the peaty mosses and the siliceous grasslands, rarely exceeding 1,500 feet in height. A broken belt on the steeply descending western side is about a mile wide, while a second belt on the gentler slopes of the east reaches a width of three miles. A third concentration occurs in the upper valleys of the Derwent and the Westend.

So bleak, open, and uncared-for does the unfenced Millstone Grit country seem, and so closely is deciduous woodland confined to narrow steep slopes on the hillsides, that it is difficult to appreciate the extent of forest clearing, or the probable effects of grazing and turf cutting. Turbary rights were held if not exercised by dwellers on the moorland edge as late as the end of the nineteenth century. Large intakes made after 1750 in the range 900–1,500 feet affected heather moor and siliceous grassland, where reclamation by burning, clearing of stones, flaking-off of shallow peat, ploughing, and seeding after oats was still in progress fifty years ago. The principal modification now under way is afforestation: Hope Forest consists chiefly of pine, in various stages of growth, while the mainly experimental Matlock Forest contains spruces and larches also.

C. E. Moss was the first to recognise ashwood as the climax community of the limestone dales of Derbyshire. Where it still survives it is typical of damp valleys, inaccessible cliffs, and screes; one of the finest examples is the dense, feathery wood of Griffe Grange Valley above Cromford, where a tunnel of elegant trees almost encloses the road. Dovedale, Lathkill Dale, and Monsal Dale are other sites beautified in similar fashion. Accessible land on the limestone plateaux is generally enclosed, supporting a biotic climax of fescue-agrostis pasture maintained by heavy grazing and occasional manuring. The distinctive green of well-managed grassland (best seen shortly after mowing) is bright and clear, but heather and bilberry come in if the land is neglected.

Soils developed on the limestone include the whole range from rendzina to podsol, even without the siliceous soils of some cherty cappings and the soils developed on igneous outcrops. There is a corresponding vegetational range from ashwood and calcareous grassland to moorland. Balme, in a detailed study of Cressbrook Dale and Wardlow Hay Cop, distinguishes a clear edaphic and vegetational zoning, closely allied to the form of the ground and to the results of weathering, as follows.

(a) Dense thickets, including ash, on the shallow immature rendzinas of lower slopes and screes, with calcareous grassland on the very shallow and mobile soils of slopes in excess of 30°.

(b) Close fescue sward, on the incipiently leached rendzinas of stable scree with slopes less than 20° but greater than 30°.

(c) Fescue-agrostis grassland on slopes of about 20°, with brown-earths distinctly acid at the surface and reddened by mobilised ferric iron.

(d) Restricted moorland flora, including bilberry, hair-grass, and mat-grass on the immature podsols of slopes of about 10°.

Mature podsols, although actually confined to such high plateaux as Bradwell Moor, Balme identifies as the climatic climax. Claims that terra rossa is present may, in part, be mistakenly based on the occurrence of Triassic fillings in sinks. The development from rendzina through brownearth to podsol—a process of chemical differentiation—can clearly be indefinitely delayed in the special circumstances of cliffs and live screes.

It has come to be widely believed, but quite without justification, that the Coal-Measure country of Derbyshire and Nottinghamshire possesses cold and unpromising soils. Natural soils developed on the extensive shales are however quite calcareous, and have long been cultivated. As Moss observes, cultivation on the Coal Measures goes higher than on the other members of the Carboniferous system, and Coal-Measure hills are usually farmed up to their summits. The main exception occurs south-southwest of Dronfield, where part of the outcrop is incorporated in the belt of intact upland (Fig. 10). Any wide view of the coalfield, apart from predominantly industrial sites, includes much farmland, with arable extensive, as, for instance, west of Bolsover. The few open and uncultivated parts carry heather associations on the sandstones and grassland associations on the shales; but in its former wild state the Coal-Measure country was probably well covered by oakwood, varying as to species with the parent material of soils which, on the shales, fell chiefly into the brownearth group. Strings and belts of oak, giving a distinctly bosky appearance to the well-dissected western part of the outcrop northwest and southwest of Chesterfield, strongly suggest former oakwood.

Although most of the backslope of the Magnesian Limestone cuesta is nowadays under the plough, the reddish coloration, the rather heavy nature of the soils, and the dominance of oak in some patches of woodland, suggest that oakwood was once extensive, and that the natural soils tended towards terra rossa. Difficulties in classification are similar to those encountered with Clay-with-Flints soils in Chalk country; and, again as in Chalk country, the scarp faces develop rendzinas. Turf dominated by broom-grass, accompanied by abundant sheep's fescue, grows on parts of the scarp; but the most remarkable plant assemblages occur where streams trench through the grips. G. Jackson and J. Sheldon characterise the cliff tops by birch, elm, oak, and yew, in addition to the ash which is rising to dominance, and describe the wedging of cliff faces, kept irregular by frequent rockfall, by the yew; elm is the principal coloniser of scree slopes, while lime grows in the grips as a native tree.

Highly specialised conditions obtain in the Bunter belt. The underlying rocks consist predominantly of coarse sand, which can amount to 90% of the total bulk; the clay fraction is very small, and the adsorptive and capillary powers of the highly friable and permeable soils are very low indeed. Lime content at the surface is of the order of 0·15%. Since the water-table lies well below the surface, except along the valley bottoms and the feet of scarps, where seepage occurs, leaching is usual; but the very permeability of the rocks, and the great depth of the water-table, are rather paradoxically capable of offsetting to some degree the obvious tendency to podsolisation. J. W. Hopkinson reports thin surface peat and patches of pan from Rufford Forest, which with Clipstone Forest was once extensively in heath; but recent exposures here alongside forestry roads usually show shallow and markedly immature podsols, no more than a foot in depth and lacking a marked horizon of illuviation. Soil erosion can take place in the absence of tree cover. The danger of blowing is greatest in dry springs, while surface wash and even gullying can follow heavy rainstorms, especially in summer. Soil erosion would be severe if the Bunter rocks were capable of sustaining steeper slopes while still developing loose soils, while even in existing conditions Hopkinson regards the area as near the limit of cultivation.

Much of Sherwood Forest was scrub or heath in the late eighteenth century (Fig. 29), by which time the plant cover had been very greatly modified. Despite the well-known presence of aged oaks, it seems unlikely that Sherwood was ever continuous. The perambulation of 1232 recorded extensive tracts of heather, gorse, and broom; the survey of 1609, dealing with a total area of 90,000 acres, classed fewer than 10,000 acres as woodland and gave 45,000 acres as inclosures [sic] and 35,000 acres as enclosures [sic]. Among the single events of clearing or devastation were the fire of 1624, which affected the area between the Maun and the Meden; felling during the Civil War, which cleared every tree from Clipstone Park; and clear felling in some parts, with military training in others, during both World Wars. Hopkinson however identifies various groupings: dry oakwood, ranging from open park to closed oakwood; scrub, mainly on the typically wide waysides; grass heath, liable to be overrun by traveller's-joy, bracken, and heather; heath proper; and various transitional communities.

Oakwood, when clear cut, regenerates with difficulty, and birch and bracken rapidly overrun sites of felling. Areas left open support abundant *Clematis Vitalba* (traveller's-joy), which deeply tinges the views of midsummer; unrecorded in the county flora of 1839, this plant seems to have spread from colliery tip-heaps. Clipstone and Rufford Forests, now in the hands of the Forestry Commission, are planted with trees selected with reference to soils, profile drainage, and air pollution: Corsican pine is the first choice on the Bunter Sandstone, with fringes of hardwood along the margins. As yet, the new forests are capable only of producing small poles for mines and farms.

K. C. Edwards states that the soils of the Keuper Marl belt are slightly podsolised, but it is uncertain what allowance should be made for the centuries of impoverishment which followed Dark-Age settlement. Although mechanical analysis shows that much of the total bulk falls into the grades of fine clay or fine silt, textural variations, from loamy on the Waterstones to clay-loamy on the marls, are significant in agriculture. The usual slight lime deficiency, in combination with the long history of tillage, perhaps suggests that the natural soils belonged to the brownearth group, developed under deciduous woodland in which oaks were prominent. In any event, the natural Keuper soils cannot fail to have contrasted with the loose Bunter soils to the west, or with the soils developed on terraces or floodplain to the east.

Conditions of the main Keuper Marl belt of Nottinghamshire are

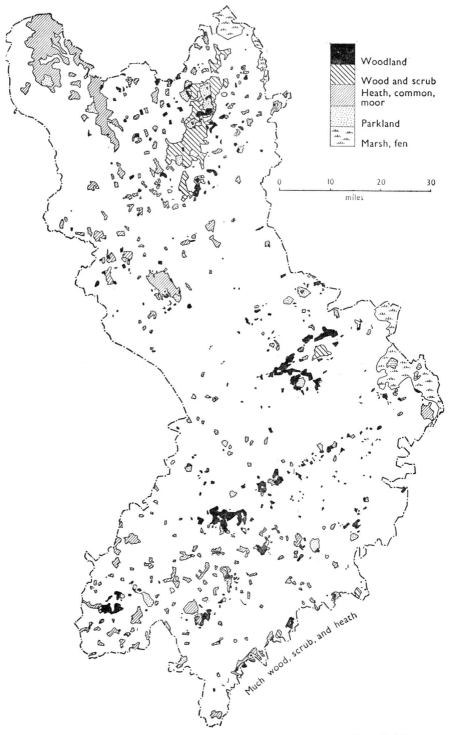

Woodland
Wood and scrub
Heath, common, moor
Parkland
Marsh, fen

0   10   20   30
miles

Much wood, scrub, and heath

Fig. 29 SOME ITEMS OF LAND-USE IN THE LATE EIGHTEENTH CENTURY. Compiled from
contemporary maps, plans, and descriptions.

reduplicated in some areas south and east of the Trent, but the main edaphic contrasts here separate boulder-clay, outwash, limestone, and solid clays from one another, with Charnwood Forest constituting a special case. Information about the profile characteristics of its soils ranges from very detailed to very scanty,[1] while the variety of outcrops would compel a full account to be both long and in some degree repetitive. Summary statements are necessarily so brief as to be of little value—such, for example, as that the clay formations suffer impeded profile drainage and tend to develop a gley horizon, that true rendzinas occur on steep slopes, both on the Jurassic limestones and on the Chalk, and that the lime content of clays, both drift and solid, varies significantly and is reflected in the composition of woodland.

Igneous and pyroclastic rocks in Charnwood Forest weather slowly into shallow and highly siliceous soils. Dry oakwood, conifers, siliceous grassland, and bracken, all characteristic of the present scene of woody parkland, result from planting, regeneration, or degeneration. The primitive cover has long yielded to the indiscriminate felling and common grazing which reduced most of the Forest to a condition of heath or scrub by the late eighteenth century (Fig. 29). Most of the remainder of the southern division of the region was at one time wooded, although the forest cover may never have been so intact, in any large area, as it now is in the best-managed woods. Deer in the once very extensive royal hunting preserves, and deer and cattle after disforestation, are unlikely to have caused less damage than in Sherwood. A. G. Tansley's general review suggests that the former natural woodland consisted of damp oakwood on outcrops of Oxford, Kimmeridge, and Gault Clays; the Lower Lias Clay, being somewhat calcareous, was suited rather to ash-oak-hazelwood, with impure ashwood on the Hydraulic Limestones. The rendzinas of the Cotswold scarps and valley sides, kept permanently immature and lime-rich by weathering and creep, still carry semi-natural beechwoods in places; but I. Hepburn holds that natural calcareous grassland is fairly represented by the rich flora of long-abandoned stone quarries. A. S. Watts, discussing the Chilterns, recognises the natural importance of juniper, beech, hawthorn, and calcareous grassland on the scarp face, demonstrating at the same time the significance of differences in slope, in depth and dryness of soil, and in biotic factors which include the grazing of rabbits.

Conditions appropriate to limestone scarps are modified on the

---

[1] The 1958 Report of the Soil Survey listed the following East Midland sheets as in progress: 125 (Derby), 142 (Melton Mowbray), 220 (Leighton Buzzard), and 254 (Henley). The Survey of Sheet 238 (Aylesbury) had been completed at this date; the map was published in 1962.

limestone plateaux, where, however, soils can still be shallow and lime-rich, and where they are typically brashy. G. R. Clarke places the red and brown calcareous soils of the Inferior Oolite limestone, the Great Oolite limestone, and the Cornbrash in the rendzina group. At their shallowest and driest, such soils appear likely at one time to have supported heath, grass heath, or calcareous grassland, but elsewhere (as on the Cornbrash and the Coral Rag) there were expanses of ashwood. Coarse sandy soils developed on the Lower Greensand of Oxfordshire fall into the brownearth group, even though they are free-draining; on the higher-standing, thicker, and highly permeable Lower Greensand of Bedfordshire, podsolic soils are common. This particular outcrop and the Gault excepted, the pedological relationships of solid formations, in the range Lower Lias-Chalk, are well summarised by G. R. Clarke (see Table 23).

The country beneath the Chiltern scarp reveals a marked dis-cordance between outcrops as shown on the geological map and distribution of parent material as mapped by the Soil Survey.[1] Drift, including sludge of various descriptions, is far more extensive than formerly suspected, and the Gault has been largely re-worked, whether by ice or by frost-stirring. With a few slight omissions, the recorded geology of a sample area measuring four miles by two is shown by outcrop boundaries in the upper part of Figure 30: most of the area is based on Gault, with Lower and Middle Chalk coming in successively down-dip. The soil map (lower part of the Figure) presents a high contrast. Most of the total extent of soil is based on some kind of sludge or downwash, or on disturbed solid material. Complex though the soil pattern is, this sample map merely indicates some of the local variations which typify the whole district. Table 24 summarises the variety of parent material and profile within the sample area.

The climax vegetation of dry oakwood on the Bedfordshire humus podsols was formerly replaced, in practice, by much heather, gorse, and bracken. The existing woods, with their prominent conifers, result principally from eighteenth-century and later planting. The woods of the interfluves farther north, however, are the direct descen-dants, greatly altered though they be, of the primitive forest. With the exception of Wychwood, the main blocks of woodland existing south of the Trent in the late eighteenth century were almost precisely located on the Chalky Boulder Clay, where that formation is most nearly intact on the least-dissected divides between the trunk rivers. The very name of the old forest of east Leicestershire had gone, and

[1] The sample map (lower part of Fig. 30), and the accompanying descriptions of soils in Table 24, have been adapted from material supplied by the Soil Survey in advance of publication of Sheet 238 (Aylesbury), and are used here by permission.

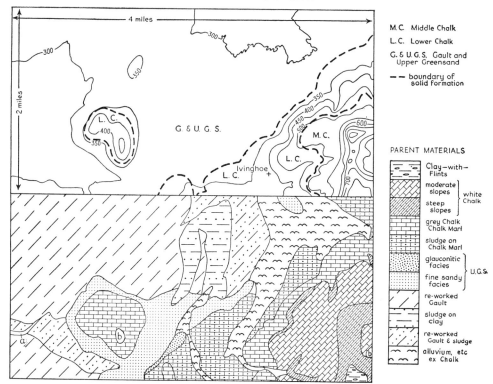

M.C. Middle Chalk

L.C. Lower Chalk

G. & U.G.S. Gault and
Upper Greensand

— — boundary of
solid formation

PARENT MATERIALS

Clay—with—
Flints

moderate
slopes   white
steep   Chalk
slopes

grey Chalk
Chalk Marl

sludge on
Chalk Marl

glauconitic
facies   U.G.S.

fine sandy
facies

re-worked
Gault

sludge on
clay

re-worked
Gault & sludge

alluvium, etc
ex Chalk

Fig. 30 COMPARISON BETWEEN SOLID GEOLOGY (*upper panel*) AND THE PARENT MATERIAL OF SOILS (*lower panel*) for part of the Chiltern scarp and the adjacent subedge. (*a*) Chalky alluvium ; (*b*) flinty and Chalky head over Chalk.

very little but the name remained of Leighfield Forest on the borders of Rutland and Huntingdonshire ; but Rockingham Forest between the Nene and the Welland, Yardley Chase, Salcey Forest and Whittle-wood Forest between the Ouse and the Nene, Whaddon Chase in the angle between Ouse and Ouzel, and a further belt of wood reaching from Oxford to Winslow, were still easily identifiable by their remnants (Fig. 29). In all these, ash/oakwood seems to have been the leading type. Oak and ash are prominent today, both in the managed woods and in the surrounding hedgerows where farmland has replaced trees. Without doubt, abundance of ash is a response to the lime content of the boulder-clay soils at depth. Little is yet known of surface conditions, which are likely to differ with the texture of the drift, but the boulder-clay soils are usually tenacious, moisture-retentive, and decalcified to no great distance below the surface. They are no more difficult to cultivate than are some of the long-farmed soils at lower levels. The persistence of woodland upon them is thus scarcely to be explained either by difficulty of clearing or by difficulty of farming; an allowance of undetermined magnitude must be made for a course of settlement which involved penetration along the valleys and left the clearing of the interfluves long deferred and still uncompleted.

Despite its close association with obstinate woodland, the boulder-clay is not uniform. In places it contains a high proportion of sand and gravel, without being classifiable as outwash. The outwash proper is richer in lime than might be supposed, decalcification rarely affecting more than a very few feet, and abundant Chalk pebbles coming in below. Even where it is thickest, as in southeast Leicestershire on part of the site of Glacier Lake Harrison, percolation can be checked by a high content of clay or silt and by flatness of interfluves; the surface soils are moreover tenacious enough to lie in ridge-and-furrow and to bear long-established permanent pasture. Coarse outwash on well-drained sites might promise to develop soils incapable of supporting woodland; but, as Moss observes for Derbyshire, *Quercus robor* has long tap-roots which can strike deeply into fluvio-glacial sands. The emparked pieces of rolling land on the outwash-train extending through Watford Gap suggest that, in the wild state, the climax vegetation would be impure oakwood, with abundant hazel and numerous bracken-clad glades. These supposed conditions are well illustrated on the Fawsley estate.

In this southern division of the region, two specific kinds of site are of special interest—floodplains and fens. They illustrate respectively the influence of severely impeded profile drainage and the development of organic soils. The floodplain of the Trent, which separates the northern and southern divisions of the region, is unique. Edwards justly states that its characteristics are inconstant: its lithology and its profile drainage are affected not only by the presence of gravel islands, but also by variations in moisture conditions which relate to intermittent rejuvenation. Differences in land use, as mapped in the 1930s, quite well reflect differing effectiveness of natural drainage. Earlier, in the late eighteenth century, most of the Trent floodplain was already improved, except for some marshy patches in the north and the badly drained carrland on the regional boundary. The carrland is, properly speaking, an extension across administrative limits of country belonging to another region: it forms part of the rim of an area where post-glacial alluvium was first colonised by woodland and subsequently by raised-bog peat, localised growth of which continued into the late nineteenth century.

The floodplains of misfit streams south of the Trent are not, in general, broken by gravel islands—certainly not in their middle and upper reaches—and, so far as is known, everywhere display the results of seriously impeded profile drainage. The uppermost 4 feet or so of a typical profile consists of silt and sand, with a matrix of clay sufficiently bulky to produce prismatic or cloddy structure on drying; colours near the surface are dull, but bright mottling sets in with depth; in the lower part occurs a deep gley horizon, with proved thicknesses exceeding 12 feet. This lower part of the profile is diversified in Cotswold valleys by malm and peat; similar intercalations are suspected in the continuation of the limestone belt towards the northeast.

Considerably detailed information is forthcoming about the Fenland margins, chiefly from the work of H. Godwin and his associates. The larger of the two extensions of fen into the East Midland region, that of Huntingdonshire, is singular in containing much acid peat. M. E. D. Poore relates the acidity of the raised bog existing at Holme ' fen ' until the mid-nineteenth century to a small catchment area based on base-poor rocks. Woodwalton Fen is also thought to have been mainly bog, with acid flushes, before it was disturbed; the calcareous meres of Ugg and Trundle formed about 2500 B.C. on the surface of bog peat. But although acid plant communities persisted into historical times, the area was easily accessible from adjacent higher ground and was early exploited. Extensive cutting removed nearly all the upper, acid, layer, and the last complete cutting in the second half of the nineteenth century exposed basic fen peat. Wooded portions include birchwood, with some oak and alder; *Molinia* forms the dominant field layer on the so-called heath, being associated there with ling and bell-heather.

CHAPTER 6

PEOPLING, SETTLEMENT, AND ECONOMY

PATTERNS of prehistoric and Roman geography in the East Midland region are traceable only in part, and then with difficulty. The relevant structures and foundations make a small total contribution to the existing landscape. A coherent system of Roman settlements and connecting roads has but recently emerged from laborious research, while the circumstances of pre-Roman times are but patchily indicated by clustered finds. Events prior to the Christian era, and their accidental imprints on the present scene, will therefore be treated summarily on the basis of accounts which are, in the main, general and comprehensive rather than local and special. This is not to deny the typological significance of Creswell or the importance of careful studies of the material equipment, agronomy, and social organisation of pre-Roman inhabitants, nor yet to minimise the absorbing interest of prehistoric sites. However, the post-glacial extensions of peat on the Pennine upland, the post-glacial infilling of large river channels, and the post-glacial erosion of some terraces, all combine to ensure that the distribution of pre-Roman remains is but imperfectly known.

Palaeoliths of Abbevillian type indicate the presence of man in the region during the Antepenultimate Interglacial. The richest finds of unrolled palaeoliths occur in the gravels of the former channel of the Thames between Caversham and Henley—beyond the regional boundary—in the gravels between Dorchester and the Chiltern scarp, and in terrace deposits at Hilton in the Trent valley north of Burton. Middle Acheulian implements, referable to the Penultimate Interglacial, have been obtained from the Summertown-Radley Terrace and the basal part of the Wolvercote Channel in the Oxford area, where finds of later type are scanty. At Hilton, on the other hand, the sequence continues with Levalloisian and Clactonian implements, which belong in part to the Last Interglacial.

Ice spread over all, or nearly all, the region during the Antepenultimate and Penultimate Glacials, when prehistoric men can scarcely have maintained themselves so close to the glacier fronts. During the Last Glacial, however, *Homo neanderthalensis* lived at Creswell, Whaley, and Ash Tree Cave near Whitwell, being dislodged only at stadial maxima. The Creswell record overlaps with that of Hilton, showing that *Homo neanderthalensis* produced implements of Mousterian type, used fire in cooking, wore skins and personal

74

ornaments, and probably practised magic. As climate improved with the onset of the second interstadial of the Last Glacial, Neanderthal man was permanently supplanted by *Homo sapiens*, who introduced at Creswell an Upper Aurignacian culture. This, evolving slowly, produced the developed Aurignacian which is styled Creswellian. The third stadial of the Last Glacial produced a stalagmite layer which sealed in the whole former deposit at Creswell.

Mesolithic penetration of the north of the region was probably wide, but the record is undoubtedly obscured in much of the upland by peat formed in the Atlantic Phase of post-glacial time. Peculiarly enough, little Mesolithic evidence comes from the limestone plateau, although a settlement has been identified near Taddington. The Neolithic and Bronze Ages, which produced earthworks and megaliths, have left signs abundant enough to show that much of the region lay, during the relevant culture-periods, outside the main concentrations of agricultural and stock-raising communities. The Peak District and the extension of the Cotswolds into Oxfordshire were the chief areas of Neolithic and Bronze Age occupance, although the Chalk belt along the southeast boundary was also well settled. The Severn-Cotswold group of chamber tombs has three certain outposts in Oxfordshire— at Wychwood (Slatepits Copse), at Rollright (the Whispering Knights), and at Enstone (The Hoar Stone)—but additional possible tombs remain to be examined. Henge monuments include the stone circles of Rollright and Cornwell, and the henges of Dorchester ; causewayed camps are known at Maiden Bower near Dunstable, and at Abingdon just outside the region. It seems likely that Neolithic immigrants worked along the Cotswold cuesta, along the Berkshire Chalk, and possibly also up the Thames. The terraces both upstream and downstream of Oxford, especially the Summertown-Radley Terrace, were firmly colonised, providing a link between the chalkland and the Jurassic limestone belt. Bronze Age barrows in this southern part of the region have suffered much from the plough, but still appear as cropmarkings on air photographs : Bronze Age finds are massed on the terraces from Standlake downstream.

Chamber tombs occur in Derbyshire at Five Wells near Taddington, at Green Low, and at Minninglow near Grangemill. At Arbor Low, 5 miles southwest of Bakewell, is an embanked stone circle 150 feet in diameter. Bronze Age circles include those of Froggatt Edge, Eyam Moor, and Harthill Moor, the Doll Tor circle which is associated with the Stanton Moor site, and the Nine Ladies circle which is incorporated in the Stanton Moor barrow cemetery. A second barrow cemetery lies at Swarkston Lows, 4 miles south of Derby.

Despite the apparently unattractive qualities of much of the region in Neolithic times and in the Bronze Age, many districts were traversed by or accessible to routes of trade. Links existed between the Peak and Ireland, and also between the Peak and the east of the region, for the Peterborough culture of Neolithic times eventually reached the upland. The naming for Peterborough of the heavy, coarse, and profusely ornamented pottery does not however imply a centre of cultural diffusion in the east: the style of potting was introduced by settlers, possibly descendants of Mesolithic peoples, from Scandinavia, while its products are concentrated mainly in the Thames valley whence they extend to the Cotswolds. In any event, the Peterborough culture forms but one variant among the Secondary Neolithic group.

Some Neolithic and Bronze Age communities throve—for instance, the Middle Neolithic pastoralists of the Peak District. At times, and in places, the pressure on land was great enough to result in clearance of woodland, as in the north of the region during the Bronze Age. But it is difficult to discriminate among the respective influences of increasing numbers, change in climate, and change in economy. Any one of these, or any combination, may have been responsible for the shift of habitation from the limestone plateau of Derbyshire to the encircling gritstone, in the interval bracketed by the Early and Late Bronze Ages. Again, some increases in population were due to immigration, as when the Beaker people suddenly irrupted into the south of the region. Movements of peoples and evolution or replacement of culture are well documented; climatic change, as a series of events, is no less clear. Against the background of mean temperatures appropriate to interglacial maximum is to be set the entry of invaders who, bringing the culture of the Iron Age, found a pattern of habitation ready-made in the most tractable districts. These districts they rapidly subdued. Fortified sites dating from the Early Iron Age, nearly all located on spurs or hilltops, appear to be systematically disposed round the Derbyshire plateau, along the Jurassic cuesta, and on the Chiltern crest. Three sites on the minor cuestas of Greensand indicate that parts at least of the lowland vales of the south had also been brought under control (Pl. 13).

If earthworks of uncertain but possibly Iron Age date are mapped alongside those authentically belonging to that period, the resulting distribution is suggestive. The Icknield Way, the Jurassic Way of W. F. Grimes, and such antique trackways as Sewestern Lane appear capable of combining with additional ridge-routes to provide a true interconnecting network.

Parts of the array of Roman settlements and Roman roads have, of course, been known for many years, but much additional information has been obtained and much detail filled in with the aid of air photog-

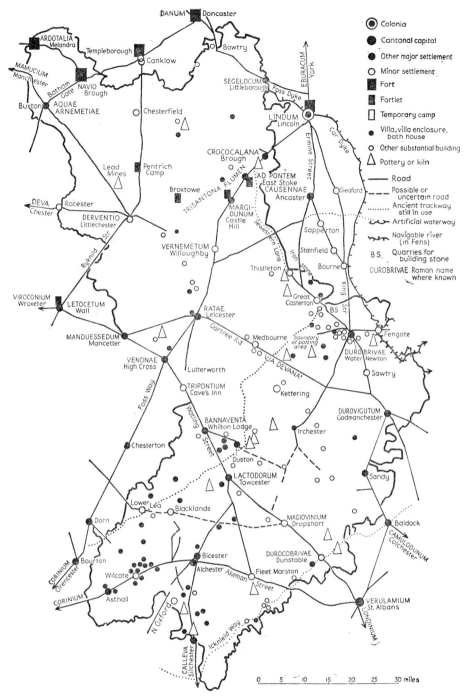

Legend

- ⊚ Colonia
- ⬤ Cantonal capital
- ◕ Other major settlement
- ○ Minor settlement
- ◼ Fort
- ▪ Fortlet
- ☐ Temporary camp
- • Villa, villa enclosure, bath house
- ○ Other substantial building
- △ Pottery or kiln
- — Road
- --- Possible or uncertain road
- ···· Ancient trackway still in use
- ⌇⌇⌇ Artificial waterway
- ⌁⌁ Navigable river (in Fens)
- B.S. Quarries for building stone
- DUROBRIVAE Roman name where known

DANUM Doncaster
Templeborough
ARDOTALIA Melandra
Canklow
Bawtry
MAMUCIUM Manchester
Batham Gate
NAVIO Brough
Buxton
AQUAE ARNEMETIAE
SEGELOCUM Littleborough
Foss Dyke
EBURACUM York
Chesterfield
LINDUM Lincoln
Car Dyke
Ermine Street
Lead Mines
Pentrich Camp
CROCOCALANA Brough
Broxtowe
AD PONTEM East Stoke
CAUSENNAE Ancaster
Sleaford
DEVA Chester
Rocester
DERVENTIO Littlechester
TRISANTONA FLUMEN
MARGI-DUNUM Castle Hill
Ryknild Str
Sewstern Lane
Sapperton
Stainfield
VERNEMETUM Willoughby
Iron stone
Bourne
Thistleton
King Str
VIROCONIUM Wroxeter
LETOCETUM Wall
RATAE Leicester
Great Casterton
B.S.
Fengate
MANDUESSEDUM Mancetter
Gartree Rd
Medbourne
'boundary of potting area'
DUROBRIVAE Water Newton
VENONAE High Cross
VIA DEVANA
Lutterworth
Sawtry
Foss Way
TRIPONTIUM Cave's Inn
Kettering
DUROVIGUTUM Godmanchester
Watling Street
BANNAVENTA Whilton Lodge
Irchester
Chesterton
Duston
LACTODORUM Towcester
Sandy
Lower Lea
Blacklands
MAGIOVINIUM Dropshort
Baldock
Dorn
CAMULODUNUM Colchester
CORINIUM Cirencester
Bourton
Bicester
DUROCOBRIVAE Dunstable
Wilcote
Alchester
Akeman Street
Fleet Marston
CORINIUM
Asthall
VERULAMIUM St. Albans
N Oxford
LONDINIUM)
CALLEVA Silchester
Icknield Way

0 5 10 15 20 25 30 miles

Fig. 31 SOME ELEMENTS IN THE ROMAN GEOGRAPHY OF THE EAST MIDLANDS.

77

raphy and of continuing excavation. I. D. Margary has contributed notably to knowledge of the road system of Roman days, which is now seen to be quite elaborate (Fig. 31). In the south of the region, Akeman Street came from Verulamium to pass Alchester on its way to Corinium. The south-centre was traversed by Watling Street, running from Verulamium to Letocetum and to Viroconium. Via Devana, taking off from Ermine Street north of Godmanchester, made direct for the cantonal capital of Ratae, beyond which it joined Watling Street at Manduessedum. In the east, Ermine Street with its alternatives north of Durobrivae continued north through the colonia of Lindum towards Eboracum, with a cross-connection from Lindum to Danum in the Don valley. The best-known transverse route is the Fosse Way, starting at Lindum, going through Ratae and on to Corinium, and so eventually to the southwest coast. A second transverse route, Ryknield Way, linked Letocetum with Derventio and Derventio with the Templeborough site. Both the Fosse Way and Ryknield Way may have served initially to supply frontier garrisons; but the establishment of Aquae Arnematiae as a watering-place belongs to the time when the southern Pennines had been brought firmly within the civil province (Pl. 14).

Pre-Roman trackways still in use included Sewestern Lane between Durobrivae and the crossing of the Trent at Ad Pontem, a cross-way entering the Fens south of Sleaford, the Jurassic ridgeway where it had not been superseded by Ermine Street, and Icknield Way along the Chalk belt on the regional boundary. At least one navigable waterway struck across the Fens towards Durobrivae, being joined at Fengate by the artificial Car Dyke which led to Lindum and connected with the Trent by Foss Dyke.

Figure 31 suggests that a number of elements of the road system remain to be located. There seems room for a direct connection from Derventio, either with Ratae or with Vernemetum. Similarly, a road could be expected between Irchester and Lactodorum, or Irchester and Magiovinium, as also between Lower Lee through Blacklands to Magiovinium. Again, the sub-equal spacing of numerous proved settlements suggests that additional members of this series have yet to be discovered.

As is well known, Roman lead mines in the southern Pennines produced for export. Ironstone was mined and smelted on the Lincolnshire border, while Durobrivae was a notable and productive centre of pottery manufacture, having the largest industrial complex known for Roman Britain.

The scale of domestic building is best known from the south of the region, where Dorchester and Alchester (the only two towns established during the Roman period) were of no great significance : they enclosed respectively 13½ and 25 acres. The first structures at Alchester were wattle-and-daub, partly replaced by stone building in the second and third centuries A.D. The plateau country west of the Cherwell, on both sides of Akeman Street, saw the establishment of a number of villas which ranged from small farms to large country houses. Calculations from the granary of the Ditchley villa suggest that the estate was a modest one of some 1,000 acres.

Dark Age pioneer settlement in the East Midland region varied widely in date, speed, and intensity. The most rapid early advances occurred in the centre, where Northamptonshire underwent intense settlement by Middle Angles. The trunk valley of the Nene was occupied in the late fifth century, and by the early seventh century settlers were established far up the tributary valleys. Thick forest on either side of the river remained obdurate, but did not forbid access to the less heavily wooded hills of the west. Angles from the east and Saxons from the southwest effected colonisation in areas farther to the south. Anglian penetration through Huntingdonshire was rather slow, and Bedfordshire was reached so late that it has very few archaic place-names. The impetus of the penetration phase exhausted itself in Oxfordshire, where invasion was checked. The vale country in the Thames and Thame valleys remained in British hands until, during the great period of West Saxon expansion, Cuthwulf in 571 captured Eynsham, Bensington (Benson), Aylesbury, and Limbury. With the British power broken, Saxon place-names of the late sixth and early seventh centuries began to appear along the Thames and the Icknield Way, that is, on terraces and at the scarp-foot. Dense woodland on the divide between the Thame and the Ray, continuous with wood and heath on the main outcrop of Lower Greensand, to some extent blocked off Saxon settlement on the one side from Anglian settlement in north Buckinghamshire on the other, although some admixture of dialect took place. The slow penetration of some southern districts, and the halt after the first advance, accord with evidence of British survival, confined though it be to scattered indications in the Chilterns, and to a few elements in the settlement-names of north Oxfordshire in the general neighbourhood of Brimsbury.

Beyond the western prong of colonies in the Nene valley, the Soar fixed a rough limit of advance in Leicestershire. The thirty or so pagan Anglian cemeteries of Leicestershire lie mainly beside the upland streams entering the Soar from the east ; although these cemeteries date from the fifth to the mid-seventh century, archaic place-name terminations are very rare. Like parts of Leicestershire, much of Nottinghamshire proved unattractive ; early settlements were restricted

79

mainly to the terraces and low hills close to the Trent, and Sherwood Forest long continued to shelter British inhabitants. Like Northamptonshire, however, Nottinghamshire possessed a trunk river as a main route of entry, which led many of the late entrants far upstream into Derbyshire and Staffordshire, the eventual heart of Mercia. In parts of the Peak District, where full British control was maintained until the seventh century, the frontier between Celt and Teuton was for a time narrow and sharp.

Scandinavian conquests beginning in the ninth century left a deep impress upon the place-names, social structure, and administrative subdivision of the region. Most of the newcomers were Danes. Exceptions were remarkable enough to be recorded in place-names, for example the five Normantons (Norwegians' villages) of Nottinghamshire. It was a Danish army which wintered at Repton in 873–4. The partition of Mercia was effected in 877, and the Danelaw gained *de facto* recognition in 878. Counties emerged within the Danelaw as army-territories or earldoms; the Danish Derby replaced the Anglian name Northworthy and the town became a Danish borough, in company with Nottingham, Leicester, Lincoln, and Stamford. Danish penetration in Northamptonshire stopped roughly on the line of Watling Street.[1] Towcester and Oxford on the English side were fortified as burhs against the Danes by Edward the Elder; Oxford, first recorded in 912, was the administrative and defensive centre of an area which, although imprecisely defined, was probably comparable to the present county. Much of the administrative classification of the region was thus established, or provoked by armed threats, during the late tenth or early eleventh century; indeed, the only subsequent major changes have been the transfer of a county seat from Buckingham to Aylesbury, the raising of Rutland to county status, and the modern re-classification of towns for administrative purposes.

The considerable freedom enjoyed by sokemen within the Danelaw may have encouraged secondary colonisation, especially since the sokeman class was spatially concentrated. Sokemen constituted up to half the population in parts of Lincolnshire and in adjoining parts of the East Midland region, and have been estimated at a third of the populations of Nottinghamshire and Leicestershire. Large numbers were present in Northamptonshire, and perceptible numbers in Derbyshire. Secondary colonisation, in places involving the clearance of wood, certainly occurred in pre-Domesday times, but, as will presently be shown, the process was vigorously renewed a century after the Conquest. With this reservation in mind, one may observe that certain place-name

---

[1] Scandinavian personal names in some Oxfordshire compounds are thought to reflect investment of tribute money in English land.

elements in the north are distributed in ways which might be expected. Concentrations of Derbyshire names in -feld, -leah, -lundr, and -wudu, and of Nottinghamshire names in -feld, -leah, -lundr, and -haga or -hagi indicate abundant wood in the Derbyshire foothills, in the Derwent valley, on the descending slopes of the extreme northwest, on much of the exposed coalfield, and on the Permian outcrop. Names indicating woodland are not lacking in Sherwood Forest, where sparsity of settlement however reduces their numbers. The Nottinghamshire distributions give a distinct impression of early attacks on the woodland of the Permian country.

A distribution map of Domesday vills (Fig. 32) suggests a fairly even scatter throughout most of the region. Areas of high density include the Chiltern scarp-foot and the inner valley of the Trent ; but the pattern on the map is partly due to the alignment of settlements in these areas upon linear elements of terrain. Sparse numbers typify the Peak, the East Moor of Derbyshire, Sherwood Forest, Charnwood Forest, and the fenland margins of the east. The map makes no allowance for variations in form of settlement, or in size, equipment, productivity, and population-density of vills. Distribution maps published in the Domesday Geographies and in the *Victoria County History of Leicestershire* show that wide variations in fact occurred ; for instance, Northamptonshire vills with many plough-teams and abundant meadow concentrated themselves in the trunk valley of the Nene, while vills in west Leicestershire were poor both in equipment and resources by comparison with those in the trunk valley of the Soar, the Wreake valley, and the Belvoir country. Generally speaking, however, much of the region was well settled by Domesday times.

Although the density map of recorded Domesday population (Fig. 33) is affected by the sizes and shapes of the divisions used, patches of high or low density can readily be associated with geographical units. High density appears for the country bounded by the Chiltern scarp-foot and the Thame, the open plateaux of northwest Oxfordshire, the lower Ouse valley, for a hilly belt north of the Welland, the neighbourhood of Leicester, and for the Belvoir district. The two most common physical facts in this group are drift-free limestone and wide river-terraces. Densities of recorded population not exceeding 5 per square mile correspond to Wychwood, the drift-based woodland stretching from Whittlebury Forest to Yardley Chase, the fenland margins, the country south of Charnwood, the marly foothills of Derbyshire, the exposed coalfield, and the marshy extreme north of Nottinghamshire. The lowest recorded densities of all, under 2·5 per square mile, correspond to Charnwood Forest, Sherwood Forest, the East Moor of Derbyshire, the limestone plateau, and the High Peak.

0 5 10 15 20 25 30 miles

● Boroughs
· Vills

5 7
7

Fig. 32 DOMESDAY SETTLEMENTS. Figures represent unlocated vills for which group totals are stated. Based on the *Domesday Geographies*.

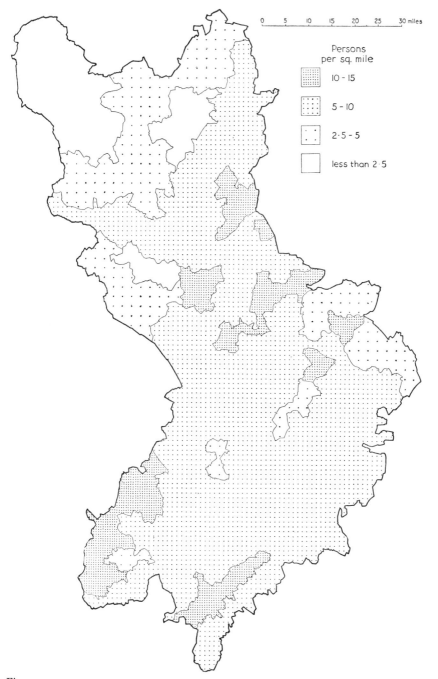

Persons
per sq. mile

10 - 15

5 - 10

2·5 - 5

less than 2·5

Fig. 33 DENSITIES OF RECORDED DOMESDAY POPULATION. Based on the *Domesday Geographies*.

83

Bold contrasts in degree and success of exploitation clearly reflected variations in land quality, and underlay the more delicate variations resulting from local differences in site and situation or from the accidents of history.

According to the estimates of J. C. Russell, the total Domesday population of the nine counties was little more than 160,000 (Table 25). Even though some 95% were in the landed group, the average density of rural population at the time of Domesday was below 50 per square mile, so that large parts of the region would be classed as sparse-rural on the scale used for modern times (Chapter 11). Russell's estimates of density, by counties, give eight means in the range 20–31 per square mile, the lowest values relating to Rutland and Nottinghamshire which included extensive wood. Derbyshire, estimated below 10 per square mile, had large areas useless for farming which did not entirely overlap with anciently established hunting forests. Derbyshire was moreover lagging in its recovery from the devastation of 1068. The whole region underwent an economic setback at the Conquest, and many districts subsequently experienced punitive action, recovery not being complete by Domesday ; values for Bedfordshire T.R.E. total £1,348, against £903 when the lands passed to their Domesday holders and £1,044 in 1086. The *valuit* total (? of 1068) for Derbyshire is £596 7s, against a *valet* total of £425, and the term *waste* is applied to a scattered 10% of the county's Domesday localities.

Towns in Domesday times were astonishingly small by present standards, and small even by comparison with contemporary rural populations. Of nine towns for which populations are estimated by Russell, Oxford was the largest, with 1,431 inhabitants. Only Huntingdon, Leicester, and Northampton also exceeded 1,000, and Newark had only 357 (Table 26). Apart from the county towns, only Newark, Bingham, and Newport Pagnell are known to have had burgesses ; on this account they are shown as boroughs in Figure 32, whether or not their official status has been proved.

For all its lack of people, the region may well have possessed more ploughland in the eleventh century than it does today. There has certainly been a net reduction in tillage since Domesday in those districts where permanent grass is now widespread. Tillage and people alike were more evenly scattered in the eleventh century than they are now, and some settlements were more populous at Domesday than at the last census ; R. Lennard cites instances from the Cherwell valley, where thirty or forty flour-mills ground bread-grain. The present variation in density of rural settlement, which is all too easily overshadowed by huge urban totals, had little counterpart in the eleventh century ; the waste and forest of that period do not match the thin peopling of certain agricultural parishes in the twentieth century.

Eleventh-century land tenure could be as complex as the aims of farming were simple. At one extreme, Ramsey Abbey held extensive lands which were highly concentrated in Huntingdonshire, Cambridgeshire, and Bedfordshire. With some 430 plough-teams on demesne or belonging to direct tenants, and with so little sub-infeudation that additional ploughs numbered below 40, the Abbey profited by owing few knights' services. Having little need to raise cash, it could largely dispense with rents. In Oxfordshire, on the other hand, there was already much sub-infeudation. Although the fee of six tenants-in-chief accounted for about half the agricultural land, and although more than 90% of the available plough-teams were located on the 42 estates valued at £10 or more, the actual tenurial arrangements were highly complicated. Even in Derbyshire, with its huge and well-consolidated estates, four distinct types of tenurial organisation were common, ranging from coincident manor and vill to subdivided manors. Differentiation in the bordar-cottar class already foreshadowed the social changes and redistribution of land which took effect later in the Middle Ages.

Troubled conditions in the twelfth century may have included checks on population. They certainly favoured a wide total extent of waste, which in parts of the region was increased by afforestation. H. C. Darby calculates that waste accounted in the twelfth century for more than half the area of the three northern counties, and from one-fifth to two-fifths of the remainder. Rutland, Leicestershire, Huntingdonshire, and Northamptonshire were at one time wholly subject to forest law. M. L. Bazeley's maps for the early thirteenth century show huge blocks of royal forest in the Peak, Sherwood, the whole of Rutland and Huntingdonshire, and a great tract called Rockingham which, running down to the Nene, adjoined Salcey Forest. Salcey in turn adjoined Whittlebury, and this Bernwood, which extended into Oxfordshire; Wychwood formed a western outlier. The royal forests probably attained their greatest extent under Henry II (1154–89). Growing hostility to the forest system resulted in drastic changes in the early fourteenth century, but a thick residue of tradition, custom, and administration persisted in places as late as the nineteenth century. While the application of forest laws by no means implied the spread of wood, or even the disuse of farmland, it must surely have involved checks on clearing and upon secondary settlement.

Such checks can have been serious in the late twelfth and early thirteenth centuries, when population was increasing. Russell's general conclusion that numbers increased greatly between Domesday and the mid-thirteenth century, and more slowly thereafter, is strongly supported by place-name evidence for the East Midland region. Place-name endings in -*cote*, -*leah*, and -*thorpe*, for the seven counties for which place-name handbooks have been published, are classified in Tables 27 and 28 by date of first known record. The frequency seems to indicate much secondary colonisation in the period 1150–1300, with a peak roughly between 1200 and 1250.

The frequency distribution is admittedly affected by some uncertainty about the use of these elements, and also by accidents of documentation. Endings in -*cote* and allied forms present little difficulty, even though they include a few special cases, for example Bearwardcote (Derbyshire). Endings in -*thorpe* or -*throp* have been ignored by Buckinghamshire and Oxfordshire, where they are English, not Scandinavian ; seventeen items have been rejected on this count. Elsewhere, the significance is clearly daughter-settlement : as W. G. Hoskins points out, numerous *thorpes* were founded in Scandinavian Leicestershire as daughter-settlements of neighbouring -*bys*. Terminations in -*leah* are the least satisfactory, in view of changing usage ; but post-Domesday names in -*leah* are likely to mean clearing rather than wood. In any event, the totals of names in -*leah* seem high enough both to offset doubts arising from variable use and to obliterate the effects of special cases.

Accidents of documentation, although possibly serious, may yet apply rather to pre-Domesday than to post-Domesday times. They can scarcely account either for the similarities in distributional frequency between county and county, or for the distinctiveness of Derbyshire. County totals of the three elements strongly resemble normal frequency distribution ; indeed, a perfect distribution is obtained for Northamptonshire. It seems entirely reasonable, then, to infer a post-Domesday wave of clearing and secondary settling, coming earliest in the south and in parts of Nottinghamshire and notably delayed in Derbyshire. Although some of the secondary settlements may have been large and compact enough to rank as nucleated from the outset, others were certainly small and formless enough to be classed as dispersed. The movement, although impressive in total, was locally piecemeal. Hoskins, concluding that the work of clearance was still unfinished in the mid-thirteenth century in Leicestershire, suggests felling and grubbing of five or six acres a year as a probable task for the inhabitants of a single parish. Again, although the pressure on land was considerable, it could be eased by conversion from two-field to three-field working—a conversion accomplished in most parts of Leicestershire before the end of the fourteenth century.

During the early medieval period, as is well known, religious houses possessed great aggregates of land and exerted a strong influence on economy. Some establishments pre-dated the Conquest. Peterborough Abbey was first founded about 655, and was re-founded about 966 after being destroyed by the Danes in 870; Ramsey Abbey was founded about 966. But it was in the fifty years after the Conquest that Black Monks became most numerous, and it was during the early thirteenth century that foundations spread from the plantations of Cistercians and Carthusians at Waverley, Rievaulx, and Fountains. The East Midland region came to possess twenty-eight monastic establishments of the first rank (Table 29). Some of these (for example Rufford, Welbeck, and Chicksands) were set in sparsely peopled territory where they could exert full tenurial and economic control. Others, located in well-peopled country, left the way open to depopulation when their holdings passed into lay hands; Lavendon is a leading instance. Others again were set in towns, dominating and controlling urban activities; such were Peterborough and Ramsey. It is difficult to assess the early economic significance of religious houses, especially since their economic functions had been drastically modified well before the Dissolution. R. H. Hilton shows that the main early source of profit, from production on the estates of Leicester Abbey, was wool, and that some wool was bought in for sale to Italian merchants in the late thirteenth century; however, there was no sign of disproportionate meadow on the Abbey lands, and the corn tithe was considerable. Changing prices led, not to an increase in grazing by the Abbey organisation, but to leasing out of land. The Abbey had become a *rentier* by 1500.

Coinciding with, and presumably related to, the thirteenth-century increase in rural population, came signal changes in the functions of towns. These changes may have helped to reduce the economic power of religious houses, if only where markets and crafts were not under ecclesiastical control. The great upsurge in urban activity during the thirteenth century can be associated in the wider view with progressive change towards a money economy and thus connected with the wage-payments and commutations of service which became increasingly common in the fourteenth century. Charters were granted for a striking total of fairs and markets during the thirteenth century. There was as yet little sign of the disproportionate growth of towns (Tables 26, 30) or of their detachment from their surroundings, but there was indubitably a great increase in commercial activity at all levels. The four greatest fairs were those of Winchester, St Ives, Sturbridge, and St Bartholomew; those of Northampton and Boston also ranked high. The original grant of St Ives fair, in 1110, was for eight days; by the early fourteenth century the fair lasted forty days, and until the Black Death St Ives strongly challenged its neighbour Huntingdon, handicapped as this was by deteriorating channels on the navigable Ouse. Twenty-three places in Leicestershire gained fairs, markets, or both, between 1200 and 1300 ; fifteen markets and fairs were granted in Nottinghamshire, Lenton fair rising to supremacy. Nearly all the ancient market charters of Bedfordshire date from the thirteenth or fourteenth century, and even the tiny Rutland secured seven markets and six fairs during the same period.

Status and powers of towns were enhanced as functions were elaborated. New Leicestershire boroughs appeared at Hinckley (1209), Lutterworth (1279), Castle Donington (1311), and Ashby de la Zouch (1330). Partial immunity from distraint was secured by Nottingham, Retford, Northampton, Oxford, and Stamford ; Derby and Nottingham agreed not to exact tolls from one another. Town gilds established during the twelfth and thirteenth centuries assumed control of craft industries and not infrequently obtained local monopoly at the expense of their surroundings. Fulling, dyeing, or weaving flourished at Dronfield, Tideswell, Chesterfield, Derby, Retford, Newark, Nottingham, Leicester, Huntingdon, Stamford, Northampton, and Oxford— that is, in the county towns and in some of the leading commercial centres outside.[1] This first start, however, was a false one. The woollen industry declined seriously in the early fourteenth century. Northampton, said to have had 300 cloth workers in the reign of Henry III (1216–72), was unable to pay its farm in 1334 ; here, and at Leicester, increased tallage was a sign of depression. Oxford, with 60 or more weavers in the time of John (1199–1216), had none in 1323. It was not until the second expansion of the woollen industry, in the second half of the fourteenth century, that the region took full advantage of its medieval resources and not until the fifteenth century that the long-lasting organisation of town clothiers and country weavers became general.

Strengthening of towns was accompanied by growth of roads. Leicester and Northampton were foci of local medieval road systems. It is difficult to discuss long-distance transport overland owing to lack of evidence, although something can be made of the circuits of fairs, of ancient road-names, and of the Gough map. F. Stenton's summary of the road system of the mid-fourteenth century, as represented by the Gough map, includes reaches of main routeways which, radiating from London, crossed the East Midland region. The road from London

---

[1] H. C. Darby observes that the Pipe Rolls of 1130 and 1156 indicate Oxford, Northampton, Nottingham and Derby (combined), Huntingdon, Stamford, and Bedford, in that order, as the outstanding towns of the region and its immediate neighbourhood ; the tallage of 1225 gives Oxford, Northampton, Bedford, Stamford, and Nottingham as the first five, in that order.

to St David's ran through High Wycombe to Oxford, where there was a branch to Bristol, and continued north of the Thames through Witney, Burford, and Northleach, and so to Gloucester. One London–Carlisle route followed Watling Street from Dunstable to Stratford (? Fenny or Stony), where the road forked; one branch went through Northampton and Market Harborough to Leicester, and thence to Nottingham, Worksop, and Doncaster, while the other made a detour (possibly as far west as Buckingham) to run through Daventry to Coventry, where it crossed a transverse road connecting Coventry with Leicester, Melton Mowbray, and Grantham. A second cross-road, coming from the lower Severn valley, ran from Lichfield through Derby and Chesterfield to Doncaster. The route from London to Carlisle by way of Stainmore Pass came in along the line of Ermine Street to Huntingdon, but made a westward detour before crossing the Nene at Wansford. Beyond Wansford it took the modern route through Stamford, Grantham, and Newark to Tuxford, but then swung west of Retford on its way to Doncaster.

Saltways and saltstreets in the west relate to a lengthy trade in salt from Droitwich. Perhaps the most striking of the anciently named roads, however, is the portway which joined the south of the region to Southampton. The prefixes North and South were attached to the two Hamptons before the Conquest; their connecting road, on which lay Brackley, Oxford, Abingdon, Newbury, and Winchester, provided part of the circuit system of medieval fairs. The portway on the east side of the Cherwell above Oxford seems to have been a branch, or rather an additional part of the chief portway system, for the name portway occurs at intervals beyond Banbury, suggesting a trading route from Oxford to Leicester by way of Daventry and Husbands Bosworth, that is, along the hilly belt which parts the Cherwell and Avon on the west from the Ouse, Nene, and Welland on the east. Thus Leicester, like Northampton, seems to have had well-known commercial associations with Southampton, sharing in trade on the Channel in addition to that on the North Sea.

From the fourteenth century onwards, when wool production was associated with cloth-making for export, the grazing and textile-working of the region increased hugely. Oxford became the main urban centre of broadcloth production, just as the Jurassic cuestas were the chief areas of long-wool sheep. Chipping Norton vied with Gloucestershire's Chipping Campden as a wool-market, surpassing Oxford, Burford, and Banbury. These and neighbouring towns, notably including Witney, were heavily committed to the wool trade and to cloth-making. But the Jurassic limestone country of Oxfordshire, Rutland, and the Lincoln border shared a common prosperity; large flocks were kept elsewhere, for example, on the Bedfordshire manor of Grove, with a flock estimated at 4,000, and in the north, where much waste was improved in the early fourteenth century. In the second half of this century small tenants followed the example already set by great land-owners in increasing the sizes of their flocks.

The two main concentrations of population in fourteenth-century England were in Norfolk, Suffolk, and the silt fen, and in the east-central part of the East Midland region. The main outlets at Boston and Lynn engaged in vigorous trade. At least the northern part of Oxfordshire was highly prosperous. The rankings obtained by J. E. T. Rogers show that in the wool-tax assessment of 1341 Oxford-shire ranked third in England, after Middlesex and Norfolk, by ratio of demand to acreage. Bedfordshire, Rutland, Huntingdonshire, and Northamptonshire occupied the fourth, seventh, ninth, and twelfth places among 37 places. Closely similar placings occur in the grant of archers of 1453, and no great change is indicated by the assessment of 1503. Throughout the whole period from 1350 to 1500, distinct economic success favoured all the south and southeast of the region, Buckinghamshire excepted; the three northern counties, by contrast, developed little and slowly (Table 31).

Progressive success of grazing and textile production were associ-ated with enclosure and grassing-down of tillage. These in turn were accompanied by rural depopulation which, continuing into the early seventeenth century, caused the loss of numerous villages and hamlets. Although it is impossible to discuss this matter without reference to the Black Death and other epidemics of the fourteenth century, it would be erroneous to hold disease responsible for all the observed effects. The Black Death was long preceded by the beginnings of enclosure and by commutations of service. Its attack, disastrous in total, was yet locally uneven, and wage rates responded unevenly to shortage of labour even where epidemics were most severe. Demo-graphic trends had already reduced the populations of some settlements before the outbreaks took place: M. Beresford observes that two in five of the 225 lost villages in Midland counties had very low tax assessments in 1334; from Leicestershire to Oxfordshire, the 1334 quotas for settlements later to be depopulated ran 40% or 50% below the average. Population totals in these weak settlements were, at most, half or two-thirds as great as the totals in villages which were to resist depopulation. Similarly, settlements eventually lost ranked low in the scale of relief in 1352–4 and in the poll tax returns of 1377.

Beresford, noting the need of detailed research to show if early depopulation was concentrated on marginal cornland, suggests that population pressure may have declined in the early fourteenth century, and that climatic change may have made it difficult to hold on to land colonised in the land-hungry thirteenth century. However, a comparison between the lists given by Beresford with the place-name handbooks for the five southern counties shows that nearly two-thirds of the settlements undergoing depopulation already existed at Domesday. Even when names of lost, but probably once-inhabited, medieval places are added from the handbooks to the lists of Beresford, 57% occur in Domesday. More than 70% of the places suffering depopulation in Nottinghamshire and Derbyshire date from before the Conquest. Depopulation, therefore, was by no means confined to, or even typical of, the secondary settlements of the twelfth and thirteenth centuries; it affected very many old-established settlements which, for whatever reason, were underpeopled at the time. Nor, of course, did depopulation always mean complete destruction; often not more than a few houses were thrown into ruin, or a family or two made homeless on any occasion, but some wholesale evictions did occur, and some sites were lost entirely (Pls. 15, 16).

The distribution map of lost settlement sites (Fig. 34) is drawn from information given by Hoskins for Leicestershire, and from Beresford's data for the remaining counties; the forms in which information is presented cause all Leicestershire depopulations to be classed as certain, at known sites, while a range of uncertainty applies elsewhere. When the distribution of sites is considered, without reference to severity, marked concentrations appear in the centre, southwest, and northeast of the region. Depopulation was facilitated here because the land was highly convertible, able to grow either corn or grass as required, and the relative prices of wool and wheat ensured heavy pressure upon tillage. The depopulating movement was most intense between 1440 and 1520, when small freeholders were systematically bought out, and unopposed squires could act largely as they pleased. The dissolution of monasteries in 1536–40 led to wholesale transfers of ecclesiastical estates to lay owners, who proved far more rapacious than their predecessors. A sixth of the medieval villages and hamlets of Leicestershire were obliterated between 1450 and 1600; between 1516 and 1568 the convertible lands of the Midlands supplied the locales of three-quarters of the cases of depopulation. Something between 1% and 2% of the area of Derbyshire and Nottinghamshire was affected by depopulating enclosure; in the resistant arable lands of Huntingdonshire, the fraction was little above $5\frac{1}{2}\%$; in Bedfordshire, Buckinghamshire, and Oxfordshire it rose to $8\frac{1}{2}\%$, and in Rutland, Northamptonshire, and Leicestershire to 9%. Where complete depopulation occurred there was rarely much, if any, rebuilding during the late fifteenth century or subsequently, when the pressure on tillage

Fig. 34 SITES OF LOST VILLAGES and of other settlements depopulated in medieval and early modern times.

eased. The distribution pattern of rural peopling had been permanently changed by the elimination of many small settlements.

It is unfortunate that the returns of 1377 cannot be compared with equally full records for the period before the Black Death. This and associated epidemics reduced numbers of population by at least one-third; Russell, indeed, infers a reduction of 40% in the country as a whole between 1348 and 1377. If this proportion, and Russell's estimates of density in 1377, are of the right order, then population in the East Midland region had by the early fourteenth century reached average densities exceeding 80 per square mile in Leicestershire, Rutland, Northamptonshire, and Bedfordshire, and between 68 and 71 per square mile in all other counties but Derbyshire, where the calculated value is 46 per square mile. These tentative figures suggest that a very great deal of the region had become densely peopled enough to fall into the rural density class, as opposed to the sparse rural class which applied widely at Domesday. Furthermore, county totals of population in the early fourteenth century may not have been equalled or surpassed until about the end of the sixteenth century; for two centuries or more, epidemics kept the level of population down (Tables 25, 32).

Reductions in numbers by pestilence cause the totals of single village populations in 1377 to appear unduly low. Russell finds that peak numbers of villages in Oxfordshire and Bedfordshire lie near the range of 100 inhabitants, while populations of 100–200 were common in Northamptonshire. Allowing for the epidemics, these figures suggest that many southern villages had populations of 150–300 in the early fourteenth century. Of 35 parishes in a Northamptonshire Rural District selected at random (Daventry), 16 had fewer than 200 inhabitants in 1951, and 8 had fewer than 100. The separate or combined effects of disease and depopulation were at some places never offset.

Beneath the pervasive themes of sheep grazing, woollen manufacture, depopulation, and disease, could be heard persistent undertones of agricultural and social change. Some 622 acres of Leicester Abbey land at Stoughton in 1341 were held in villeinage by 26 tenants, 23 of whom held each 24 acres of arable and appurtenant meadow; by 1477, some 700 acres were held at will by 17 tenants, of whom 7 held from 50 to 70 acres of arable, with defined acreages of pasture land. Similar changes had overtaken free tenures: whereas in 1341, 19 tenants held some 160 acres, including 2 considerable tenements, in 1477 there were only 4 tenants on 230 acres, one of them holding 170 acres. Comparable developments can be readily cited. A small class of rich peasants had emerged by the end of the fifteenth century, each able to cultivate 60 to 80 acres of arable—twice as much as on the peasant holdings of a hundred and fifty years earlier. The most eminent yeomen of 1500 were often the descendants of well-to-do peasants of the fourteenth or even of the thirteenth century. There was a spectacular outburst of land-buying by the greater yeomen from about 1540 to 1600. Rural domestic architecture was transformed at about the same time by the introduction of an upper floor, first as a loft-bedroom and then as a storey with fixed stairs. Social, economic, and tenurial changes were accompanied by changes in the aims of agriculture, additional to those related to the spread of grazing. Leicestershire farmers appear to have extended the acreage of spring corn (barley, oats, and pulses) at the expense of winter corn (wheat and rye) in the period 1350–1600 (Table 33). In some degree the swing probably represents a change from food grain to cash crops, and certainly indicates improvements in distribution.

Saxton's maps, Leland's *Itinerary*, and Camden's *Britannia* shed a modern, not a medieval, light upon the sixteenth century. Saxton's influence on subsequent cartographers needs no comment; the *Itinerary* consists partly of geographical field-notes; the *Britannia* stands at the head of a line of topography which leads direct to the *Victoria County Histories*. Although a connected sequence of geographical change in the East Midland region has been traced from the fifth to the sixteenth century, the contrast between, say, 1150 and 1550 seems of a different order from the contrast between 1550 and 1950, notwithstanding that sixteenth-century industrialisation was slight, or that sixteenth-century farming had a distinctly medieval cast. There occurred no sudden break; but population totals by about 1600 had regained the levels of 1350, after two and a half centuries of halting recovery. It was to be another hundred and fifty years before sustained and vigorous increase set in; but the worst effects of pestilence had at last been remedied. The region's coalfields had secured permanent markets, even though these were as yet modest, liable to depression, and confined within rather narrow limits of distribution. Trials of textile manufacture in factories were made early in the sixteenth century. Depopulating enclosures had increased the numbers of vagrants and poor, exacerbating the problem of surplus labour which was eventually to encourage official promotion of textile working in attempts at poor relief. In all these ways the sixteenth century produced significant changes.

Leland portrays much of the region as champain country, dotted with numerous parks, variegated by unevenly distributed woodland, and with an inconstant ratio of grassland to tillage. Those districts which are woody today were woody in Leland's time. Parts of

Leighfield Forest and Bernwood still remained in addition, the latter surrounded by coverts for its venturing deer. Charnwood was still well timbered, and Leicester Forest, although much diminished, was still recognisable. Extensive tree cover in parts of Sherwood contrasted with wide heathland near Worksop. Leland's frequent notes on woodland are, needless to say, referable to the growing contemporary crisis in timber supply.

Some of the parks which Leland recorded were newly established. The squirearchy was rising : most Northamptonshire villages had their gentlemen. Mr Gostewick, born in Willington (Bedfordshire), had bought the local lordship from the Duke of Norfolk, and, buying some five or six other lordships also, built a sumptuous house of brick and timber. Timber and stone, according to locality, were the main building materials in the towns. Oundle was all stone-built. The old buildings in Northampton were stone, the new timber ; the town walls, directing traffic through their four gates, were adjoined by two suburbs, the larger outside Southgate. Leicester and Nottingham were both timber-built, while Nottingham seemed large and handsome in timber and plaster. Nottingham however had not thrown out large suburbs, even though its walls and gates were ruinous. Newark and Retford among the lesser centres had well-known markets, although naturally overshadowed by Nottingham ; Bawtry was failing, its market being base and poor. The markets at Banbury and the timber-built Aylesbury were celebrated, and the Luton market was noted for barley. Brackley's Wednesday market, however, was desolated. The town itself, failing as a centre of the wool trade, was much decayed.

The decay of Brackley is perhaps symptomatic of depression— depression severe enough to reduce the prosperity index of Oxfordshire to the regional average (Table 31). The movement is difficult to explain, except in the rather general terms of price changes, that is, the rise in wheat prices, by comparison with prices of wool, which is known to have occurred at this time. Oxfordshire had certainly been heavily committed to grazing and cloth-making. One Tucker, a clothier from Burford, attempted to take over Abingdon Abbey as a factory in 1538, and Stumpe, the Malmesbury clothier who already held Malmesbury Abbey, actually rented Osney Abbey in 1546. His project to employ two thousand cloth-workers was, however, defeated by the terms of the contract imposed on him. Wool marketing and the broadcloth industry seem during the recession to have retreated from the Marlstone benchlands into the oolite plateaux in the west, where Witney, Burford, and Bampton continued in production. The fall in wool prices may have been due in part to over-production, which became intensified as the century drew on. Enclosure and conversion to pasture accelerated at

95

the Dissolution, and not only in Oxfordshire. Camden saw Northamptonshire as overspread and beset by sheep; in the vale country of Buckinghamshire flocks of sheep pastured most plenteously in mighty numbers, loden with fleeces, to the great gain and commodity of their masters. Great flocks were maintained in east Leicestershire, and the Derbyshire uplands fed sheep very commodiously. Tillage nevertheless displayed signs of expansion in the late sixteenth century. Apart from the fenland, which was still in grazing, Huntingdonshire was highly arable, and it was the barley of south Bedfordshire which supplied the Luton market. Not surprisingly, the main blocks of tillage were in the dry east.

The distributions of the sixteenth century, already modified by depopulating enclosure and by felling of woodland, were to be still further modified in the seventeenth century by severe and widespread felling, by neglect of standing timber, by the continued decline of some towns and the rise of others, by the extension of metal working in the north, and by changes in the textile industry which particularly affected northern and central districts. The beginning of these changes are clearly specified in contemporary accounts.

Wright's *History of Rutland* (1684) imitates the model of Camden, but includes a map classifying settlements. Forty-eight places are marked as *villae parochiales*, six (including five thorpes) as *pagi minores*, and no fewer than fifteen as *sedes, vel loca devastata, olim villae*. Comparison of lists shows that depopulation in Rutland was even more widespread than claimed by Beresford.

Morton's *Northamptonshire* (1712), making a geographical subdivision of the county, records assessments both of terrain and of soil. The main subdivisions for Morton were fen, heathy upland, and fielden. The fen had been partly drained, but North Fen, Burrow Little Fen, and 6,000 acres of Burrow Great Fen remained in common grazing. Heathy upland (underlain either by bare Northampton Sand or by glacial outwash) provided furze as fuel in bakers' oven and lime-kilns, and supported rabbits and sheep of small breed. Whittlewood and Salcey Forests were subdivided and largely coppiced. Rockingham Forest also lay dismembered. All three forests suffered damage as common grazing, and Rockingham was additionally depleted by charcoal-burners. Birmingham smiths drew on the west of the county for ash-timber. The fielden, the champain tract, was worked on the three-field system, but brashy soils were not always ridged up. Turnips and sainfoin were already known, and wheat was kiln-dried in places in wet seasons. A considerable part of the fielden lay enclosed and in pasture; the richest pastures were located on the broad clayey divide between the north branch of the Nene and the upper Avon, and in a belt extending from the clay and outwash east of Daventry along the divide between the Tove and the Cherwell. Stock in these areas was fattened for the London market. The county's tillage yielded a surplus of grain, which went to Spalding, Wisbech, Bedford, and Derby. Northampton had recently acquired a highly successful horse market, presumably at the expense of King's Cliffe which, although well connected by roads, was scarcely worthy of the name of market town. Rockingham had also declined; the rise of Wellingborough had depressed Higham Ferrers, and that of Kettering had equally depressed Rothwell, in the last fifty years or so before Morton wrote. Wellingborough profited especially by its corn market, Kettering by its manufacture of woollens.

Plot recorded nine kinds of soil for Oxfordshire, where cropping systems varied with soil, and where heaviest sowing was limited to the best land. As in Northamptonshire, there was much working of clay for making beaten floors, and localised production of pipe-clay and pottery. Caversham practised the specialised manufacture of twenty-two-inch bricks for malt kilns. There were at least 60 blanketers at Witney, with 150 looms in work and 3,000 poor employed. Wagons took blankets to Leadenhall and Southwark markets each week, returning with loads of wool; red and blue blankets were produced for use in barter by merchants in Virginia and New England. The leather industry, long centred at Oxford, had undergone dispersal, for fell-mongering was located at Bampton, gloving at Woodstock, and saddlery at Burford.

Navigation on the Thames had been improved by locks or sluices, but Henley, Marlow, and Maidenhead were better placed as ports than was Oxford, which suffered from low water in summer. The Great Ouse, its navigation deteriorating throughout the Middle Ages, was improved during the early seventeenth century by the installation of sluices and by the scouring of shallows; but the works were the cause of constant disputes and became neglected when trade decayed during the Civil War. Improvements after the war allowed boats to reach Bedford; the town sent grain down to King's Lynn for coastwise shipment, and received coal, salt, iron, and fish. Bedfordshire, taking an ever-greater interest in stock-fattening for the London market, had its roads constantly impaired in Defoe's time by droves of store animals coming from Lincolnshire and the Isle of Ely. Buckingham town had been replaced as its county's chief market centre by Aylesbury, which dealt largely in corn, although set in country where all the gentlemen were graziers.

Leicestershire appeared to Defoe about 1700 a vast magazine of wool for the rest of the nation; it was also noted for mutton, work-horses,

97

and cattle. Sheep for droving were sold off in September and October, going chiefly to London ; fat cattle, passing in large numbers through the market of Melton Mowbray, also went to London. Leicestershire thus resembled Northamptonshire and parts of Bedfordshire and Buckinghamshire in its stock-farming, but was developing industrial connections with the two northern counties. Hand-knitting of woollens was widely disseminated throughout the southern half of the region, but framework knitting (principally of cotton stockings) never became firmly established except in the north. Defoe exaggerated grossly in saying that the whole of the three northern counties seemed to be employed in framework knitting, for the total of frames in Leicestershire, Nottinghamshire, and Derbyshire in his day can scarcely have exceeded 2,250 ; but the framework-knitting industry of the Midlands had made a firm beginning on its expansion.

Nottingham, accessible by barges without the aid of locks, pursued a vigorous trade along the Trent during the early eighteenth century, receiving iron, block-tin, salt, hops, grocery, wine, oil, tar, hemp, and flax. Downgoing cargoes included lead, coal, wood, corn, cheese, and beer—malting and brewing were widely practised in the Trent basin, which grew much of its own barley. The import of iron is significant : although industrialisation was well advanced in Derbyshire, the manufacture of iron had, for a time, ceased to develop.

The return of able-bodied men in Derbyshire in 1635 showed 65% of the county total in the semi-industrial districts of Wirksworth, the High Peak, and Scarsdale, that is, in the areas of leadmines, coalmines, stonepits, ironstone quarries, and ironworks. Derbyshire iron-making increased considerably during the late seventeenth century, in response to demands from Birmingham and London, but the phase of increase was followed by one of stagnation. R. D. Chambers infers that true industrial entrepreneurs had not appeared in the late seventeenth century and that the early gentlemen-ironmasters saw industry as a means of acquiring land. A self-contained organisation of ironworks arose in Derbyshire, unchanging either in output or in method between 1690 and 1750. Swedish competition was not met. Derbyshire had only four furnaces in 1740, their combined output a mere 800 tons a year ; the 10 bar-iron forges of 1750 produced only 650 tons. Nottinghamshire possessed an additional four forges and a solitary furnace. The exposed coalfield had been repeatedly scratched, but not yet industrially devastated. Not until the yeasty later years of the eighteenth century, when population trended sharply upwards, did iron-making enter another and permanent phase of development.

Between 1570 and 1800, according to Rickman's estimates, the population of the region approximately doubled (Table 34). Except in Derbyshire and Nottinghamshire, where industrial concentrations were appearing towards the end (Table 35), increase was generally slow throughout this period. It was as yet continuous in no part of the region, being liable to check or reversal. Chambers, examining changes in the Vale of Trent, concludes that expansion of industry and increase in numbers of people typify the period 1690–1720, only to be followed by a slowing of industrial development, and some actual reductions in numbers at times, between 1720 and 1740. The previously noted stagnation of the iron industry overlaps with the period of general stagnation, and this in turn overlaps with the recurrent and severe farmers' depressions of 1730–50. Chambers concludes that epidemics were more, and food supply less, influential on population trends than is usually recognised. Nottinghamshire records show very heavy mortality beginning about 1678 and continuing in some villages almost to 1700; little or no increase of population between 1710 and 1730 is typical of the country as a whole. With parts of its industry hidebound, and with its people intermittently savaged by disease, the north of the region could not be expected to develop economically. Only in the second half of the eighteenth century did population permanently increase, or the economy permanently expand.

Accompanying the halting developments and the progressive changes of 1550–1800 was a remarkable degree of personal and social mobility. Peyton (quoted by Chambers) finds a rapid change-over of surnames associated with no appreciable change of population total in a group of Nottinghamshire villages between 1544 and 1641. Chambers calculates that no less than 90% of the increase of population in Nottingham town, between 1700 and 1739, was due to migration; the corresponding fraction for 1739–79 is 66%, and for 1779–1801 50%. Industrialised villages simultaneously outstripped their agricultural neighbours. Representative industrialised villages were already in the late seventeenth century nearly half as large again as representative agricultural villages (Table 35); by the mid-eighteenth century the industrialised villages were the more populous by a factor of almost two, and by 1800 by a factor of more than three. It was largely at this time that the permanent cleavage between town and county, and between agriculture and industry, was effected.

With the census of 1801, population trends can be discussed in greater detail, and more comprehensively, than hitherto. In this respect the opening of the nineteenth century introduces a change of treatment. The expansion of coal mining, iron making, and framework knitting belong however both to the eighteenth and to the nineteenth centuries, as do the hand-working of lace and the straw plaiting of the south, and the lead mining of the north; but most of the industrial climaxes were reached after 1800. The description presented in Chapter 8 is, in some ways, an artificially crystallised sample of a period of violent change, for industry, agriculture, economy, and society were all being transformed. Nevertheless, the sample is well worth taking. The situation in 1800 is validly regarded as the climax of protracted piecemeal and mainly small-scale development. Changes continuing into the nineteenth century had already begun, but the conditions of 1770 and 1830 were those of different worlds.

CHAPTER **7**

FABRIC AND FORM OF RURAL SETTLEMENT

FORMS of rural settlement and rural domestic architecture can scarcely be treated together, and for the whole region, with reference to any period earlier than the late eighteenth century. It is true that individual, local, or otherwise specialised studies contribute notably to the understanding of the layout of villages, and of changes in material and construction of houses. Only during the late eighteenth century, however, did county maps capable of showing the details of settlement form make their first appearance. The region at that time was at the end of a run of late-medieval and subsequent centuries during which the impulse of secondary dispersion had been weak: although some early villages had vanished, and others had declined, that strong tendency to partial disintegration which set in during the nineteenth century had yet to be felt. A rich variety of local structural materials was expressed in an even richer variety of building styles, and traditional forms were far more numerous than they are now. The region had not yet acquired much of the urban, suburban, and industrial housing which today accounts for a large fraction of the present total of architecture. On all these counts, the forms of settlement and the character of rural housing can suitably be discussed in the context of 1800, that is, in the context of the latest period when the regional scenery was still almost wholly rural. That scenery included many villages arranged on plans closely resembling the plans of the original foundations, and fabric which, although very different from that of the first dwellings, was of local origin, was handled in ways directly evolved from those of the first settlers, and was durable enough to survive to the present time.

Understandably enough, the buildings described by writers in the *Victoria County Histories*, by Nikolaus Pevsner, and by the contributors to journals of local societies, are in some way exceptional—churches and other religious establishments, castles, mansions, and private houses which pretend at least to some grandness, or which are unusually old. Since the present aim is to review the generality of ordinary houses, striking survivals will be passed over. Farm buildings in areas of late parliamentary enclosures will also be omitted, since many of them date from the mid-nineteenth century.

Despite their appearance of placid antiquity, observable rural dwellings belong to the modern rather than to the medieval period.

W. G. Hoskins describes medieval peasant houses in Leicestershire with stone footings, walls of rammed mud or of wattle-and-daub, and roofs of thatch. Cruck-framed buildings—very few of which still exist —were at one time predominant, but probably died out as a type before the end of the sixteenth century, being superseded by post-and-truss during the Great Rebuilding of 1570–1640. Not only Leicestershire, but the whole region, seems to have been affected at about this time by that drastic re-design of structure which allowed ordinary dwellings to possess two floors, even though the upper floor was initially no more than an attic inside a low roof.

Frequency of survival from the Great Rebuilding depends chiefly upon the durability of local materials. Where Jurassic rocks are used in stone walls, many structures survive from the early seventeenth century or even from the late sixteenth. Houses supported on wooden frames endure best when the frames are filled with brick ; thus half-timbered brickwork of respectable age is well represented in the south-east, whereas almost everything but plain brick has gone from the northeast. In the Trent valley above Nottingham local sandstone walls have crumbled and have been replaced by brick. Available information is unluckily too scanty either to establish the nature and incidence of wholesale conversion on a regional scale at about the turn of the sixteenth century, or to reveal any large-scale reconstruction or replacement which may have taken place between 1600 and 1800.

More than 500 sets of observations (excluding re-checks) are located, and partially analysed, in Figure 35. They inevitably include the results of modification during the last 150 years, and are coloured in some districts by new building of the early nineteenth century. Certain clear patterns of distribution emerge, however, and a number of distinctive combinations of walling and roofing can be located with reasonable accuracy.

In the rather small villages of the northwest, stone walls in houses consist of Carboniferous Limestone or Millstone Grit. Gritstone, which can be sawn, takes a clean face ; where combined with limestone it usually forms cornerstones, lintels, and sills. Handsome effects can be obtained with both types of stone.[1] Limestone-built houses on a hot summer day look as sun-bleached as do stone houses near a sea-shore, while walls of faced gritstone are true and shapely. Outside the bounds of severe atmospheric pollution in towns the gritstone does not easily become grimed with dirt, and thus escapes the dinginess which afflicts it on industrial sites, although gritstone blocks in field walls commonly assume very dark tints. Gritstone roofing slabs, thick

---

[1] Specific localities where local materials are effectively used, or are unusually combined, are cited in Table 36.

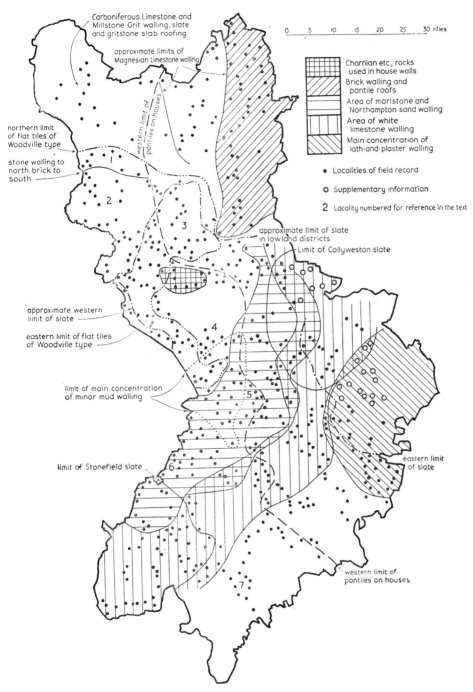

Fig. 35   DISTRIBUTION OF CERTAIN ELEMENTS OF RURAL DOMESTIC ARCHITECTURE.

and heavy but escaping clumsiness, are darkened by lichen. Slate roofs, common in the Peak District, accord well with the Carboniferous Limestone of walls. Stone houses in a narrow transitional belt to the south (1 in Fig. 35) are roofed with flat bluish tiles of the type made at Woodville (Pl. 19).

Very little has been done to identify rural styles among the swollen settlements of the exposed coalfield, although Coal-Measure sandstone and Millstone Grit have been recorded in a few walls, and roofing slabs of gritstone or of fissile Coal-Measure sandstone are known to exist. Local shales were much used in brickmaking in the late eighteenth century, so that brick may have been common in such rural housing as then existed. As part of the exposed coalfield falls within the western limit of pantiles on houses—a limit which runs from north to south across the whole region—roofing materials in 1800 may have been quite varied.

Matters are clearer on the Permian outcrop, where Magnesian Limestone is pleasantly combined with pantile roofs. Some of the limestone used in minor walling, for example of yards and barns, has weathered badly, but that of house walls is enduring well, suggesting that variations in quality of stone were fully understood by the original builders. The frequency of limestone walling decreases towards the east in favour of brick, until the whole northeastern part of the region is characterised by walls in brick of a soft but quite warm red, and by roofs of slightly pale pantile. Here is the region's greatest single concentration of rural housing in uniform style—a style probably dating from the late eighteenth and early nineteenth centuries, for houses are quite large by rural standards (Pl. 20).

Examples of brickwork dating from 1600 or earlier show however that in this area brick is a truly traditional material. Few of the brick-built villages can be called picturesque, but none can be called ugly; their very uniformity demonstrates the strength of the local style of building, and their colours harmonise well with the colours of the surrounding country.

A large triangle in the west of the region is dominated by red brick walls. Its southeastern boundary is the northeast limit of brownstone; the boundary northwest of Nottingham has not been precisely fixed, but farther west it lies at the southern limit of stone walling in the Pennines. Within this triangle the widespread brickwork seems to have superseded other types of fabric: half-timber and local sandstones appear in occasional walls in the Derbyshire foothills and in nearby parts of the inner Trent valley. Although half-timber and brick may once have been quite common, they may already have been largely superseded by brick in 1800, for brickworks were exploiting the whole

Carbo-Permo-Triassic sequence of red beds in the late eighteenth century.

In this area it is particularly difficult to make due allowance for the new building associated with nineteenth-century industrialisation, especially since the two commonest types of roofing are Welsh slate and bluish flat tiles. Although a few thatched roofs are on record, there is no reason to conclude that thatch was ever universal ; thatched roofs are indeed known to have been confined in some areas, during the late Middle Ages, to the poorer houses. Now the local tiles are of the kind produced chiefly in the west of the Leicestershire coalfield, with production centred at Woodville. Their approximate limit of distribution (Fig. 35) suggests that many come from Woodville itself. It seems impossible to distinguish tiles made before 1750 from those made later in truly industrialised plants, so that one particular tradition of building seems unaffected by industrialisation. In the Derbyshire foothills (2 in Fig. 35) flat tiles are almost the sole type of roofing, but between Nottingham and Charnwood Forest (3 in Fig. 35) slate and pantiles also occur. Local crystalline rocks form house walls in and near Charnwood Forest and Mountsorrel, either alone or with corner-ings of brick. South of the Forest, a small area which encloses Leicester is outside the limits both of pantiles and of flat tiles of the Woodville type. Few but slate roofs occur here (4 in Fig. 35). Most of the slating is of Welsh blues. Charnwood slates have a limited range, probably because reserves were always small, and also because the cleavage of Charnwood slates is inferior to that of Welsh slates. In combination with the solid red of brick walls, the smoky colour of Welsh blues is by no means unattractive, especially in summer ; villages which have not been industrialised evoke none of the revulsion inspired by brick-and-slate building in Midland towns. The associa-tions of Welsh slate are nevertheless with the improvements in bulk transport which accompanied industrialisation, and their limits of use suggest that Leicester was a leading distributing centre ; it can scarcely have become so before the navigational works of the late eighteenth century were undertaken.

A belt of brownstone walling—of walls built of Marlstone or of Northampton Sand—extends from east Leicestershire into north Oxfordshire. The notation in Figure 35 is not meant to imply that, within the belt, brownstone is the exclusive type of walling ; on the contrary, there is a great deal of brick of various dates, some of it certainly as old as the very early nineteenth century. Some villages in this belt are nevertheless almost entirely stone-built. Very many stone houses were originally thatched, and thatch was certainly used on quite large and elegantly constructed dwellings. Thatch has however been slowly disappearing for many years. One most regrettable practice is the covering of thatch by corrugated iron, which, if applied during the depressed inter-war period, is often today ugly with rust. Where thatch has been replaced by flat tile the original high pitch of the roof is usually unchanged, but replacement by slate has involved the raising of the outer walls in order to reduce the pitch ; such raising was especially likely when the original roof came down to the top of the ground floor. Excellent examples of surviving high-pitched thatch, on houses built of Northampton Sand and with two full storeys, occur north of Northampton (5 in Fig. 35) ; thatch on Marlstone is best seen north and northwest of Banbury (6 in Fig. 35). In the northeast of the brownstone belt, where the solid rocks are much obscured by boulder-clay, little brownstone remains amid the predominant red brick of the villages ; here, too, some pantile roofs come in.

Marlstone and Northampton Sand are to some extent mutually exclusive ; the one occurs chiefly where the Middle Lias thickens into the Banbury ironstone field, the other in the Northampton district. The principal differences between them, as building-stones, lie in colour and in ease of working. Although some Marlstone can be sawn and faced, most of the ashlar used in ordinary houses is little more than roughly shaped. It is also commonly overgrown by lichen, so that its varying browns are overlain by grey. Northampton Sand, by contrast, can be cut true, and the best building, even in ordinary houses, has remarkably clean lines. This stone appears to discourage lichen, so that its rich apricot tints are not obscured with age.

Walls of white limestone from the Inferior and Great Oolites are numerous in a belt of country slightly overlapping the belt of brownstone walls. White and brown stone may be combined in the region of overlap in formal combinations ; Northampton Sand is usually employed as cornering to walls of white limestone, or, on occasion, as whole decorative courses. Roofs are of thatch, flat tiles, or slate, in the central belt of white limestone, with pantile coming towards the northeast. At either end occur roofs of stone slab—Stonesfield Slate in the southwest, Collyweston Slate in the northeast. The limits of stone slab on ordinary houses are quite well defined, but limits on large houses and on churches are wider and less regular. In few villages in the areas of stone-slab roofing is there no flat tile, thatch, or slate, but slab predominates in the centres. The beauty and effectiveness of the stone-slab combination are unsurpassed among the architecture of the region (Pls. 21, 23).

Within the belt of white limestone there is room for much variation in the detailed quality of stone, in accordance with vertical and lateral variation in limestone facies ; indeed, the two areas of slab roofing are themselves responses to particular modes of bedding in two depositional basins. Generally speaking, the variation amounts in practice to a range from ragstone to freestone. The best architectural effects are naturally achieved with freestone, which imparts distinction to large buildings, but even the rougher rags can achieve elegance by their soft creamy tints and the care with which they have been laid (Pl. 22).[1]

Adjoining the belt of white limestone walling on the southeast comes a strip of clay vale extending to the Chiltern scarp and merging eastwards into the Fens. Although this area has not been reconnoitred in much detail, certain facts of distribution have been established. The part coinciding roughly with Huntingdonshire has strong architectural affinities with country farther east, lying as it does within the main concentration of lath-and-plaster building (Fig. 35). There is little overlap between the distribution of lath-and-plaster walls and that of white limestone, or between slate roofing and roofing of flat tiles. Thus in Huntingdonshire and adjacent parts of Bedfordshire, lath-and-plaster with flat tiles seems to represent an indigenous style, and was certainly common in 1800 despite the presence of some thatch and pantiles. The pitch of tile roofs is high enough to give, by itself, an air of age. Walls are washed with pale colours on the outside ; some are jettied, but jettying seems characteristic less of villages than of towns, where it is often obscured by reconstruction of shops. A few instances of clap-board walling in the extreme southeast indicate additional links with East Anglia, but pargetting is uncommon.

Numbers of decaying walls demonstrate the derivation of lath-and-plaster from earlier wattle-and-daub—chiefly minor walls, such as the end-walls of barns. Lath-and-plaster is itself vanishing, having already been replaced to a marked extent by brick. Pale yellow brick, abundant for instance in east Bedfordshire, is probably the result of rebuilding in the nineteenth century : it is quite widely used in nineteenth-century rural schools. Associations, and some formal combinations, of yellow and red brick come in towards the southwest, and the limit of distribution of yellow brick is reached not far beyond the western limit of pantiles. Half-timber work is scattered throughout this whole southwestern part of the region, filled mainly with red brick ; but in south Buckinghamshire, where patches of Upper Jurassic limestone crop out, fillings consist not infrequently of cob (7 in Fig. 35). Stone fillings, and plain stone walls, are also present. The combination of half-timber, cob, and red-tile roofs richly encrusted with dark lichen

---

[1] Variations in type of stone, with locations of quarries, are given by W. J. Arkell. Twelfth-century distribution of fine building stone from the Great Oolite is mapped in the Oxford B.A. Handbook, Fig. 40.

is as attractive as the more familiar combination of lath-and-plaster with flat tile (Pls. 24, 25, 26).

Where stone is available close at hand, it has been freely used in field walls in many parts of the region. The stone walls of the Cotswolds and of the limestone plateau in Derbyshire are outstanding cases. But since stone for walling fields is rarely carried far, abrupt changes occur from walls to hedges, or in the material used in single walls : immediately north of Buxton the colour of stone walls changes midway across fields from the bleached tints of limestone to the sombre darkness of grit. Stone in the brownstone belt is rarely used in minor walling except within villages, where it encloses gardens, yards, and paddocks. Limestone from the Rhaetic and Lower Lias is scarcely found in walls of any kind within the region, although it remains as footings on the margins of the Vale of Belvoir ; nothing compares with the light blue-grey stone houses of east Warwickshire. The only type of minor walling mapped in Figure 35 is that in which mud is used— in fact, boulder-clay mixed with straw. Mud walls in some ancient dwellings are undoubtedly concealed by rendering, but mud in minor walls is usually bare. It resists weather surprisingly well, so long as it be soundly coped ; but many of the surviving mud walls, their coping gone, are falling into ruin. On the regional boundary the mud walls are lightish brown in colour, but farther east they take on rich tints similar to, but darker than, those of Northampton Sand. The few mud walls in the north of the brownstone belt are too rare to allow limits of distribution to be drawn.

Large barns in villages would justify study on their own. They often contrast strongly in fabric with the nearby houses, either because they represent antique styles, or because they are made of materials little esteemed by local builders of houses. Houses, barns, and farm-steads in the northeast of the region are alike of brick and pantile, but in the south-centre pantiled barns and especially pantiled lean-tos are far commoner than pantiled houses. Black-painted clapboard barns, some with massive roofs of thatch, extend in the southeast far beyond the limits of house-walls of clapboard ; this same area includes clap-board barns roofed with pantiles or with flat tiles. Preliminary obser-vations of this kind imply not only that barns are as highly characterised as houses but also that the two sets of distributional limits of style may not coincide (Pl. 27).

Parts of the East Midland region are notably rich in great houses, which combine the theme of form of rural settlement with the theme of location ; indeed, fabric is by no means irrelevant to this topic, even though most of the building is in stone. Especially if farmhouses be included, country houses in this region exemplify widely ranging styles.

Lesser country houses of the early nineteenth century vary from plain to pretentious, farmhouses of about the same period from shapeless to solid. In these two groups the austere lines of the eighteenth century were being abandoned, while the nineteenth-century expression of worth and wealth was beginning to appear, although less rapidly than with the romantically-minded architects responsible for certain major structures. In general, the best-known country houses are naturally the largest. These are also the most closely associated with deliberate changes of landscape, not merely because of their own size but because of the emparking, planting, and—in places—the depopulation which they involved. To some extent the great houses record the political, social, and economic history of the region. No selection or brief survey can do justice to all the available treasures (or offences) of architecture which date from Norman times onward. Many of the outstanding examples are illustrated and discussed in the works listed in the bibliography for C. Hussey, H. A. Tipping, and Nikolaus Pevsner.

South Wingfield Manor House (Derbyshire) and the quite unmistakably Norman manor house at Northborough (Northamptonshire) pre-date the Tudor period. Haddon Hall (Derbyshire ; see Plate 29) ranges in date from the twelfth to the sixteenth century. Early Tudor times produced Fawsley House (Northamptonshire) on a depopulated site, while the vigorous Bess of Hardwick built Hardwick Hall (Derbyshire) in the 1590s. In 1512 the grazier Sir John Spencer was licensed to empark 300 acres at Althorp (Northamptonshire), which he depopulated ; by Restoration times the Spencers were earls, and the diarist Evelyn called Althorp a palace. Successive owners have left their imprint on interior and exterior alike, but externally the present house is due to the architect Holland who worked upon it between 1786 and 1800. Late-Stuart times produced Chatsworth House (Derbyshire) under the first Duke of Devonshire (1687–1707) ; but here also an Elizabethan house is incorporated in the existing structure. The present house owes much to the activities of the sixth Duke between 1820 and 1842 (Pl. 29).

Ten years before Palladianism was introduced at all widely to architects in England, Sir John Vanbrugh in 1705 made the colossal plan of Blenheim Palace (Oxfordshire ; see Plate 31). Pevsner describes the front of Blenheim as theatrical and ostentatious, in comparison with Baroque structures of the European mainland, but also as illustrating the forcing of English aloofness into the services of an overmighty plan. Other products of the Vanbrugh school in the East Midlands are Stowe House (Buckinghamshire) and Shotover Park (Oxfordshire). Aynho Park (Oxfordshire ; see Plate 30) expresses the rigorous lines favoured by Sir John Soane, a pupil of the junior George Dance and of Henry Holland ; he remodelled both the house and parts of the village for the Cartwright family. Aynho, with peaches and apricots trained up house-walls fronting on the village street, and with the severe interiors of the great house itself, possesses to some minds the most exquisite of all domestic architecture in the East Midlands. It forms a complete contrast with Belvoir Castle (Leicestershire ; see Plate 32), which the Duchess of Rutland and her husband's chaplain Sir John Thoroton constructed in the early nineteenth century. The Belvoir site, on the very summit and tip of the Middle Lias scarp above the Vale of Belvoir, is dramatic ; it was occupied by a Norman castle soon after the Conquest, subsequently by structures which underwent various extension, rebuilding, and ruination, and was to have carried a building designed by Capability Brown until the project was stayed by the death of the fifth Duke. The Duchess, now in charge, embraced romanticism, which suddenly irrupts into the region with the building of the castle. In the 1830s the work was characterised as very faulty, but so grand as to sink criticism in admiration. Certainly the castle is massive, impressive, and commanding. Although Belvoir is remarkably functionless, and deliberately so in keeping with the artistic ideas of the nineteenth century, its appraisal today is surely tinged by its strong resemblance to Windsor Castle, which Belvoir matches with remarkable closeness in the history of its building.

Although the fabric of rural dwellings and outbuildings has been renewed and supplanted, the forms of some settlements appear to have changed little between the time of the original foundation and the end of the eighteenth century. In the year 1801, parishes belonging to the rural or sparse-rural classes of population density (Chap. 11) still contained more than three-quarters of the inhabitants of the region. Few of the villages which are today perceptibly industrial had begun to spread ; some did not even exist. Few of the lesser towns had gone far beyond their very early bounds ; indeed, some of the principal towns were still uncomfortably constricted by ancient limits. Now, this was precisely the time when the forms of rural settlement were first documented in detail for the whole region, first on the county maps of the eighteenth century and then on the First Edition of the Ordnance Survey. Because some of the county maps fail to supply so complete a range of information as the First Edition O.S., this map will principally be drawn on for illustrations to the following discussion. It marks individual buildings in plan, carries symbols for gardens, and distinguishes between village and hamlet by style of lettering. Although it refers to a time when, in parts of the region, secondary dispersion had already begun as an accompaniment or sequel of parliamentary enclosure, this circumstance is perhaps not unduly serious in the context of the plans of nucleated settlements.

The villages of 1800 were the end-products of twelve centuries, more or less, of habitation. By no means all of them can be expected to have remained substantially unaltered, even where the epidemics of the fourteenth century and the enforced depopulations of the early modern period had exerted little influence upon form. It is because of the effects of disease and depopulation that no regional map of the respective distribution of villages and of hamlets will be attempted : numbers of settlements which were functionally hamlets, in any reasonable sense of the term, still had village status in 1800, having been originally founded as villages or having risen early to village rank. In complementary fashion, a number of nucleated secondary or daughter-settlements, originally small, had flourished well enough to become villages in their own right. Little is yet available for England to match the profound studies of rural settlement which have been made on the European mainland ; furthermore, English settlement forms may prove less easily classifiable than those, for instance, of the North European Plain. Any but a purely descriptive classification of rural settlement in the East Midland region seems indefensible in the present state of knowledge. Nevertheless, the thesis that numbers of settlements still preserved in 1800 something very like their original plans seems justified by the recurrence throughout the region of at least one clearly distinguishable form, the linear. This, well documented from sites of depopulation, is certainly early (Pl. 18).

H. M. Keating identifies four types of village in south Nottinghamshire—strung, spread, asymmetrical, and clustered ; the clustered group is located on valley sides and subclassified according to relationship to roads. Hamlet settlement and dispersed settlement complete Keating's list. E. Paget distinguishes four main types of village for the country around Oxford—street-line, loose and irregular, composite with street-line tentacles, and twin villages. Estate villages, which Paget also names, may be omitted from the present discussion ; settlements smaller than villages he classes together as dispersed. Certain principles already emerge : that the forms of villages range considerably in both parts of the region, and that village settlement is, as usual, distinguishable from settlement in hamlets and in single farms.

Now, the linear plan appears safely acceptable as characteristic of the whole region. Perhaps it may prove the single type of original plan which is really widespread. Variations upon it appear with the presence or absence of back lanes, which can occur to one or to both sides of the main street.

Fig. 36 LOCATION MAP, FORM, AND PATTERN OF RURAL SETTLEMENT. Named settlements appear in the text and in Fig. 37. Framed areas are shown to larger scales in Figs. 39–42.

112

At Hickling (Nottinghamshire [1]; Fig. 37a) and Liddington (Rutland; Fig. 37b) no back lane exists. A continuous lane runs parallel to the main street along the whole north side of Braunston (Northamptonshire; Fig. 37c), while at Woodnewton (Northamptonshire; Fig. 37d) its place is taken by the through road. Ravensthorpe (Northamptonshire; Fig. 37e) and Ibstock (Leicestershire; Fig. 37f) lie on valley sides, each with a through road branching at the end of the village to run along the crest of a hill; at each village the through road is somewhat built up, and its origin as back lane is dubious. Tingewick (Buckinghamshire; Fig. 37g), although possessing one through road which includes the main street, and having a parallel street to the south, is probably to be classed as a twinned settlement rather than as a village with a built-up back lane, for the two parts of the village lie on opposite sides of the little stream. Tingewick thus invites comparison with Podington (Northamptonshire; Fig. 37h) and with Dean-Upper Dean (Bedfordshire; Fig. 37i), both indubitably twinned. However, Upper Dean ranks also as a hamlet of Dean, for the second hamlet of Nether Dean lies a mile away to the northeast. Helmdon (Northamptonshire; Fig. 37j) appears linear at first sight, illustrating the fact that the main street of a linear settlement need not always be straight; but Helmdon is best taken as a twinned village, relying for its water supply on wells and springs on the two sides of a valley.

The foregoing illustrations of Hickling, Braunston, and Woodnewton show that roads crossing, or diverging from, a main village street were by no means everywhere followed by buildings in 1800. Liddington seems to incorporate some extension along side-roads. At East Haddon (Northamptonshire; Fig. 37k) the main street runs east–west; whether the processes of the village along side-roads to north and south are original, or at least very early, is a matter for investigation. Wollaston (Northamptonshire; Fig. 37l) may have grown selectively at its south end, complicating an original simple north–south alignment. The plan of Gotham (Nottinghamshire; Fig. 37m) may result from the addition of angular back streets to an early linear form, in which event its apparent compactness in 1800 is deceptive. Stanwick (Northamptonshire; Fig. 37n) is linear as to the main street in the southwest, but also twinned on the two sides of the valley, with five cross-connections between the two parts.

Any thorough investigation of form would need to allow for variation in the closeness of building along the main frontage. It is here particularly that some of the county maps of the late eighteenth century fall short of what is desirable, generalising into continuous lines buildings which did not actually abut on one another. Continuous

[1] Places mentioned in this section are located in Figure 36.

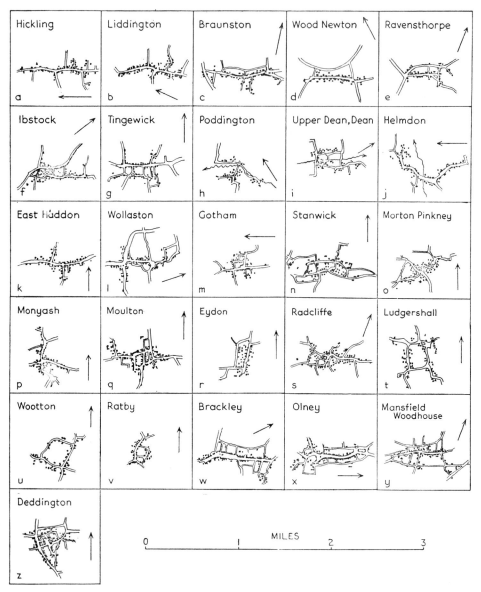

Fig. 37 EXAMPLES OF THE FORM OF SETTLEMENT (villages and small towns). For location see preceding Figure.

frontages existed at least as early as the seventeenth century in some villages, for example Rockingham (Northamptonshire) ; but the First Edition O.S. suggests that they were still uncommon in 1800.

The relationship of dwellings to streets is complicated in many villages by small courts, around each of which a few houses are grouped. M. Beresford has recorded such courts in depopulated settlements ; they are, then, early features. Hellidon (Northamptonshire ; Fig. 38) illustrates the way in which they influence the layout of a village. They suggest a direct link with the courts and alley-ways of early towns, which are in turn reflected by the backyards and entries of late-nineteenth-century industrial housing.

Located on a hillside where four aquiferous horizons occur, Hellidon cannot be called linear ; on the other hand, it straggles too much to be classed as compact. Although much of its oldest (seventeenth-century) housing is clustered about the Y of its central lanes, equally old houses occur in other parts. In direct contrast, Morton Pinkney (Northamptonshire ; Fig. 37o) seems firmly grouped around its central crossroad, as also does Monyash (Derbyshire ; Fig. 37p). Moulton (Northamptonshire ; Fig. 37q), although complicated by interconnecting ways, was also a compact settlement in 1800. Eydon (Northamptonshire ; Fig. 37r) possesses an undeniable main street running north–south on its eastern side, but gains an appearance of compactness as opposed to linear form from the second parallel road on the west. Radcliffe (Nottinghamshire ; Fig. 37s) appeared radial in 1800, but the allowance to be made here for selective growth is difficult to judge.

A check on most of the region from the First Edition O.S. reveals that, of 1,256 settlements, 628 (precisely half) possessed linear plans in the very early nineteenth century. A few small towns were included in the check, which took account also of settlements of hamlet rank but large enough to be comparable to settlements of recognised village status ; small groups of, say, five or six dwellings were not considered. Compact settlements accounted for 25% of the total, radial or loosely grouped settlements for 19%, and cruciform settlements for the remaining 6%. The tally of 6%, relating to alignments on the four arms of crossroads, not outgrown or substantially elaborated by 1800, is probably too small to indicate original or very early plans. The 44% of compact, radial, and loosely grouped settlements on the other hand is enlarged by numbers of transitional or dubiously classifiable plans, some likely to have evolved from earlier linear or cruciform groupings.

Village greens in the East Midland region range greatly in size, in form, and in location with respect to the villages. In many linear villages quite wide verges exist along the main street without being reflected on the eighteenth-century county maps or on the First

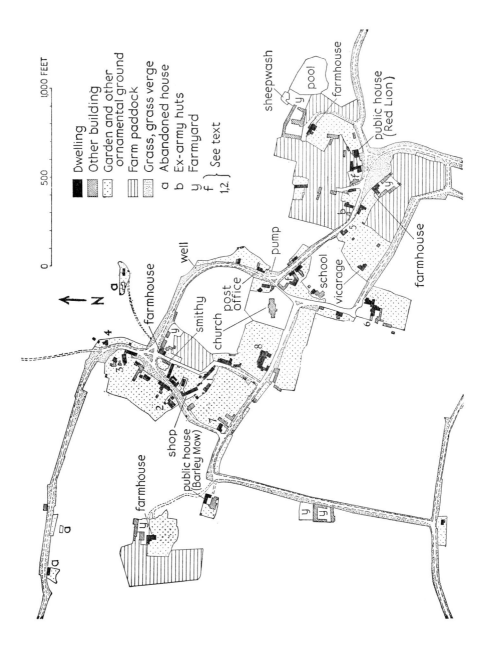

N ←

1,000 FEET
0   500   1,000

Dwelling
Other building
Garden and other
   ornamental ground
Farm paddock
Grass, grass verge
a   Abandoned house
b   Ex-army huts
y   Farmyard
f   } See text
1,2.

farmhouse
a
well
pump
smithy
church
post
office
farmhouse
y
shop
public house
(Barley Mow)
farmhouse
y
a
a

school
vicarage
farmhouse
y
b
5
6
8
7
2
3
4

sheepwash
pool
y
farmhouse
public house
(Red Lion)
farmhouse
f
y

y   y

Fig. 38 FORM OF THE VILLAGE OF HELLIDON, NORTHAMPTONSHIRE. A frequent design of dwelling-house, here as in neighbouring villages, involves a square plan; both the ground and the upper floors contain, or originally contained, only one room each. The design goes back at least to the early seventeenth century. Common internal modifications include partitioning, the merging of two houses into one by a passage, and the boarding-over of ceilings to conceal the faggots which underlie the thatched roofs.

Where small square houses abut on one another, the effect of the plan can be misleading. Thus, the court numbered 1 (actually, two courts) is lined with square houses, such as appear clearly in the smaller court 2. At one time the court 3 was also enclosed by houses of this type, but some had been pulled down by the 1920s, while others were in use merely as barns. The house 4 dates from the late nineteenth century; it represents colonisation of the wayside verge. Outlying houses of similar location but earlier date lay abandoned early in the twentieth century (a, a in the northwest). Two of four outlying dwellings on the northeast were also abandoned and unroofed.

The dwellings numbered 5, 6, 7, 8 are substantial; 8 is the great house, at one time the headquarters of a racing stable, but liable to stand empty between tenancies. Manor Farm lies outside the village on the west; two other farmsteads are on the edge of the village on the east. One older and smaller farmstead adjoins the main village green near the smithy, while two former farms now used as dwellings (f, f on the plan) occur near the church and near the Red Lion public house.

Apart from nineteenth-century building, the village consists mainly of three clusters of ordinary houses. The principal cluster surrounds the main green on three sides and includes the courts 1, 2, 3; the smithy and its attached garden encroach on the green. The second cluster of dwellings, east of the church, contains 15 dwellings, not however all occupied, or used as dwellings, in the 1920s. Here, on a tiny wayside green, is the village pump. The third cluster is far looser than the other two, comprising short rows at the east end of the village, where a second large green occurs at the Y of incoming roads. This green was virtually functionless in the 1920s, when nearly all the village children lived in the northwest of Hellidon and played traditional games on the main green; but the Bicester Hunt assembled on the green in the northeast. Rights of common watering in the large pool in the northeast (Leam Pool, the reputed head of the River Leam) have long fallen into disuse, although the sheepwash and the adjoining dip operate regularly for the benefit of all local farmers.

Edition O.S.; such is the case at Rockingham. Large central greens occur elsewhere, as at Quainton (Buckinghamshire) and Haddenham (Buckinghamshire). However, some large greens which now appear central were originally marginal, as at Newnham (Northamptonshire), lying at the divergence of outgoing ways, as can still be seen at Yelden (Bedfordshire). The greens at Foolow (Derbyshire) and Leafield (Oxfordshire) may also have developed as marginal elements. Where greens contain watering-ponds, as at Leafield, Staverton (Northamptonshire), Tissington (Derbyshire), and Kirtlington (Oxfordshire), one at least of their functions is clear. But the true analogue of the market-square and place of assembly in small towns is supplied in some villages by quite tiny greens, such as the central green of Badby (Northamptonshire) which at one time held the village stocks (cf. Pl. 28).

Too little is yet known of the development of East Midland villages to sustain comment on the relationship of certain greens to clearance of, or encroachment on, woodland. Ludgershall (Buckinghamshire; Fig. 37t), Barton in the Clay (Bedfordshire), Wootton (Bedfordshire; Fig. 37u), and Shillington (Bedfordshire) suggest the looping of villages round approximately circular roads. If the suggestion is valid, the original function of the area within the circle needs study. On the other hand Ratby (Leicestershire; Fig. 37v) suggests that transition may occur from the linear to the twinned/rectangular and thence to the apparently ringed form.

Colonisation of verges alongside outgoing ways has produced, in some villages, widely spaced dwellings with gardens elongated parallel to the remaining way. In this manner a kind of loose radial pattern has arisen. Certain influences of broad ways, both within and at the margins of nucleated settlements, are discussed by E. M. Yates with reference to an early map of the town of Ashbourne.

R. E. Dickinson notes three market forms as constantly recurring in the medieval mercantile settlement of western Europe: the long wide street thoroughfare, the rectangular market, and the triangular market situated at the convergence of two main highways. All these forms can be matched among the village greens of the East Midland region: the small rectangular market, as stated above, in Badby; the triangular market by the triangular open space at the east end of Braunston (Fig. 37c, above); and the long central market, excellently displayed by Thame (Oxfordshire; see Plate 40), by the long verges at Rockingham. These are, of course, merely a few of very many possible examples. The small market towns of the East Midlands resemble villages drawn large. Brackley (Northamptonshire; Fig. 37w) has a broad street thoroughfare, wider at one end than at the other so that it forms a long narrow triangle; parallel to the main street run a continuous back lane on one side and elements of a second on the other. The axial street of Olney (Buckinghamshire; Fig. 37x), widening into a triangle at one end, is accompanied by two complete back lanes. Mansfield Woodhouse (Nottinghamshire; Fig. 37y) in 1800 possessed one main street, two back lanes, and cross-connecting ways

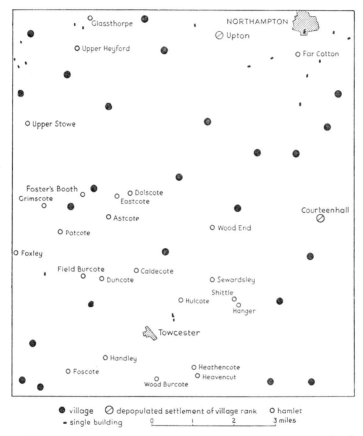

Fig. 39 PATTERN OF SETTLEMENT IN A PART OF NORTHAMPTONSHIRE in the late eighteenth century. From Eyre's County Map, as revised by Jeffreys and engraved by Faden in 1779.

which at the time were little built up. Deddington (Oxfordshire; Fig. 37z) exemplifies the central marketplace of a compact settlement; like the tiny market-square at Stony Stratford (Buckinghamshire) and the larger square at Bingham (Nottinghamshire), the Deddington market-place is off the main road.

In what has been said above, form has been emphasised at the expense of site. Future work will presumably take into account not only such elementary matters as water supply and natural drainage but also modes of colonisation, manners of settling forest land, and structure of human societies in early villages, especially at the times of secondary settlement.

With the emphatic stipulation that they describe conditions at the time of mapping, the county maps of the late eighteenth century can be used to illustrate patterns of rural settlements. With the aid of the

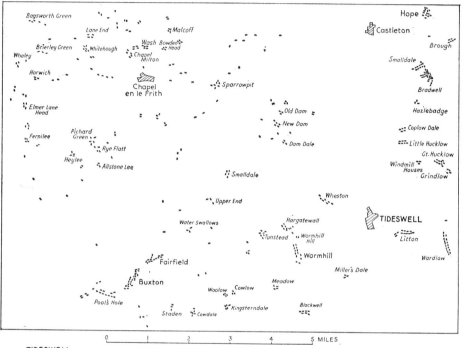

Fig. 40   PATTERN OF SETTLEMENT IN A PART OF THE PEAK DISTRICT in the eighteenth century.   Re-drawn from Burdett's Survey of 1762–7.

place-name handbooks, however, matters can be taken further than mere exemplification. For instance, Eyre's map of Northamptonshire (Jeffreys' revision of 1779) shows that parts of the county were characterised in the late eighteenth century by villages and hamlets, with few intervening single buildings. *The Place Names of Northamptonshire* reveals that, of the hamlets named in Figure 39, all but three were recorded at least as early as 1203 ; Wood End appears by 1275, Eastcote by 1277. Foster's Booth is alone late, being first known from 1675. This was probably, at the outset, a single dwelling, whereas the others were hamlets from the beginning. So much is indicated by the frequent ending -*cote*, of which the plural form is still preserved in Far Cotton. Heathencote and Heavencut are not separated in *The Place Names of Northamptonshire*, although distinguished from one another on Eyre's map; the two names appear to be variant forms, applied to each of two nearly adjacent hamlets. The two hamlets which Eyre calls Shittle and Hanger combine today in the village with the single name Shutlanger which, known from early records, suggests

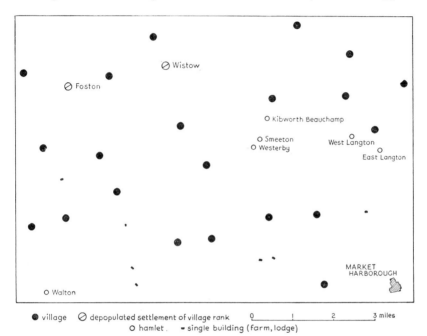

● village ⊘ depopulated settlement of village rank   0   1   2   3 miles
O hamlet   ■ single building (farm, lodge)

Fig. 41   PATTERN OF SETTLEMENT IN A PART OF LEICESTERSHIRE in the eighteenth century.   From Prior's map (1775–7).   Compare next Figure.

that the two hamlet-names may be back-formations. Eyre gives the name Stow Nine Churches to the present Upper Stowe, calling the present Church Stowe simply Stow. However, it seems likely that Stow=Church Stowe was the original foundation, and Upper Stow(e) the daughter-settlement. Aside from these minor points of doubt, Figure 39 represents the authentic effects of early secondary settlement. Whether the movement outward from the villages be called secondary dispersion or secondary nucleation depends on the classification of the hamlets as dispersed or nucleated.

Figure 40, re-drawn from Burdett's eighteenth-century map of Derbyshire, locates individual buildings for part of the Peak District, except in the closely built-up settlements of Castleton, Chapel-en-le-Frith, and Tideswell. Whether or not Burdett conscientiously recorded all buildings and refrained from symbolising those of the larger settlements is not critical in the immediate context ; the type of distribution represented by Burdett's map, and his ranking of settlements in order of importance, as shown by size of lettering in place-names, resemble the distributions and rankings of the 1954 O.S. and of the O.S. First Edition closely enough to seem accurate in the main. Now, *The Place*

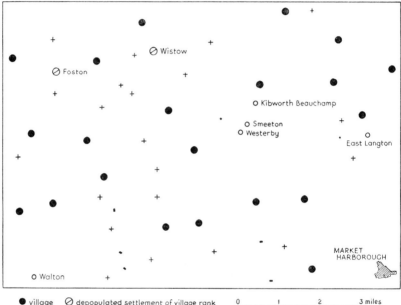

● village   ⊘ depopulated settlement of village rank   0   1   2   3 miles
O hamlet   + single building (lodge, grange, hall) not mapped in 1775-7   ■ single building mapped in 1775-7

Fig. 42   PATTERN OF SETTLEMENT IN A PART OF LEICESTERSHIRE in the mid-nineteenth century. Compare preceding Figure.

Names of Derbyshire gives dates for the settlements named by Burdett which place them nearly all in two groups, one known to be recorded before 1300, the other not known to be recorded before 1540. In the first group fall Allstone Lee, Heylee, Tunstead, and Whitehough, in the second Smalldale, Sparrowpit, and Upper End. Not surprisingly, this area of scattered settlements provides more queries than does the simple example from Northamptonshire presented above ; Burdett seems to have omitted a few place-names which pre-date his lifetime by centuries, and to have misapplied a few others. Nevertheless the separation into two groups is quite clear ; Old Dam (1405) and Burbage (1417, apparently included in Pool's Hole by Burdett) alone make their first-known appearance in the records between 1300 and

1540. Because places with village rank are so few on the earliest maps, while minor settlements are numerous, this piece of country seems to represent original settlement consisting very largely in hamlets. Some of the names appearing after 1540 relate to industrial activity, but others belong to a second series of hamlets which were superimposed on the pattern of the earlier series.

In the absence of a place-name handbook for Leicestershire,[1] Prior's county map of 1775–7 will be sampled for comparison with the mid-nineteenth-century distribution recorded by the O.S. (Figs. 41, 42). Villages were typical of the district immediately northwest of Market Harborough in the 1770s ; isolated dwellings and hamlets were alike few, although at least two villages had suffered depopulation without losing rank. By the mid-nineteenth century the hamlet of West Langton was mapped as Langton Hall, while country houses called lodge, hall, and grange had appeared in number. Names recorded by Prior for country houses existing in his day conflict with those on the current O.S. ; check-lists of landowners and their addresses cannot therefore be used to trace the sequence of building, but—assuming Prior not to have omitted numerous houses from his survey—the net result is obvious. The two accompanying Figures illustrate that movement of secondary dispersion which accompanied parliamentary enclosure of farmland and developments in middle-class society.

[1] Not published at the time of writing.

CHAPTER 8

AGRICULTURE AND INDUSTRY IN 1800

MUCH of the available information about the East Midland landscape in the late eighteenth and very early nineteenth centuries is contained in the two series of reports to the Board of Agriculture. The authors of the first series produced reports uniform but rather limited in scope. The writers of the second series reveal at least as much about themselves as about their allotted counties. In a comparison between the two sets of recorded conditions it is necessary to allow for idiosyncrasies of opinion and treatment, and to disentangle reportage from polemics.

The reporters of the 1790s wrote when parliamentary enclosure was rapid, but when its lasting effects could not be surely foreseen ; its immediate effects varied from parish to parish. Tillage and the output of grain were on balance reduced, at least temporarily, while the extent of grass and the yield of milk, meat, and butter increased. The first reports already show marked contrasts between one part of the region and another, even under open-field working. Specialisation had been promoted by enclosure and depopulation, by estate management of former monastic lands, and by the sometimes high-handed practices of the eighteenth-century gentry. But the ordinary strip-holder of the open fields felt the influence of urban markets, local soils, and local climates.

About a third of Derbyshire was classed as non-agricultural land in the early 1790s. A fifth of the county's farmland was in corn, the remainder in old sward or artificial grasses. Oats dominated the arable of the higher ground ; barley and peas were also grown in the lower hill country, while wheat made a fourth leading tillage crop in the Trent valley lowlands. To the great total extent of grass corresponded a lively interest in quality of stock, especially in the south, where improvements were already well in hand with the aid of Bakewell's animals. Remote cattle-farms concentrated on cheese and pigs ; dairying was commoner than fattening.

Lowe, in his first report of 1794, clearly specified agricultural variations in Nottinghamshire ; exceptionally, however, the same writer produced a second report within four years, which was reprinted in 1813 as part of the second series. The paragraphs immediately following are based on the report of 1798.

Livestock on the Pennine flanks was generally indifferent. Liver-fluke—a menace on all ill-drained land in the eighteenth century—

was endemic on the Coal-Measure shales. Tillage on the exposed coalfield was extensive merely because leys degenerated rapidly with disappearance of their best grasses. Sherwood Forest was in a poor state. Of the 10,000 trees recorded for 1790, many were well advanced in decay. The 7,200 acres of new plantations included patches of conifers. The Dukes of Newcastle, Portland, and Norfolk, with the Savile family, led the movement to enclose, plant, and empark. The Duke of Newcastle alone enclosed 4,000 acres in Clumber park, greatly improving the whole and putting 2,000 acres to tillage ; the Duke of Portland improved more than 2,000 acres, planting some 500 or more with new trees, and the Saviles took in 3,000 acres. Lesser permanent enclosures meant large farms on low-yielding land, even with a turnip course. Temporary enclosures ranged from 4 to 250 acres, being tilled for five or six years, but their cultivation ranked little above catch-cropping.

Open fields were still extensive in the Keuper Marl country west of the Trent, with the usual rotation of fallow ; wheat or barley ; beans, peas, or a bean-pea mixture. Undersowing of barley with clover was on the increase, and stock-carrying capacity in open fields was rising. Livestock remained poor, however, by contrast with that of low levels near the Trent where cattle were markedly improved, and sheep, much altered by Lincolnshire and New Leicester tups, were far better than the small polled sheep of the Forest. Ploughland worked by turnip husbandry intermingled with pasture on the terraces, while grassland covered the floodplain, parts of which had still to be drained (Fig. 29).

Dairying replaced stock-fattening on the south of the Trent and in the Soar valley, where dairy farms carrying 20 or 25 cows concentrated, as in south Derbyshire, on cheese. The low ground of the Smite basin still lacked effective drainage. Poor sandy land, low moors liable to flood after heavy rain, and old turbaries combined in a landscape dismal to the eye and offensive to the reporter. There were market gardens near Newark, however, comparable as really specialised cultivation to hop-growing near Retford and to orchard cultivation around Southwell.

Sheep were few in low-grade land of the Nottinghamshire Wolds. These Wolds and the Vale of Belvoir were alike handicapped by lack of transport ; the Vale, still partly open, yet recorded some specialisation in cattle rearing and fattening, but cattle were losing favour to sheep crossed with New Leicesters. Leicestershire as a whole was deeply committed to highly organised stock farming ; grassland was at least three times as extensive as tillage on the claylands, and accounted for nine-tenths of the farmland around Melton Mowbray. Sheep, dairy cattle, beefstock, and horses were kept in large numbers. Stores were bought from many parts of England ; fat beasts went outside the county to Birmingham, Rotherham, and London. Although many graziers paid little attention to breeding, individual tup-letters were making rapid fortunes. Turnips fed off by sheep became common in Leicestershire in the late eighteenth century, normally being planted after fallow. Dairy farms were especially numerous in the Melton Mowbray district, famous for its Stilton cheese. Ill-drained land supplied winter hay. The pattern of grazing changed repeatedly as leys were broken, but much permanent grass remained untouched. The extent of grass increased with enclosure, which was said to be accompanied by a decline of population. In Charnwood Forest and its gravelly southeastern borders the degenerate local sheep still persisted.

All the open fields of Rutland were under the three-shift system, except where turnips had been introduced on light soils. Enclosed tillage was almost wholly confined to light land, where it provided surplus wheat for sale in Lincolnshire, and where three-year or four-year clover leys were grazed by sheep. About three-fifths of all enclosures consisted of heavy land in permanent grass, lying in high ridges and deep furrows which, impeding drainage, were studded by anthills. Sheep of the Lincolnshire and Old Leicestershire breeds were the chief stock. Cattle were few and poor and dairying was uncommon. Most of the beefstock was Irish or Scotch, bought for a year's fattening before sale to London. Fat sheep went either to London or, through Melton Mowbray, to the north. As elsewhere, the first parliamentary enclosures had been followed in some parishes by an increase in grassland and decline in population, but increasingly heavy stocking by the 1790s was increasing output and demand for labour alike.

Nearly three-quarters of the parishes of Northamptonshire were already enclosed. The vanishing open fields incorporated a turnip crop and a partially developed six-course shift. Management of enclosed farms was varied, even though based on open-field practice : enclosed fallow was partly grazed by sheep and partly sown to turnips, wheat followed grazing while barley followed turnips, and in the succeeding year came beans or peas ; but then came barley undersown with red clover, two years of clover, and then beans or oats. Yields of grain were reasonably high in open fields, but increased after enclosure. Despite the requirements of workers in the leather and textile industries there was a surplus of grain, sent down the Nene for export through Wisbech ; flour went by wagon into neighbouring counties.

Northamptonshire shared in the production of fat sheep,

supplementing turnips by rye for spring feed. London took the surplus sheep, but Yorkshire made the first demand on wool, so that the delivery of wool to spinners in the Kettering district fluctuated from year to year. Output of mutton and wool rose as the breed improved. Bullocks, bought from Shropshire and Herefordshire in March and April, were fattened for London. Commercial dairying with Yorkshire Shorthorns concentrated in the southwest ; calves went to markets in Buckinghamshire, eventually for producers in Essex. Hay-meadow on floodplains, estimated at not less than 40,000 acres, was often flooded by rivers checked by mill-dams ; flooding must have been especially severe in the broad alluvial trough immediately below Northampton, but the Nene as a whole was so extensively dammed that its floodplain descended in steps.

Considerable tracts of woodland remained, but most was poor. In Rockingham, Whittlebury and Salcey Forests, and in the Chases of Geddington and Yardley, undergrowth was cut in rotation every 12 or 18 years for hurdle-making and firewood. Large timber was not a leading product. Privately owned purlieu woods were the most profit-able, selling underwood at 11 to 14 years as bakers' firing.

Huntingdonshire experienced agricultural difficulties no less marked than those of the 1930s. Its enclosure was slow, over half the country being still held in common. Common arable was divided into three (except at Stilton, where there were four fields), but each of the three divisions was halved, so that a six-course rotation was at least possible. Old pastures lay ill-drained and littered with anthills, floodplains were frequently inundated, fenland soils were often soaked, and tillage was discouraged by covenant. Fleeces ran very low at three or four pounds each on the neglected commonable pastures, those on enclosed pastures averaged but seven pounds. Beef cattle were poor and dairying was rare. Although agriculture was almost the sole means of livelihood, harvest labour was deficient, for many workers went outside the county and had to be replaced by Irishmen.

Oxfordshire, Buckinghamshire, and Bedfordshire, with wide stretches of clayland and with carrier-links to London, contained numerous farms depending upon butter and pigs. Pressure from London was strongest in the south, and standards of farming fell away northwards. Oxfordshire was the most varied of these three counties. The red soils of its Marlstone shelves were mostly still in the arable of open fields. In the western angle of the county, on the shallow brashy soils of the oolite belt, woodland and grass dominated. Overlapping through the strike vales into Buckinghamshire, there lay on both sides of the Thames a belt of interlocking tillage, pasture, and meadow, wherein certain areas were distinctive—the unprofitable common of

Otmoor, the broad pastures in the Thame valley, and the grazing and fattening country of central Oxfordshire. This area supplied calves to London, and maintained Shorthorns as milkers.

Shorthorns were also common in the vale country and on the boulder-clay soils running through Buckinghamshire into Bedfordshire. Long years of continuous grazing had here allowed anthills to overrun permanent pasture, grazing-lands were ill-drained, and flooding of valley bottoms was frequent. Buckinghamshire was deeply involved in dairying. Its clayland farms were not thought to favour sheep, although North Wiltshires were bought as stores and Berkshire ewes for breeding. Sheep on the common fields of Bedfordshire were indiscriminately bred, but farmers on enclosed land were using Lincolnshire-Leicestershire combinations and experimenting with crosses. Cattle in Bedfordshire (Holderness, Lancashire, Leicestershire, and Alderney) indicated a strong interest in dairying and attempts at selection, but little progress had yet been made.

The Duke of Bedford was planting many hundreds of acres of trees in the south of the region on the podsolic Lower Greensand soils near Woburn Abbey. Tillage increased from the vale floors towards the scarp-foot of the Chilterns. The scarp itself, and part of the crest, were in pasture for sheep, while the backslope carried tillage, rough grazing, scrub, and diversifying woods of oak and beech.

Variations in soil, climate, and accessibility had clearly made possible, by the early or middle eighteenth century, agricultural specialisation far more pronounced than is sometimes assumed. Many of the agricultural subdivisions of the region today, or those apparent in the reports of the Land Utilisation Survey, were strongly foreshadowed before parliamentary enclosure. What combination of factors made early specialisation technically possible is difficult to judge. Even the inspired Bakewell and his predecessor Allom seem to have worked by trial and error. The spread of the new breeds of stock, like the spread of old and of parliamentary enclosures and of the new techniques of farming, was effected by diffusion. Antiquated methods were able to co-exist, in the late eighteenth century, with new methods both wise and unwise. The contemporary scene was both lively and confused.

This scene was treated in diverse ways by the authors of the second series of reports in the years about 1810 to the reconstituted Board of Agriculture. These second reports were based usually on observations made some four years earlier, so that no more than twelve or fifteen years came between the two series. Short though this interval was, it permitted enclosure of many of the open fields of the 1790s, improvement of livestock, and numerous trials of rotation and soil management.

The second group of reporters could observe the emerging pattern of nineteenth-century farming.

Young, writing on Oxfordshire, continued his pursuit of improvement in accordance with his own strong views ; Parkinson, the author of the reports on Huntingdonshire and Rutland, supplied summaries of land-use by parishes and contributed similar figures to Priest's report on Buckinghamshire. Pitt's reports on Leicestershire and Northamptonshire include estimated statistics for the two whole counties. Bedfordshire was treated in no great detail by Batchelor. Lowe's second report on Nottinghamshire appeared, as already stated, in 1798. Farey's huge report on Derbyshire is only in part agricultural ; used in conjunction with the first report, however, it supplies rough estimates of the use of land. In all, summaries of land-use are possible for six of the nine counties (Table 37) ; despite the omission of the three remaining counties, contrasts appear both between the north and the south and also between the east and the west of the region.

Perhaps a fifth of Derbyshire was in tillage in the early nineteenth century ; a quarter—mainly open moors on the Millstone Grit—lay unproductive, while the remainder was in grass. Farey's lists of grass-seed mixtures indicate improvement of pasture by re-seeding ; lime was produced, mainly in the Ashover district, for use on farms. Hay, grown on the floodplains in the south of the county, maintained during the winter cows which grazed the Keuper Marl country in the summer. The opening of the Trent and Mersey, Derby, and Erewash Canals had altered the direction and changed the organisation of the trade in cheese : cheeses were now assembled in canal-side warehouses, where a single factor buying on commission for London dealers could handle 2,000 tons a year. Few dairy farms concentrated on butter, but fresh milk was supplied to Derby, Chesterfield, and Sheffield. Parts of the limestone plateau were annually shut up for hay ; large fields were rented for summer pasture, with herdsmen provided by the landlords.

Nine breeds of cattle, and nine crosses, were known. Ten breeds of sheep and seven types of cross included New Leicesters and Southdowns. The small Woodland sheep of the High Peak, the Old Limestone sheep of the central Dome, and the Forest sheep of the east were being replaced by New Leicester stock. Dairy farms carried many pigs, and black work-horses were raised in large numbers.

Open arable survived in but thirteen parishes, twelve of them on Keuper Marl belt or Coal-Measure shales. Rotations on enclosed farms were becoming adjusted to soils, but there was considerable production of grain in the county as a whole. Oat bread remained the food of many poor people. Several breweries produced for public sale, and flour mills had recently been built at several places to use steam-power when the rivers ran low in summer. The mill at Measham ground flour by night and supplied power for cotton-working by day. Specialised cultivation included woad growing for Manchester dyers at Beighton and Eckington, potato growing in the market gardens of Darley-in-the-Dale, and general market gardening on the outskirts of the rapidly expanding cotton-manufacturing town of Belper.

Changes were probably taking place in Nottinghamshire broadly similar to those of adjacent counties. Reclamation of the badly drained land on the lower Trent and in the Smite basin was certainly increasing the total of farmland.

Grazing continued to be the main interest in Leicestershire. Pitt estimated the proportion of non-agricultural land at 8% of the total area (Table 37). About half this fraction consisted of the wastes of Charnwood Forest and Rothley Plain, the other half of woods, inland water, gardens, buildings, and roads. The 92% of the county in farmland was thought to be half in permanent grass, and half in occasional tillage. Pitt estimated 30% of the county in tillage, 46% in permanent grass, and 62% in grass of some kind. Three-quarters of the stiff clay soils and valley floors were in permanent grass, where many farms had no tillage. A prosperous breeder or grazier might hold 500 acres, with no more than 100 acres in tillage and with no fallow. Enclosure induced grassing down of the best land, while the ploughing of old sward was usually forbidden. Land continued to be laid in ridges, not all of which, therefore, correspond to the selions of open-field working (Pl. 17).

Where experiments were allowed, barley was a leading tillage crop, following green crops and preceding grass. Leicestershire had a surplus of barley but a deficiency of wheat. Pitt estimated its percentage distribution of tillage (excluding rotation grass) as: barley 26, green crops and roots 26, oats $19\frac{1}{2}$, wheat 16, beans $6\frac{1}{2}$, peas and vetches 3. The remaining 3%—a mere 5,000 acres—was fallow. Leicestershire tillage was made to serve animal husbandry and cash sale.

Bakewell's influence on stock was very strong. Improvements were most notable in beefstock, but also affected the dairy farms of the north, where farms produced their own straw and turnips, recording a higher-than-average fraction of tillage. Part of the wool clip was sold to stockingers in the county, but most went to west Yorkshire; fat sheep were sold to dealers from London and Birmingham. Work-horses went to fairs at Market Harborough, Ashby de la Zouch, and Loughborough, and to fairs outside the county, many eventually reaching London.

Exceptions to the broad pasturage stood out sharply. Common land at Glenfield was still worked on three shifts. Ashby Wolds had been lately enclosed and were cultivated, but Charnwood Forest and Rothley Plain were still sheepwalks supporting the Forest breed. In direct contrast the Belvoir estate had been drastically changed by the Duke of Rutland, who, enclosing between 1766 and 1792 more than 20,000 acres of poor woodland and common fields, had consolidated farms, planted trees, built houses, and made roads. The new Grantham Canal gave the hitherto remote Vale connections with expanding towns. Former sheepwalk went under the plough, and the richer land was grassed down.

The boulder-clay soils of west Rutland were largely in pasture. This area at the beginning of the nineteenth century had close affinities with the adjoining wolds of Leicestershire ; its already numerous sheep increased with the continued spread of the New Leicester breed and of fattening for London. Parkinson estimated the county's flock at 80,000 ; cattle, less than one-tenth as numerous, were also on the increase, mainly because of increased fattening, for store and dairying were uncommon.

Seven Rutland parishes, and large parts of two others, were still in open fields, lying between the heavily grassed west and the highly arable east, and possessing much sandy loam and brashy rendzina. Their yields per acre and per bushel of seed were lower than the yields of enclosed farms, especially in oats.

Since Pitt wrote both the Leicestershire and the Northamptonshire reports, the reported qualitative differences between the two counties are likely to be valid (see Table 37). Pitt gave tillage in Northamptonshire as 35% of the total area, that is, as 5% higher than in Leicestershire ; grassland he again estimated at well over half the area of the county. Distribution of tillage among crops differed strongly from that of Leicestershire : wheat took 27%, barley $14\frac{1}{4}$%, beans, green crops, and fallow each $13\frac{1}{4}$%, oats $10\frac{1}{2}$%, peas and vetches 7%, and rye $1\frac{1}{2}$%. Northamptonshire had a surplus of wheat, wheat flour, oats, and beans. Potatoes had appeared as a field crop, hemp was grown in the fens of the eastern borders, and market gardening had developed around Northampton.

Four types of management were known. The seventy unenclosed parishes operated variations of the three-shift system, but had lost some land to permanent pasture in closes. Old enclosed land was generally in grass, either for feeding or for hay : the early depopulated Fawsley was all in grass. Some enclosures were in alternate tillage and pasture but also included permanent grass for dairy cattle. Many new farms rotated tillage and sheep pasture, keeping cattle on old-enclosed grass. As in Leicestershire, grazing was the main single interest of farming. Bullocks for fattening came from Scotland, Staffordshire, and the

Welsh border; as many as 17,000 went to London each year, and as many again to other markets. Fat sheep were sold in autumn fairs at 250,000 a year, London again taking half. Pitt claimed that Northamptonshire met one-seventh of the metropolitan demand for butcher's meat. Dairy farms in the west of the county sent butter and cheese to London by road.

Huntingdonshire, like Rutland, was more markedly arable in the east than in the west; but, with more than two-thirds under the plough, there was little scope for internal contrasts. In few parishes did grassland exceed tillage. Large, old enclosed estates in the hands of single owners affected the distribution of pasture. Little had yet been done to improve cattle, which remained far fewer than sheep—9,250 against 141,500. Huntingdonshire was well inside the limits of New Leicester influence and its sheep were generally much improved, although indiscriminate tup-breeding had had unfortunate results, principally on the weight of fleece. Large numbers of sheep and much ploughland indicate a sheep-arable combination.

Oxfordshire, where enclosure was unusually late, contained many farmers who still viewed the new ideas with deep suspicion. Nevertheless, mixed farming was highly successful on the red loams of the Marlstone shelves. The main limestone belt still had numerous open fields, but enclosure brought turnip growing, folding, and experiments in breeding. Wychwood Forest had degenerated into waste. The vale country possessed strong links with the adjacent dairying grounds of Buckinghamshire. Its in-calf shorthorn cows were brought at three years old and kept for three years. Wagons plying between Bicester and London collected ten tons of butter a week. Home-bred pigs were kept on the dairy farms, and there was some fattening of Herefordshire bullocks. The undulating dairy grounds of Oxfordshire ended southwards in the tillage beyond Thame, westward in the meadows of the Cherwell and Thames, and northwards along the edge of the limestone cuesta, abutting sharply on the large common of Kidlington and the ineffectively managed Otmoor. Some open fields remained west of Oxford on the low ground near the Thames, but enclosure and grassing down were in hand: 4,000 of the 10,000 acres of Bampton were under grass.

The data for Buckinghamshire (Table 37) exclude the Chiltern plateau and country farther south, that is, the most solidly arable districts, where 80% of the land was reported in tillage. Parkinson's obviously rounded-off figures for single parishes give 40% of northern and central Buckinghamshire under the plough—5% more than Pitt's fraction for Northamptonshire. Grassland, however, was almost as extensive as in Northamptonshire, there being little woodland, waste, or common; grass was especially widespread in the west of the vale country, while concentrations of tillage appeared beneath the Chiltern scarp, on the Lower Greensand belt, and west of the Ouzel, increasing eastwards towards Bedfordshire.

London exerted a strong effect on Buckinghamshire. Dairying dominated many central districts, parts of the Vale of Aylesbury excepted. Yorkshire shorthorns were well known as dairy animals, while Leicestershire longhorns and Guernseys appeared in lesser numbers. Horse-driven churns were used in the twice-weekly operation of butter making. Surplus calves were sold for veal; Hereford and Devon bullocks were fattened for sale before Christmas, unless they were sustained through the winter by oil-cake and hay. The chief aim of sheep farming was the supply of fat lambs to London, but Southdowns, kept for their wool, were on the increase. Sheep farmers could hire flocks to farmers on the common fields, or to the enclosed arable farms of the Chilterns. In-lamb ewes for fattening and pigs for store were bought into the dairying districts. The Aylesbury neighbourhood had acquired a reputation for tame rabbits, as also for ducks, which had initially been raised by the poor.

Dairymen in Buckinghamshire did so well that the average rent per acre was three-quarters as high again on dairy farms as on arable farms. Steady profits, however, did little to encourage attention to the permanent grass, where anthills were still numerous and drainage was still poor. Wheat, if it succeeded, remained the great profit-maker of open arable. Short leases and rack-rents discouraged change on enclosed farms, whereas rotations as long as nine years were operated by farmers secure in tenure and free to experiment.

Although enclosure now affected most of Bedfordshire, the general esteem of fallow was deplorable, as was the rotation of corn, corn, fallow reported from some enclosed farms. Crop and fallow alternated on two farms in Stotfold. Rotations in the surviving open fields had so degenerated that two-thirds of the fallows were annually sown to wheat. A clover course on the common arable was prohibited by the expense of fencing, and rye was still being grown on sandy soils.

Batchelor's data for single parishes well reveal the effects of old enclosure. Holcut, supposed to have been enclosed about 1590, had 808 acres of pasture and 35 wood against but 77 arable; Potsgrove, thought to have been enclosed for a hundred years, had 1,500 acres of pasture and 35 wood against 150 arable. Cranfield, which had not yet been subjected to parliamentary enclosure, had 900 acres in open field and 50 acres of wood; in addition, however, there were 300 acres already enclosed. The open field in Flitwick had been similarly reduced before the parliamentary enclosure of 1807, for its open arable amounted to no more than 620 acres and its open pasture to 470 acres —a total of 1,090 acres out of 2,130 acres for the parish, which included 360 acres of old-enclosed arable and 680 acres of old-enclosed pasture.

All the clayland of Bedfordshire lay in high ridge-and-furrow. Old ridges were usually levelled after enclosure on dry soils, but old level pasture was, in places, deliberately ridged up. Here again some of the existing ridges post-date parliamentary enclosure. Livestock was less improved in Bedfordshire than in the broad grazing lands to the north ; horned sheep were still pastured on clayland. Nor had much progress been made in cattle-breeding, for the dairy herds serving the London butter market were typically mixed. Experiments were most vigorous on light soils, where turnips and clover entered rotations up to six years long. Courses were however variable on many farms, because of uncertain yearly tenancies. Market gardens in the southeast of the county had extended their reputation and widened their distribution. Running from Sandy and Potton, past Biggleswade, and north of Shefford towards Ampthill, they dispatched green peas and beans, cucumbers, potatoes, parsnips, carrots, radishes, cabbage plants, turnips, and onions for distances of sixty miles. Ducal plantations around Woburn Abbey were spreading ; but woodland was vanishing from the remainder of the county, including the Chiltern scarp.

Whatever allowance be claimed for the opinions, prejudices, and statistical methods of agricultural reporters of the early nineteenth century, their identified contrasts seem geographically reasonable today. No great effort of imagination is required in following the reports through the subdivisions of the region. A more difficult task is to create a picture of farmland where many fences were new, where patches of open field lay treeless amid the new farms, where sheep were far more numerous than they are now, and where little secondary dispersion had yet occurred. All reporters dealing with areas of village settlement state that the farmhouses of the new owners or tenants still lay chiefly in the villages themselves. Neither capital nor tenure yet permitted that outward migration which later removed the most prosperous residents from the villages, emphasising the separation of class by a separation of dwelling.

Industry in the southern half of the region in the years about 1800 took three main forms : the production of woollens, of lace, and of leather. The woollen textile industry of the southwest was gravely depressed. Shag-weavers were very short of employment both at Bloxham and at Banbury, where a thousand had been employed in the 1790s ; at Witney, where 500 weavers had been employed in 1760 and 400 in 1800, no more than 150 were working in 1807. Nevertheless the Witney industry drew on a force of some 3,000 hands, and had met some of its difficulties by introducing spinning jennies and spring looms in the late eighteenth century. An estimated 5,000–6,000 hands were employed in making woollens in Kettering and some neighbouring smaller places of Northamptonshire. Wellingborough shared in the woollen industry but was interested chiefly in hand-worked lace, which employed 9,000–10,000 hands in the Wellingborough district and in southwest Northamptonshire during the late eighteenth century. Lace making was also widespread in Buckinghamshire, flourishing during the eighteenth century and into the nineteenth, with chief centres at Newport Pagnell, Olney, and Aylesbury. The domestic lace industry extended through Bedfordshire into Huntingdonshire, where Kimbolton was its main focus. Lace making was everywhere a task for women and for children, who were taught the trade as early as the age of six ; it relied on the import of Flanders thread, when this import was possible, and mainly upon the home market, although exports went to Ireland, the West Indies, and North America. So dominant did it become that it was locally the greatest employer ; for example, at Hanslope (Buckinghamshire) 500 out of a population of 1,275 were in 1801 employed in lace making.

In the specialised leather manufacture of Woodstock 1,500 women were needed to produce up to 400 dozen of gloves weekly. Commercial production of footwear was expanding at Northampton and some neighbouring towns and industrialised villages. Most of the leather came from London ; most of the product went either to London shops or to the army. A labour force of a thousand or more produced 7,000–8,000 pairs a week in peacetime, but disturbances in Ireland, and the threat and eventual outbreak of war, provoked a 50% increase in output by 1794. As the footwear industry of Northampton developed, so did the now-depressed woollen textile industry of Kettering and Wellingborough decline. The balance of employment between leather and woollens swung over. So marked was the decline of the textile industry in Northamptonshire—lace making excepted—that the county took scarcely any share in the development of framework knitting.

Leicestershire occupied a peculiarly intermediate industrial position between the south and the north of the region. Its textile manufacture was still dominated by wool—wool combing, wool spinning, the weaving of worsted, and the hand-knitting of woollen stockings which were the principal manufacture sold outside the county. Cotton manufacture was flourishing at Hinckley, but had as yet secured no more than southerly outposts. Nottinghamshire and Derbyshire, on the other hand, were already deeply involved with cotton. There were 31 cotton mills in Nottinghamshire in 1794, and well over 100 in

Derbyshire in the early nineteenth century. The main single concentration lay in northwest Derbyshire, belonging to the Lancashire industry rather than to the East Midlands; but mills occurred throughout the Derwent valley, up to and including Edale. Those on the lowermost Derwent lay not far from Nottingham, which possessed its county's main concentration; the rest of the Nottinghamshire mills were located in a belt from Hucknall to Worksop. Associated with the spinning mills were calico-weaving mills, but calico printing was confined to northwest Derbyshire. A large part of the demand for spun cotton came, however, from the framework knitters, with a lesser demand from Manchester.

Factories making woollen cloth in Derbyshire lay mainly in the northwest, in or near Glossop and Whaley Bridge, although Brassington specialised in blankets and Chesterfield in carpets. Two worsted mills operated in Derby, and others at Mansfield, Cuckney, Arnold, and Retford. Silk spinning was almost confined to Derby town, which had seven of the eight mills; the eighth was at Chesterfield. Miscellaneous textile mills produced hopsack, fustian, linen, tape, and whipcord; like the cotton mills, these too were concentrated in northwest Derbyshire, in the Derwent valley, and in the belt Nottingham-Mansfield-Worksop.

Mechanisation in the textile industries included the use of frames, which did not necessarily involve concentration in factories, and the application of power in large mills. Mechanical silk spinning failed at the first attempt in Derby in 1702, but a new essay in 1718 succeeded with the aid of great water-wheels constructed by the engineer Sorrocold. The cotton industry made technical advances through the inventions of Strutt of Blackwell, who perfected a system of ribbing in 1750; of Hargreaves, who produced the jenny in the late 1760s, and in partnership with the hosier James established a workshop of jennies in Nottingham in 1768; and of Arkwright, who, producing his water-frame in 1768, erected a cotton mill near Hockley in 1771. This first mill, however, was horse-driven; it proved over-costly, and Arkwright removed to Cromford where a water-driven mill was erected to work from the mine-sough. By 1785 a steam-driven cotton mill was built at Papplewick; some others of the Nottinghamshire mills were steam-powered in the 1790s, but the Derbyshire mills continued to rely on water-power.

It was not long before textile mills were strikingly reduced in number. To a climax of textile milling at the turn of the century succeeded depression grave enough to leave Nottinghamshire with only 8 mills, and Derbyshire with 56, by the year 1836. More than one mill in two failed. The readjustments left Derby supreme as a manufacturer of silk, Leicester supreme in worsted, and Nottingham the leading manufacturer of cotton. Simultaneously the largely dispersed industry of framework knitting was spreading to more and more settlements, and, despite the poor rewards which it offered, drawing on a surplus of labour. Lee's invention of the stocking frame in the late sixteenth century was represented, a century later, by fewer than 700 frames in the whole country (Table 38). London dominated the rapidly growing industry of the early eighteenth century, but there was much transfer to the Midlands during the 1730s, and half the country's frames were in Nottinghamshire, Leicestershire, and Derbyshire by the mid-century. By 1800 the fraction had risen to two-thirds. Further expansion was to come, and concentration of hosiery production in factories was to be deferred for at least another fifty years ; but one particular development—the making of frame-lace—belongs to the period now under review. Frame-lace working was made feasible by inventions of the late eighteenth and the early nineteenth centuries ; some 15,000 were employed in the trade by 1810, mainly in Nottinghamshire. By 1828, however, frame-lace making had been superseded by bobbin-net manufacture, and the framework industry as a whole had undergone one of the reductions which were, in the end, to extinguish it completely.

In the circumstances outlined, the East Midland region cannot be said to exemplify at all directly the industrialisation of an originally domestic textile craft. The dispersed lace making of the south and the framework of the north remained well dispersed at least until 1850. Furthermore, their organisation was—or at least purported to be—distinctly late-medieval in structure, even though they were largely the outcome of eighteenth-century development. In diametrical contrast, the mining and metallurgical industries had roots striking deep into medieval and even earlier times ; but it was these industries which, with varying success, carried the north of the region through the industrial revolution as that period is usually understood.

The lead industry had passed its peak by 1800. All the readily accessible ore had been removed. There had arisen a massive series of mining laws and mining custom, enforceable by special courts, which included the protection of old workings. Abandoned mines and open rakes were consequently subject only to weathering, soil-formation, and overgrowth. Working mines were still required to possess a stowse (manual haulage gear) on each concession of 29 yards ; where improved equipment was used, small model stowses signified legal occupance. Steam-engines were introduced for winding and pumping as mines went deep. The orefields were technically ahead of the coalfield, and lead-mining practice was adapted for use in coalmines, for example the driving of soughs to carry off underground water.

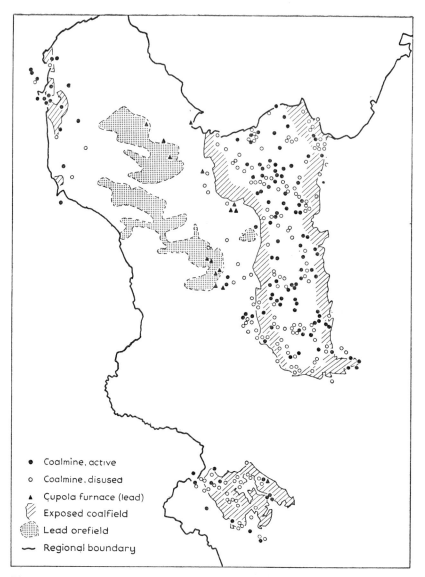

Coalmine, active
○ **Coalmine, disused**
▲ **Cupola furnace (lead)**
Exposed coalfield
Lead orefield
Regional boundary

Fig. 43   MINING IN THE NORTH OF THE REGION ABOUT 1806. Compiled from Farey's lists.   See also the next Figure.

Up to the sixteenth century ore was smelted over wood fires. The succeeding hearth furnaces, also fired by wood, lay either on the western brows of high hills or near streams where bellows could be driven by water-wheel. In the mid-eighteenth century a company of Quakers introduced from Wales the coal-fired reverberating cupola furnace, which was exclusively in use in the earliest years of the

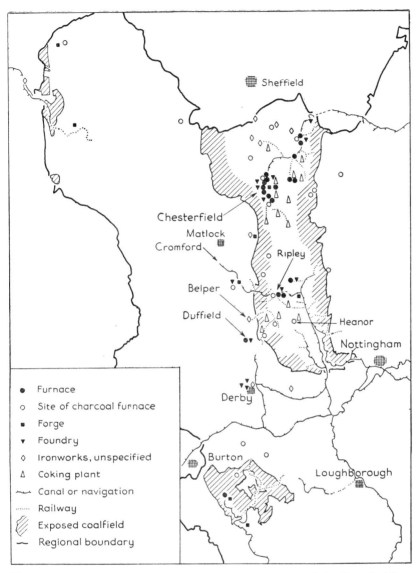

Fig. 44 METAL-WORKING IN THE NORTH OF THE REGION ABOUT 1806. Compiled from Farey's lists. See also the preceding Figure.

Legend:
- ● Furnace
- ○ Site of charcoal furnace
- ▪ Forge
- ▼ Foundry
- ◇ Ironworks, unspecified
- △ Coking plant
- ～ Canal or navigation
- ⋯⋯ Railway
- ▨ Exposed coalfield
- ～ Regional boundary

nineteenth century. Cupolas stood near the eastern limits of the orefields, or near the western edge of the exposed coalfield (Fig. 43); there was a solitary cupola on the exposed coalfield of Leicestershire.

Pilkington estimated the annual production of lead at 5,000–6,000 tons, at a time (1789) when production was falling. During earlier and more productive years the Gregory Mine in the Ashover inlier had alone yielded an average of 1,511 tons between 1758 and 1783. Zinc ore, mainly from the Castleton and Wirksworth districts, was extracted at an approximate rate of 500 tons a year in the late eighteenth century. Declining output of ore, increasing difficulties of mining, and technical improvements in smelting were reflected in more than one phase of slag-milling. Much ancient slag had either been re-processed or had been used as road metal. In 1806, when bellows-blown slag-mills had fallen into disuse, improved mills were associated with five of the active cupolas. At these places especially, sulphurous fumes greatly damaged vegetation in the near neighbourhood.

Coal mining in 1800 was almost entirely confined to the exposed fields (Fig. 43). Farey listed 86 active mines for the Derbyshire and Nottinghamshire field, in about 1806, none lying on the Permian outcrop, although 7 were at or very close to the eastern limit of the exposed measures. An additional 7 active mines occurred beyond the western limit of the coalfield, presumably working seams in the Millstone Grit, and at least 3 of the active mines of northwest Derbyshire were sunk in rocks older than Coal Measures. Of the 13 active mines in the Leicestershire field, 5 were possibly outside the bounds of the outcrop. Shafts were yet of modest depth : Pilkington seemed to regard depths of 222 feet (West Hallam), 190 feet (Ilkeston), and 184 feet (Alfreton Common) as exceptional.

Some of the mines listed by Farey as formerly in use may never have produced coal at all, although the 31 on the Leicestershire field are well within possible limits of mining, and no more than 17 of those associated with the Derby and Nottinghamshire field lie west of the outcrop boundary. Four unsuccessful pits had been sunk in the concealed field, very close to its western edge. More than a hundred collieries lay already abandoned on the exposed field ; considerably exceeding the number of pits in work, they were well distributed over the outcrop.

Coal-Measure shales were used for brick-making at 15 works in the valleys of the lower Derwent, Erewash, and upper Rother. In the same areas were 15 manufactories of pottery, some associated with the brickworks. Ganister, occurring as seat-earth immediately beneath seams of coal, and raised from colliery shafts or quarried for its own sake, was used as road-metal or for making crucibles. Fire-bricks were produced at Swadlincote, Dronfield, and Bolsover.

Coal-Measure ironstone, chiefly occurring near the central axis of the exposed field, was widely exploited. The most valuable ores of the late eighteenth century were raised in Morley Park near Heage, and at Wingerworth, Chesterfield, and Staveley. The first workings were simple diggings at the outcrops, but by 1800 rakes had been superseded by bell-pits which, going as deep as 50 feet, yielded up to 72 tons of ore. Adits in some places penetrated the gently dipping beds. The small furnaces and bloomeries, where cast iron and bar iron was made, were charcoal-fired up to about 1765; one of them, blown with the aid of a water-wheel, remained in use at Wingerworth until 1784. By the very early nineteenth century, however, coke-firing and steam-powered blast were general. Little seems to be known about the early history of coking in this part of the region, although the use of coke instead of straw in Derby malt-kilns suggests that the technique of coking may have developed hereabouts independently of the well-known activities of the Darbys at Coalbrookdale.

The greatest single concentration of ironworks lay in and near Chesterfield, with 8 furnaces, 4 foundries, a forge, and 6 coking plants (Fig. 44). In addition to these works, the upper Rother valley contained another 5 furnaces, 2 foundries, 4 coking plants, and various mills of unspecified kind, grouped round Staveley, Renishaw, and Duckmanton. A second and less compact series of ironworks included those of Derby, Duffield, and Belper in the Derwent valley, and Crich, Ripley, and Somercotes in the cross-connecting valley between the Derwent and the Erewash. Coking for this group took place in the Belper-Heanor district, south of the gap. The Leicestershire coalfield had one furnace and two forges. Many of the works shown in Figure 44 were built in the late eighteenth century; to their increasing size and number corresponded a fluctuating but generally increasing output of pig iron: 7,650 tons in 1788, 5,600 tons a year some ten years later, over 10,000 tons in 1806, and 29,000 tons in 1829. The output of 1806 amounted to some 4% of the national output; about three-fifths of it came from the furnaces of the northern group, which however averaged only 500 tons a year each against the 1,000 tons per furnace in the south (Table 39).

Waterways were vital to the ironworks of 1800. The industrial axis of the northern group was the Chesterfield Canal, which, tunnelling through the high ground to the east, ran through Worksop in the Ryton valley, East Retford on the Idle, and so to the Trent at Stockwith near the Idle confluence. Completed in 1776, the Chesterfield Canal gave craft of 50- to 60-tons burden access to Retford, but was limited to 22-tons burden in its higher reaches. The chief wharves and warehouses were constructed at Retford and Chesterfield. Downgoing cargoes included coal, lead, cast iron, limestone, freestone, and pottery; ascending cargoes were mainly grain, timber, and bar iron. Short canal spurs led to some industrial plants close to the trunk waterways, but it was numerous feeder railways that completed the system (Fig. 44).

Derby had prospects in the early eighteenth century of becoming a transport centre. An Act for the improvement of the Derwent was passed in 1719, and the first boat reached Derby in 1721, bringing in timber, tobacco, and fish, and taking on lead. But the Derwent Navigation was no longer in use in 1800; traffic in lead had been diverted to Chesterfield and the Chesterfield Canal, and Derby was to some extent by-passed by new waterways. The Erewash Canal (1775-6) was effectively extended by the Cromford Canal (1789), which tunnelled from the Erewash to the Derwent valley, bringing Matlock and the Cromford mill into connection with the Trent downstream of Derby, and supplying axial transport to the Crich-Ripley-Somercotes district. When the Nottingham Canal was opened in 1792, Nottingham instead of Derby had direct access to the Cromford Canal system, with its branches to Pinxton wharf and Somercotes furnace, and with its cuts to lime kilns. Links between the Trent and the Mersey were less effective than was hoped. The last thirteen miles of the Trent, at the approach to the Trent and Mersey Canal, were difficult to navigate, being encumbered by shoals where dry-season depths could be as little as eight inches. Despite warping, and despite the use of gravel ploughs, a lasting and vigorous commerce between the Mersey and the middle Trent did not develop; Derby cannot fail to have suffered on this account by contrast with Nottingham.

The coal-producing districts of northwest Derbyshire and of Leicestershire had difficulties of relief to overcome. The Peak Forest Canal (1800) connected the Manchester, Ashton, and Oldham Canal to Bugsworth (=Buxworth) wharf, close to Whaley Bridge, and a railway which included a large inclined plane brought the Dove Holes furnace and nearby limestone quarries into the regional ambit of Lancashire, not Midland, industry. When the Soar Navigation (including the Loughborough Canal) opened in 1788, coal from the Erewash valley immediately began to compete with Leicestershire coal, and local coal-owners resisted extension of the waterway to Leicester until Loughborough had been connected with the nearby mines. The required transport route was supplied by the high-level self-contained Charnwood Forest Canal, and the railway from Nanpantan to Loughborough, but the canal failed to offset competition from the Leicester Navigation and was abandoned when the Blackbrook Reservoir burst in 1779. Mining in the east of the Leicestershire coalfield was set back, and several mines closed. The Ashby Canal in the west, with its railway extensions, was better designed for internal traffic of the coalfield than for external trade; completed in 1804, this canal could take craft of 60 tons, but the Coventry Canal which it joined was limited to a maximum of 24 tons.

Coal and coal products dominated traffic on the Soar valley system, and were prominent everywhere in cargoes on the various canals and navigations. Early estimates of the prospects of through connections were never realised, and the waterways resolved themselves into district systems among which there was little interchange, even if there was physical connection. Certain branches, constructed with high optimism, were doomed to fail : the Melton Canal up the Wreake valley (1800), extended to Oakham in 1802, and the Grantham Canal round the Vale of Belvoir, which was meant to distribute coal brought down the Trent, lacked markets from the outset, and failed to introduce heavy industry. Thus the impetus of canal building was already exhausted well before the coming of steam locomotives and through railways.

CHAPTER 9

FARMING, HOSIERY, LEATHER

LAND-USE, mining, and metal working are none too comprehensively recorded for the first half of the nineteenth century. When the stimulus of war ceased to apply itself to the economy, and when the inquiring students of natural history of the eighteenth-century type died off, much that could be directly set to geographical uses disappears from contemporary writing. Furthermore, both in agriculture and in some divisions of industry, the first half of the century was a time of stagnation or of depression, of unsuccessful experiment, and of groping transition from one age to another. In direct contrast, domestic manufacture of textiles increased both in extent and in range until well into the mid-century. Despite the activities of Turnpike Trusts, the net of roads was unsuitable for the carriage of heavy goods or large bulks. Some of the canals of the East Midlands were able to compete successfully, for an unusually long time, with the new railways ; in any event railway building was long-drawn-out in this region, one main line being added in the 1890s. The chief geographical changes of the nineteenth century were out of phase with one another. By the end of the century, however, the region possessed factory industries of leather, iron, cottons, and woollens ; coal was being raised from hidden measures, and iron ore extracted from the Northamptonshire field ; railways had prevailed over canals, while market towns had carrier services directly ancestral to the bus routes of today. The acreage of improved farmland had reached its peak, without preventing a decline in numbers of rural population.

Not in these ways alone, strong and valid contrasts may be drawn between the opening and the close of the nineteenth century. But as some changes continued from the nineteenth into the twentieth century, it seems undesirable to make artificial breaks in the record merely for the sake of conspectus. Admittedly, a span of twenty years in mid-century introduced many of the techniques which made possible industrialisation of the modern sort, but the new inventions came at a time when the growth of towns was already well begun. Indeed, the expansion of most of the large towns of the region was a matter of the whole nineteenth century. Data on population can be regarded as supplying the necessary factor of unification to the following accounts of the nineteenth and twentieth centuries in the East Midlands. Numbers, location, density, and distribution among categories of employment set the context of development in agriculture and in industry ; alternatively, they record the outcome of these developments.

James Caird, reviewing English agriculture in the mid-nineteenth century, had no doubt of its chief handicaps—not tariff policy, not crop failure in bad years, but short leases, absentee landlords, and capricious scales of rent. For county after county he describes impeding customs. Annual leases gave tenants no security, and left them uncompensated for any improvements made. High rents unfairly burdened some farmers, low rents failed to stimulate others. Drains made by tenants from tiles provided by landlords were generally crude and ineffective. Surplus workers in the highly agricultural districts had family histories of pauperisation under the Poor Law. Migration met little encouragement and much deliberate obstruction ; unwanted hands fixed disproportionate charges on the enlightened among the farmers. Something had gone badly wrong with farming.

Caird places the Soke of Peterborough, Huntingdonshire, and most of Bedfordshire in his corn-growing, low-rented, low-waged area. Derbyshire, Nottinghamshire, and north Leicestershire were not dominated by corn, yielded high rents, and paid high wages. Oxfordshire, Buckinghamshire, Rutland, and south Leicestershire also lay outside the main corn-producing area, and yielded high rents without however offering high wages. Low wages meant heavy poor relief.

Those instances of admittedly good management which Caird observed seemed to him not so much portents for the future as successful results of struggle against past difficulties. Much depended on the attitude of great landlords. Farms on the Blenheim estate of Oxfordshire could not withstand a sudden increase of rent, portions of north Northamptonshire were scrubby with game preserves, whereas leases, and secure tenure generally, satisfied the tenants on the ducal lands of Woburn in Bedfordshire, even though rotations were prescribed. The Duke of Bedford built workers' cottages, at a time when many unsightly dwellings were being removed from the Dukeries of Nottinghamshire and their owners forced into towns and villages. The Clipstone estate was perhaps the best in the Dukeries, with drainage energetically prosecuted by the Duke of Portland, and long watermeadows running greenly beside the Maun. Freely investing industrialists of Nottingham and Leicester, expecting a return for their money, showed what capital could do ; so did Mr John Beasley, who himself farmed at Overstone near Northampton, and managed farms for the Spencers where improvement fell to the landlord.

Local specialisms were of course no less evident than they had been half a century earlier. Farmers in the Vale of Aylesbury concentrated on stock and dairy, using little tillage, buying in stock, and producing butter for London. Trade in fluid milk had not yet begun. Tillage crops in the highly arable sub-edge country were thrashed by flail, although thrashing machines dealt with the wheat crop in southeast Oxfordshire. Turnip-farms, where present in this district, did well, but density of stocking on the plateaux of north Oxfordshire was low throughout. Clayland farmers of Northamptonshire lost money despite an eight-course rotation which included two years of turnips, while tenants of redland farms fared little better with their six-course shift, except where some, practising tillage-with-feeding, competed successfully against the graziers around Northampton town.

Open arable, surviving yet near Stamford, offset the well-managed grassland of west Rutland. Leicestershire lay about two-thirds in grass, with main concentrations on the high-rented claylands; fattening dominated at the lower levels, cheese making at the higher. A species of grazing-and-feeding required conjoint holdings of grazing farms for summer pasture and arable farms for wintering. Nottingham drew on its near surroundings for fluid milk. Derbyshire was very largely in grass, although wheat reached (with some difficulty) heights at 600 feet, and oats 900 feet. Rearing and dairying were the chief interests here, with Ayrshires coming in beside the long-established Shorthorns. Caird's report of profitable farming in Derbyshire, and of expensive clearance of boulders on the gritstone, sustains his view that industry did not damage agriculture but stimulated it.

Although his allowance for trends in the whole economy, and for commercial policy, now appears too small, Caird's low assessment of farming practice generally seems reasonable enough. He suspected output actually to have declined since the time of Arthur Young, but deplored the lack of statistics whereby his doubts might be verified.

Statistical recording of land use began in 1866. It embraces the maximum extent of farmland in the East Midland region, the two severe agricultural depressions of the late nineteenth century and of the inter-war period, the effects of two world wars, and the revolutionary re-shaping of farming practice which has typified the years since 1940.

According to the returns of 1866, some 82% of the whole region was then in improved farmland (Table 40, Fig. 45). Apart from a dubious allowance for inaccuracy in early returns, the increase in improved farmland to 87·3% of the whole region in 1885 presumably corresponds to increase of population; a likely contributing factor was failure to understand the growing threat of the import trade. Signs of drastic change were not however lacking. Very many sheep died of rot in Oxfordshire in 1879, when much of the grain raised in the corn-sheep combination—so far the mainstay of farming—was wasted. Grassing down of arable was already in progress in Leicester in 1866, in response to falling prices of grain. Indeed, although the extent of tillage did not begin its decline until 1875–80, the proportion of ploughland to farmland was already diminishing when the annual returns began. Tillage in 1866 was slightly more extensive than permanent grass; by 1910 grass was twice as extensive as tillage. Meantime the total area of farmland had begun to shrink; just over 2% of the whole region was lost to farming between 1885 and 1910, and a further 1½% between 1910 and 1915.

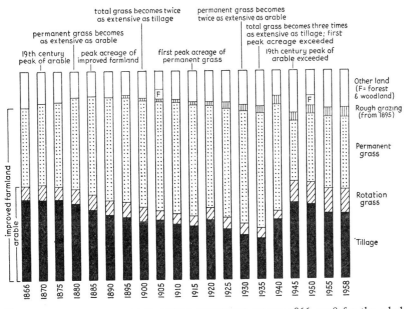

Fig. 45   DISTRIBUTION OF LAND AMONG CATEGORIES OF USE 1866–1958 for the whole region.

Data for single counties (Fig. 46, Tables 40, 41, 42) do something to reveal variations within the region, both in the proportions of land in the main categories of land-use and in the impact of change. Tillage in 1870 amounted to a third or more of the land area, and more than two-fifths of the farmland, in all but two counties—Derbyshire and Leicestershire. Almost half of Oxfordshire, and more than half of Bedfordshire and Huntingdonshire, were then under the plough. Although the map for 1870 suggests the influence of climate (for example, in the contrast between Derbyshire and Nottinghamshire, and in the eastward and southeastward increase in the proportion of tillage elsewhere), it is obvious even from county statistics that other factors were also in play. The high proportion of tillage in Buckinghamshire in 1870 corresponded to the practice of sheep-folding and to a tradition

147

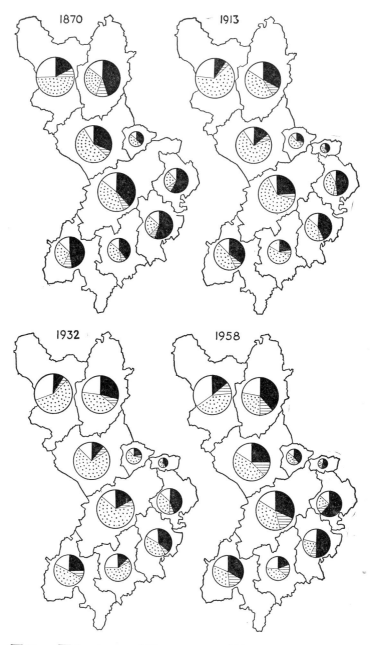

Tillage ▤ Rotation grass ⣿ Permanent grass ☐ Other land, including rough grazing

Fig. 46 LAND USE by whole counties and for selected years. Soke of Peterborough not distinguished from Northamptonshire in 1870. Wheels for Oxfordshire and Buckinghamshire scaled down, in accordance with passage of regional boundary across these counties.

of grain growing which, from this distance, appears almost a fixation. In Northamptonshire, where much of the land is readily convertible, tillage was still no more than slightly less extensive than permanent grass. The low proportion of tillage to grass in Leicestershire reflected a long-established concentration on grazing in the east of the county. Moscrop's contemporary description records many grazing farms in this area with no tillage whatever, although farms which combined breeding with grazing had modest extents of ploughland. Dairying in east Leicestershire was confined to the poorest pasture, while in the

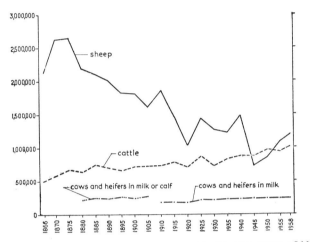

Fig. 47   TRENDS IN THE REGIONAL TOTALS OF CATTLE AND SHEEP 1866–1958.

west of the county it preponderated over grazing. But farms in the west were in any event typically mixed, with about half their land tilled.

All counties experienced a loss of ploughland by 1915. The Soke of Peterborough (not separated from Northamptonshire in earlier returns) alone had more than half its farmland in tillage in that year. The slightest percentage loss of arable between 1870 and 1915 was recorded by Derbyshire; but Derbyshire's proportion of tillage was low to begin with. Convertible land in the centre and southwest of the region was extensively grassed down. The percentage of farmland under the plough was reduced by nearly one-fifth in Buckinghamshire, where the movement has not been effectively reversed in later times. Reductions almost as great affected Northamptonshire, and—perhaps surprisingly, in view of its tradition of grazing—Leicestershire also. Simultaneously with the restriction of tillage, numbers of sheep declined markedly from over $2\frac{1}{2}$ million in 1870 to below $1\frac{1}{2}$ million in 1915 (Table 43, Fig. 47). However, the two reductions were by no means linked in any simple fashion. The greatest proportional reduction in flocks occurred in the southeast, precisely where tillage best resisted the extension of grassland.

A reversal of grassing-down during the First World War soon gave place to a renewed decline in tillage. Permanent grass was twice as extensive as ploughland by 1930, while by 1935 tillage accounted for no more than one-fifth of the region and one-quarter of the farmland. Some land went out of production altogether, partly to non-agricultural use, but partly by mere neglect. The simultaneous increase in rough grazing, although in part reflecting improved records, was real. Rotation grass declined to 5% of all land. Numbers of cattle, however, continued to show the steady increase which had begun at least as early as the mid-nineteenth century. Breeding, rearing, and fattening shared the movement with the dairying side.

F. A. Barnes has traced that rise in dairying for the London market which was suddenly made possible about 1860 by railway transport. Cheese factories opening in Derbyshire in 1870–5 were soon reduced essentially to depôts for fluid milk, using only their summer surplus to produce cheese. London by 1921 was taking milk from Leicestershire and much of Derbyshire, but little from Nottinghamshire, where numbers of dairy cattle were not great and where the surplus, if any, was small. North Derbyshire now sells milk to industrial towns in Lancashire, but the chief market for the rest of the region is still London. Sales have increased by about 30% since the mid-1920s.

Conditions in the 1930s, described in considerable detail for some counties in the reports of the Land Use Survey, corresponded to the distribution of farming-combinations illustrated in Figure 48. Dominantly arable farming was then concentrated mainly in the dry east of the region, whither it had retreated to border almost solidly arable fenlands. Arable-stock combinations were reported from much of Huntingdonshire, from the extreme south, from west Leicestershire (arable and dairying), and from Sherwood (arable and sheep). Mixed farming typified the coalfield belt, much of the country flanking the valley floor of the Trent, the plateaux on either side of the upper Nene, and (in combination with dairying) the plateau west of the Cherwell. Specialist cultivation diversified the pattern of some of the most highly arable parts of the region—market gardening in Bedfordshire and in the Melbourne district, and orchard cultivation near the little towns of the Keuper belt in Nottinghamshire. A wide belt which included large parts of the clay vales in the south, portions of the main Jurassic cuesta, and broad clay-floored expanses on the Lower Lias and its mantle of boulder-clay, were mainly under grass. Stock-farming interests in this belt ranged from dairying in the south, through dairying and sheep

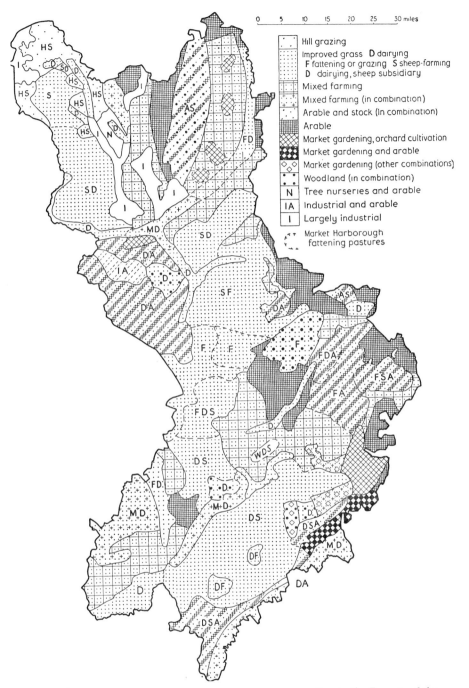

Scale: 0   5   10   15   20   25   30 miles

Hill grazing
Improved grass D dairying
   F fattening or grazing S sheep-farming
   D dairying, sheep subsidiary
Mixed farming
Mixed farming (in combination)
Arable and stock (in combination)
Arable
Market gardening, orchard cultivation
Market gardening and arable
Market gardening (other combinations)
Woodland (in combination)
N Tree nurseries and arable
IA Industrial and arable
I Largely industrial
Market Harborough
   fattening pastures

Fig. 48 FARMING COMBINATIONS OF THE LATE 1930s according to the Reports of the Land Utilisation Survey.

151

farming in west Northamptonshire, fattening on the Northampton-shire–Leicestershire border, and fattening and sheep farming on the Wolds south of the Wreake, to sheep farming and dairying north of the Wreake. Beyond the Trent, in the Low Peak and its foothills, the sheep-dairy combination was also prominent, giving way in the High Peak to dominant sheep farming, and eventually to sheep grazing on the unimproved hill pastures of the gritstone rim (Pls. 4, 17, 34).

Naturally enough, the statistics for whole counties obscure much local variety. Table 44, based on data supplied by C. E. Fitchett in the Land Use Report for Bedfordshire, indicates for the early 1940s a range from 16% arable in a sample of the Greensand belt, and 19·5% arable on the Gault, to 80% arable in the market-gardening district. Considerable variation also occurs in the ratio of dairy to beef cattle, which is lowest on the claylands in the east of the county, and in the ratio of numbers of sheep to numbers of cattle, which is highest in the claylands, in the mixed farmland of the north of the county, and on parts of the Greensand. That is to say, it occurs in areas with some of the worst and some of the most effective natural drainage.

Changes during the Second World War included sufficient breaking of grassland to bring the total extent of arable above its nineteenth-century peak in the East Midland region. Permanent grass was not at first greatly reduced in extent, but by the end of the war had been effectively encroached on by tillage and rotation grass on the one hand and by non-agricultural use on the other. Whereas permanent and rotation grass combined had been three times as extensive as tillage in 1935, ten years later they were but slightly more widespread. Although the acreage under the plough declined somewhat after 1945, it remained by 1959 greater than it had been for eighty years. Part of the land lost to military depôts and to airfields was regained, although the slow fall in the total extent of improved farmland which has been taking place since 1890 seemed to be still in progress. Drastic slaughtering of sheep during the early years of the war made the total flock less numerous for a time than the total herd of cattle ; subsequent recovery has so far not re-established the large numbers of sheep which typified the farms of the late nineteenth century.

Considerable improvements have occurred since 1940 on the lime-stone plateau of Derbyshire, where ploughing and cropping during the war years have been followed by re-seeding of pasture. Pedigree herds of Ayrshires, Friesians, and Dairy Shorthorns have been established here, while beefstock has benefited from the introduction of Galloway cattle, which winter out. Cash cropping is on the increase in the Permo-Trias country of Nottinghamshire, where potatoes and sugar-beet are increasingly grown. The former arable-sheep combination is much less evident than it once was, partly because sheep are liable to worrying by dogs from towns and from the growing villages of the concealed coalfield. More than 1,500 acres have been disturbed by opencast working of coal; against this, parts of Sherwood which lay derelict in the inter-war period have been cleared, ploughed, heavily fertilised, and brought into production. In Leicestershire, where ley farming was little known before 1939, wartime ploughing did not reduce the quality of grassland; the present trend is towards mixed rotational farming with leys. Among the cash crops of Leicestershire, wheat, barley, and potatoes all record marked increases in extent between 1939 and the mid-1950s, as do oats and mixed corn among the fodder crops. Broadly similar increases occurred also in Nottinghamshire. H. C. Chew observes that the combined extent of the chief cash and fodder crops rose by some 15% to 30% in these two counties in the fifteen years in question (Pls. 33, 36).

T. J. Coppock, although concerned mainly with the Chilterns, presents data applicable to nearby portions of the East Midland region; these data show a striking increase in the extent of grain and of rotation grass in the clay vales, which in immediately pre-war years were extensively under permanent pasture (Table 45); arable in this subdivision occupied ten times as much ground in 1951 as in 1938. Less dramatic but still impressive changes of the same kind affected the Vale of Aylesbury, while even in the market-gardening district of Bedfordshire the proportion of arable was far higher in 1951 (nearly 75%) than in 1931 (nearly 47%). Intensity of stocking rose slightly in some parts and fell slightly in others; there is nothing to show that the heavy new emphasis on cash crops applies at the expense of animal husbandry.

Figures 49 and 50 illustrate the distribution of cattle and sheep in 1958. The main concentrations of sheep occurred in the central districts, with extensions into the Ouse valley and with an outpost in the High Peak. The east and southeast of the region, the west of Leicestershire, the Derby and Nottinghamshire coalfield, and the Permo-Trias country of Nottinghamshire, had few. Cattle were more evenly distributed, although here again the scatter became thin in the southeast; Sherwood, highly arable and with light soils, and the sheep-dominated pastures of the High Peak also recorded small numbers.

Distribution of land in 1958 among the main categories of use is mapped by counties in Figure 46, which brings out the marked proportional increase in tillage and in rotation grass which has affected all eastern and some central parts of the region since pre-war years. A more detailed, and consequently more accurate, representation of post-

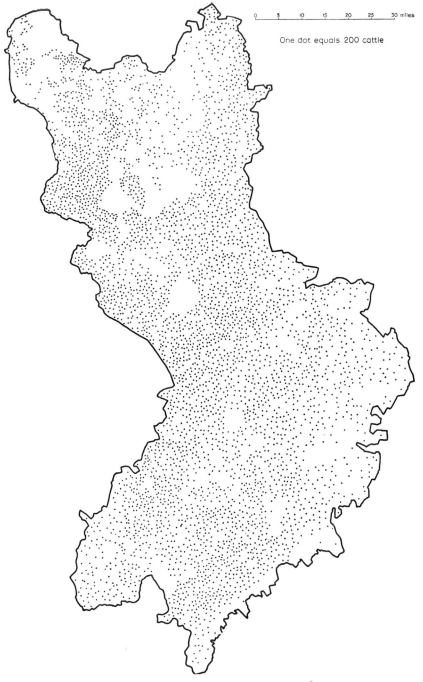

One dot equals 200 cattle

Fig. 49   DISTRIBUTION OF CATTLE IN 1958.

154

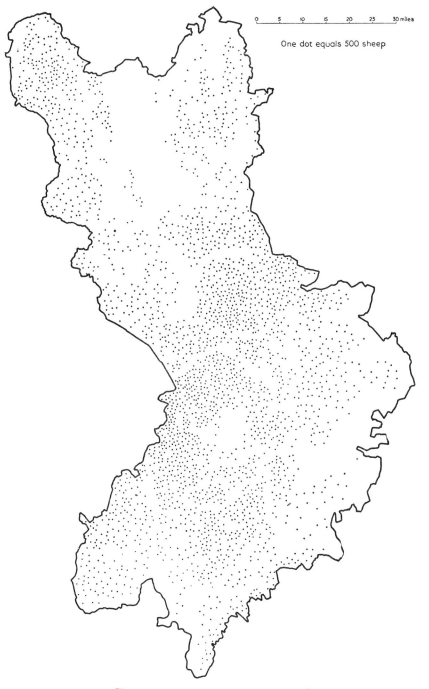

One dot equals 500 sheep

Fig. 50   DISTRIBUTION OF SHEEP IN 1958.

155

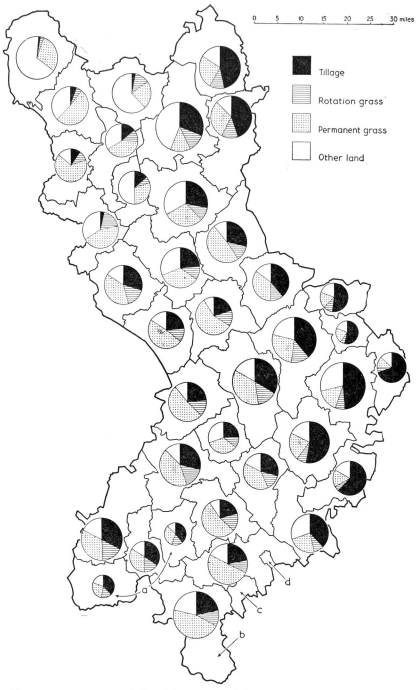

Fig. 51   LAND USE IN 1958, by advisory areas of the National Agricultural Advisory Service : (*a*) two parts of a single advisory area ; (*b*) advisory area extends across regional boundary : wheel-diagram scaled down accordingly ; (*c*) part of an advisory area which lies mainly in the Chilterns ; (*d*) part of an advisory area in Hertfordshire.

war distributions appears in Figure 51, where counties are subdivided into Advisory Areas of the National Agricultural Advisory Service. This map reveals the highly arable character of the east of the region, where some Advisory Areas have more than half their total area in tillage. Between one-third and one-quarter in tillage is characteristic of most of the remaining lowland ; but permanent grass dominates north of the Trent and west of a line drawn roughly midway through the exposed coalfield from north to south.

Table 46 gives data on ten selected groups of parishes for the years 1870, 1913, 1932, and 1958. The samples (Table 47) relate to blocks of land, somewhere of the order of 10,000 acres in size, representative of distinctive farming combinations of the 1930s. Figure 52 illustrates the percentage distribution of each sample, for each of the four years, among tillage, rotation grass, and permanent grass, and also shows numbers of stock converted to the 10,000-acre base for the sake of comparability. The statistical Table and the diagram exemplify, with reference to the chosen areas, the effects of those changes which have been outlined above for the region as a whole ; in addition, they include something of the wartime and post-war alterations which have also been described, but set these in the perspective of trends throughout the period of record.

Nine of the ten sample areas reflect the decline of tillage from 1870 through 1913 to 1932. The sole exception is the market-gardening district of Bedfordshire, where however the increase in tillage from 1870 to 1913 preceded a decline from 1913 to 1932. Of the samples given, the parish blocks in North and South Oxfordshire, North Bedfordshire, and the upland parts of Huntingdonshire seem the most readily convertible, although the pastoral upland of Northamptonshire, the Leicestershire Wolds, the dairy belt of Central Buckinghamshire, and the Keuper belt of Nottinghamshire all record considerable changes in the proportion of tillage to grass. Except for the market-gardening district of Bedfordshire, all the samples illustrate the wartime and post-war spread of rotation grass, especially where farms in the late inter-war period were heavily committed to permanent pasture as opposed to mixed farming. Most of the samples well illustrate the steady rise in numbers of cattle, which in 1958 exceeded the numbers of sheep in the Derbyshire, Nottinghamshire, and South Oxfordshire samples ; indeed, cattle already outnumbered sheep in the Derbyshire sample as early as 1913. In the sample from the Bedfordshire market-garden district, numbers of livestock are so low that the excess of cattle over sheep is not very significant, although here also the reduced state of sheep farming is of long standing.

While wheat is the leading grain crop in most groups (Table 46), oats took at least half the limited tillage in the Derbyshire sample in each of the years listed, and was as extensive as wheat during the depression years in the grazing districts of the Leicestershire Wolds and Central Buckinghamshire. Barley and wheat dispute the leading position among the grain of North Oxfordshire, while barley assumes the lead in South Oxfordshire and North Bedfordshire during the post-war period. Here it is grown principally for stock feeding, not usually being up to malting standard.

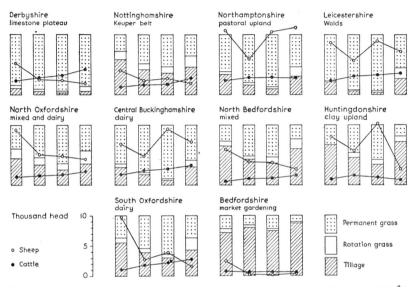

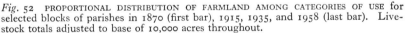

Fig. 52 PROPORTIONAL DISTRIBUTION OF FARMLAND AMONG CATEGORIES OF USE for selected blocks of parishes in 1870 (first bar), 1915, 1935, and 1958 (last bar). Livestock totals adjusted to base of 10,000 acres throughout.

Like the rest of England, the East Midland region is strongly affected today by mechanisation of agriculture. While mechanical reapers, binders, and threshers came into general use before the First World War, it was the Second which, suddenly imposing a simultaneous reduction in the labour force and a demand for increased production, made mechanisation the rule. Despite what had previously been urged about the unsuitability of combines to English conditions, combines are now familiar (Pl. 35)—not, admittedly, without some dependence on grain drying. Straw bales replace the former stooks of grain. Milking is increasingly mechanical. Irrigation (see Chap. 4) and spraying depend progressively on the versatile tractor, while selective weed-killers change the aspect not only of grainfields but also of many roadside verges. Some farms are being laid out anew, so that the whole pattern of hedgerows is changing and fields are being enlarged. Mechanisation both reflects the farming policy of the central government, and combines with it to effect the notable increase in output since 1939; mechanisation also helps to explain how intensive working can be performed with a labour force equivalent to one full-time worker to 70 acres, and one part-time worker to 450 acres,[1] in the region as a whole.

Nineteenth-century change in the manufacture of textiles included the climax and the subsequent virtual extinction of framework knitting. As Table 38 shows, and as has been observed previously, the framework-knitting industry by the mid-eighteenth century was located principally in Leicestershire, Nottinghamshire, and Derbyshire. In 1833 the hosiery industry was said to employ 28,000 people in Leicester—more than half the population of the town. By the 1840s the three counties possessed more than 44,000 frames—nearly all those recorded for the nation (Table 38). The distribution map (Fig. 53) locates especially large numbers in and about Hinckley, Leicester, Nottingham, and Sutton-in-Ashfield; but since the totals represent frames distributed singly or in small groups in the homes of knitters, rather than concentrated in workshops, the industry was far more dispersed than Figure 53 suggests. Most knitters worked in their own cottages down to 1850 and later, although shops to hold 40 or 50 frames appeared in the 1840s at Leicester, where experimental shops equipped with machine-driven circular frames were also at work. About 1840 Loughborough acquired the first power-operated factory to produce textiles in Leicestershire. Circular frames driven by steam power began to come into general use from about 1845: Townsend of Leicester patented his circular rib machine in 1847, while German machinery was first introduced (in Nottingham) in 1851. The straight-bar knitting machine, patented by Cotton of Loughborough in the same year, could make fine goods. It was not however concentration in factories or the competition of mechanical power which depressed the framework-knitting industry: depression of the most savage kind had already been chronically inflicted on the domestic producers.

As early as the Restoration period some capitalist hosiers owned as many as a hundred frames each. In the late eighteenth and early nineteenth century there emerged companies owning thousands of frames. Frame renting, truck, stinting, and price cutting forced knitters to take on additional frames and to use child labour. The huge numbers of frames existing in the mid-nineteenth century thus represent desperate attempts to subsist rather than a vigorous industry. Owners were averse both from mechanical improvement and from

[1] These figures are calculated from returns which include the whole of Buckinghamshire; they omit occupiers and their families.

workshop production, either of which would have reduced numbers of frames and income from frame rent. Riots provoked by depression and high prices occurred in Nottingham from 1779 onwards, while the

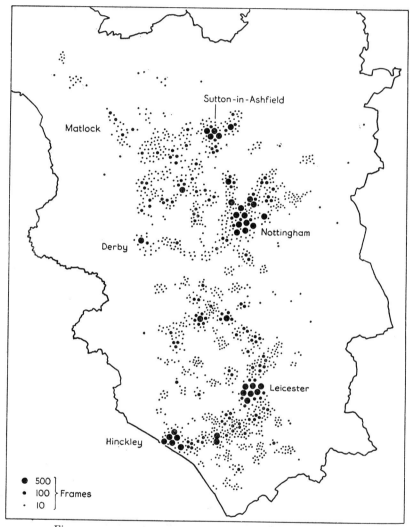

Fig. 53 DISTRIBUTION OF KNITTING-FRAMES IN THE MID-1840s.

Luddite disorders of the early nineteenth century were directed specifically to frame wrecking. Political attempts to ease the appalling conditions of framework knitters failed. They were eventually overtaken by the decline of framework knitting before competition from factories and by the rise of new industries which offered alternative employment. Leicester in 1871 had 74 hosiery factories and Nottingham 45, employing in all about 9,000 workpeople; although some establishments were little more than frameshops, others were truly mechanised. By 1890 some 95% of the output of the hosiery industry came from powered machinery, and the tally of hand-frames had declined to 5,000. In the interim, frame renting had been abolished by law in 1874, and the Education Act of 1870 had withdrawn part of the force of child labour on which framework knitting had once so heavily relied.

Lace making in the south of the region entered a decline which began in Buckinghamshire in about 1835, but was deferred in Bedfordshire and Northamptonshire until the 1880s. Simultaneously a swift and extraordinary expansion occurred in the craft of straw plaiting. Out of 10,000 people employed in plaiting in the United Kingdom in 1841 a quarter lived in Bedfordshire. By 1861 the plait hat and bonnet industries of England and Wales occupied more than 48,000 people, of whom more than 21,000 were in Bedfordshire, that is, some 15% of the whole population of the county was employed in plaiting. Both here and in the adjacent Buckinghamshire children were set to plaiting as soon as their hands could manage the straw. Late in the century this industry was badly hit by competition from the rest of Europe and from China and Japan. Unable to provide the novelties which fashion wished, it gave way to factory production at Luton.

Textile mills in the north of the region were handicapped from about 1820 onwards, first by lack of coal and then by the cotton famine of 1841–51. The failure of about half the early-established mills has been mentioned previously. Nevertheless the numbers employed in textile milling in Derbyshire were still increasing at the 1861 census, when at some 22,000 they exceeded the total of 14,500 miners but were fewer than the 26,000 workers in agriculture. Declining employment in textile making in later censuses reflects mechanisation on the one hand and the decline of silk manufacture on the other. Derby secured no such lasting pre-eminence in silk processing as did Nottingham in lace making or Leicester in the production of hosiery: the town and county between them possessed only 15 of the nation's tally of 238 silk factories in 1835, the industry having become concentrated principally in Cheshire. In the same year 1835, out of a total of 2,569 power looms in Derbyshire, no more than 166 were weaving silk; the remaining 2,403 were in cotton factories. As has been recorded, mechanised cotton mills came early to Derbyshire. In 1835 this was the fourth in rank among English counties by total of power looms, while Leicester had only 129. However, the cotton production of northwest Derbyshire was becoming progressively linked with the

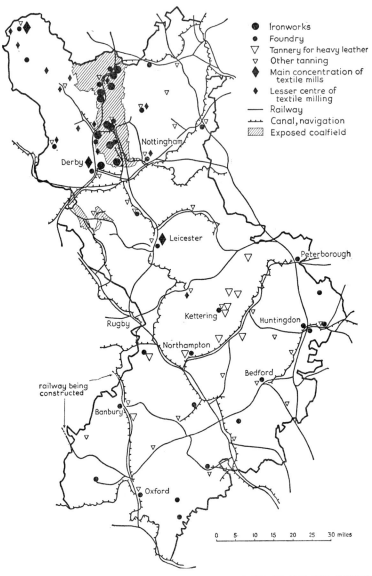

Fig. 54 SOME ELEMENTS OF THE INDUSTRIAL GEOGRAPHY OF THE MID-NINETEENTH CENTURY.

Lancashire industry, of which the mills in and near Glossop (Fig. 54) constituted an outpost. A scatter of minor centres lay between Lancashire on the one hand and Derby town and the southern part of the coalfield on the other. Framework knitting, with main groupings in the 1840s in and near Derby, Heanor, Ilkeston, Alfreton, Swanwick, Bonsall, Belper, and Horsley Woodhouse (Fig. 53), was supplanted by about 1900 by factory production at Derby, Heanor, Ilkeston, and Long Eaton.

Nottinghamshire's lace trade benefited from the bobbin machines patented by Heathcoat in 1808 and 1809, by the expiry of the Heathcoat patents in 1823, and by the machine produced by Leavers in 1813 which, in 1834, was applied through an adaptation of the Jacquard to the making of intricate designs. Here was one reason for the decline of lace making in the south of the region. The Nottingham industry from the outset depended considerably upon outwork, which still persists today in the garment trades of the Midlands; but outworking came to be concentrated within reach of Nottingham, leaving only hand crochet to be controlled by middlemen who operated far to the south as late as the 1930s.

The first steam-powered factory to manufacture textiles in Nottingham was built in 1851, to produce not lace but hosiery. At this time the lace industry was recovering from the abrupt and sharp depression of 1848. By 1871 there were 223 lace factories in the country, most of them in or near Nottingham, employing 8,300 hands. The decade 1873–83 was exceptionally prosperous, when a fashion for lace curtains coincided with considerable building of houses. By 1885 there were 431 factories in the country, employing 15,000 hands; 2,250 lace-making machines were in use in Nottingham alone.

Leather manufacture began its expansion earlier in Northamptonshire than in Leicestershire. In 1820 there were 5 tanneries in Northampton town. Tanneries for heavy leather existed by 1847 at Brigstock, Drayton, Duddington, Higham Ferrers, Kettering, King's Sutton, Northampton, Stanion, Wilby, and Warkton (Fig. 54). The perceptible grouping of some of these in Rockingham Forest or on its borders indicates the use of local tanbark, but nineteenth-century changes included the abandonment of all the tanyards of 1847. The last three to go were in Northampton itself; they were replaced by two new yards by 1906. Sixty manufacturers of boots and shoes were located in the town in 1841, and an additional 38 elsewhere (Table 48). These were evidently wholesale manufacturers, for Whellan's Directory for 1849 lists 54 wholesale manufacturers for Northampton, against 52 simple makers of footwear. Leicester in 1846 had 190 makers, increasing by 1863 to 402 makers and 35 wholesale manufacturers. Wholesale manufacture seems to have been established earlier and on a larger scale at Northampton than at Leicester, and to have been accompanied by satellite producers which Leicester did not at first match. Northampton town had 125 wholesale manufacturers by 1877, while fifteen outlying places had another 95.

Footwear production was greatly encouraged by demands from the

West Indies after the manumission of slaves in 1838, and by such events as the Australian gold rush of 1851. Riveting of soles, first introduced at Leicester in 1860, enabled that town to record a swift increase in production. Mechanical stitching of soles was quickly adopted in Northampton from 1861 onwards. These two forms of mechanisation were among those promoting division of labour and concentration of the industry in factories.

Outworking remained common for a time, however, after machinery came into wide use, for small machines were commonly hired out. In Leicester in 1890 most processing of footwear was still done in small workshops. But outworking in the leather trade had essentially ceased by the end of the century. By that time, too, the numbers of workers in the footwear industry was greater at Leicester than at Northampton —13,000 and 24,000 in 1881 and 1891 at Leicester, against 10,500 and 13,000 at Northampton. Nevertheless the difference in size of the two towns made the industry proportionally more significant at Northampton than at Leicester, even when no account is taken of Northampton's satellite producers.

Concentration of industrial production in large units has been encouraged during the twentieth century by the economies which large units permit, by the disappearance of uneconomic plant during the inter-war years, and by reorganisation during the highly competitive post-war period. Dispersal and diversification, on the other hand, deliberately stimulated by the central government especially in old-industrialised areas, have been no less effectively promoted by the post-war search for labour, and in addition reflect something of the desperate relocation of wartime itself. Broadly speaking, the leading industries of the East Midland region are now concentrated at fewer localities than formerly, although both the hosiery and the leather trades exemplify the two conflicting groups of trend.

The hosiery trade succeeded in expanding after the First World War, by contrast with all other textile manufacture except that of silk and artificial silk, and despite severe competition from Japan, Germany, and the United States. About 20% of its production of hose went for export in 1924, and about $10\frac{1}{2}\%$ of underwear and fancy goods, Australia being the chief market. Adjustments to the demands of the home market staved off the worst of the depression, although the value of exports fell abruptly in 1929–30, and restriction of imports failed to promote sales because of high prices. Leicester now produces about 30% of the national output of hosiery; more than 25% of the county's output goes for export.

While Hinckley and Shardlow are heavily committed to hosiery manufacture, with 58% of their employees in non-service industries working in hosiery, and while Leicester, Ilkeston, Mansfield, Sutton-in-Ashfield, and Market Harborough Rural District record between 24% and 36%, some incursion of the hosiery trades into former coal-mining towns is perceptible, mainly concerned with narrow fabrics, as at Coalville. In large part the post-war spread of hosiery manufacture follows directly from the wartime dispersal of engineering, the factories and the supply of labour remaining when engineering firms withdrew at the end of the Second World War. I. G. Weekley has discussed the influence of hidden reserves of female labour and of available premises on small country towns in Lincolnshire, Northamptonshire, and Rutland, showing that small-scale organisation can be both efficient and profitable. New engineering plants have arisen mainly in south Northamptonshire, but the clothing industry is the chief new employer elsewhere.

Leicestershire makes about a quarter of the national output of footwear, Northamptonshire about one-third. Spread of the footwear industry since the Second World War involves towns and villages around Northampton, such as Woodford Halse and Harrowden, reversing the strong tendency of 1924–39 for establishments to decline in number. In so far as they are prompted by policy, encouraged by premises available, or designed to take advantage of reserves of labour, all these developments contrast with those of the nineteenth century and the first half of the twentieth, but in so far as they represent the penetration of the countryside by the manufacturing activities of the great urban centres, they constitute no essential change. It remains to be seen whether far-reaching diversification will occur, for, as W. D. Holmes points out, about two-thirds of the labour force of the Leicestershire coalfield is still employed in mining, quarrying, textile manufacture, or engineering, and two-fifths in mining and quarrying alone.

CHAPTER 10

TRANSPORT, EXTRACTIVE INDUSTRIES, ENGINEERING

IN 1840 the ironworks of Derbyshire were on the point of beginning a burst of expansion which, by the end of the century, raised their combined output to 15 times that of 1840 and to 75 times that of 1800. The rediscovery of the Jurassic ores of Oxfordshire, Northamptonshire, Rutland, Leicestershire, and Lincolnshire was still to come. Few successful mines had yet been sunk in the exposed coalfields. The first railways to enter the region were still new, and the two principal canals—the Oxford and Grand Junction Canals—had as yet barely ceased to pay their peak dividends. By 1850 or shortly thereafter the scene had abruptly changed. Dividends on canal shares had sagged, never subsequently to recover. The region was traversed by two main railways coming from London, with the Great Western under construction and elements of the fourth (the Midland Railway) already present; cross-connections ran from Huntingdon through Bedford to Oxford, from Peterborough to Northampton, to Rugby, and to Leicester, along the Trent valley, and across the extreme north of the region. Exploitation of the Jurassic iron ore was imminent, as was the sinking of Shireoaks Colliery through the Permo-Trias. Engineering works were about to be established in a number of towns not located on, or particularly near, the coalfields. In these circumstances the map of elements in industrial geography in 1850 (Fig. 54) represents a glimpse at a scene of rapid change.

Among the most obvious facts of the distributions of 1850 are the closeness with which railways accompanied canals, the concentration of ironworks in and near the valleys of the Erewash, lower Derwent, and Rother, the concentration of textile milling in the northwest with a main extension through Leicester to Market Harborough, the grouping of tanneries for heavy leather in a belt running from Banbury to Peterborough, and the wide scatter of lesser tanneries and of small foundries. Nothing need be added to the previous comments on milling and tanning, except to re-emphasise that milling was to increase after 1850 while tanning was to decline and to be restricted in distribution. While the eventual extinction of tanneries for heavy leather reflected technical changes in the industry, however, the disappearance of minor tanneries should be compared to the supersession of minor foundries by engineering works established in the coming years. Seventeen places in the southern half of the region, most of them small country towns, possessed foundries in 1850 ; most of these foundries dealt in iron rather than in brass.

Wolverton acquired the first of the new engineering shops in 1838, when its railway works were opened alongside the new London and Birmingham Railway. Until 1865 the plant made locomotives, being then converted to carriage-and-wagon production. The engineer Samuelson, displaced from the railway works at Tours in 1848, bought a small implement factory at Banbury and converted it to a factory for agricultural machines ; in 1872 this factory produced 8,000 mechanical reapers. Although Oxford in 1865 rejected the offer of a large engineering plant from the Great Western Railway, heavy industry was not excluded from the immediate district : the Oxford Steam Ploughing Company began production two years later at Cowley. A new foundry was established at Buckingham in 1857 ; the Britannia Works at Bedford, constructed in 1857–9, turned from its first interests of foundry production to general engineering. Iron-founding in Leicester, located first near the canal, expanded into mechanical engineering in the 1840s, while Loughborough entered the engineering field in the 1860s. Whereas the works at Leicester and Loughborough had early connections with textile milling, and thus shared in the conversion from eighteenth-century to nineteenth-century techniques in a long-established industry, those in the south of the region represented a quite sudden invasion of the eighteenth-century scene of farmland, villages, and small country towns by heavy industry of a perceptibly modern kind. On the Northamptonshire ironfield, at Wellingborough, smelting of local ore began in 1852. Between about 1840 and 1860, then, parts of the existing industrial scene were blocked in.

Until the coming of the railways certain main lines of transport were markedly different from those which now exist. The principal waterways in the south of the region were the Thames, the Ouse (navigable to Bedford), the Nene (navigable to Northampton), and the Oxford and Birmingham Canals. Bedford was not easily in touch with the valleys of the Ouzel and the upper Ouse, which were served by the Grand Junction Canal and its branches. Kettering, Wellingborough, and their neighbours were economically aligned on the Nene valley, having yet to be traversed by the Bedford–Leicester axis of the Midland Railway. On the other hand, the Great Western Railway ran alongside the Oxford Canal up the Cherwell valley ; the London and Birmingham Railway followed the Grand Junction Canal ; the route of the Nene, with its short link of canal to the Grand Junction waterway, was duplicated by a railway from Blisworth through Northampton to

Peterborough ; the connection between the Oxford and Grand Junction canal systems was copied by a railway node at Rugby, where lines radiated to Birmingham, to Nuneaton and so to the Trent and Mersey country, and to Leicester. Railway foci at Grantham, Lincoln, and Retford involved some elaboration of the network of transportation formed by waterways alone, but the Trent valley from Newark to Burton and the Soar valley from the Trent to Leicester both acquired railways which ran alongside, and competed with, pre-existing waterways. Similarly the Ashby Canal from the Leicestershire coalfield was closely followed by the railway which later ruined it.

It was in the northwest of the region that the railways constructed before 1850 contributed principally to completing, as opposed to improving, the net of routes suitable for heavy carriage. Derby and the lower Derwent valley were served directly by a line which, passing along the valley of the Amber, entered the Rother valley and gave Chesterfield and its neighbours a direct connection with Derby which canals had failed to supply. Only in the High Peak, where the High Peak Railway and the Peak Forest Canal (not shown in Figure 54) served limestone quarries, did the eighteenth-century type of network endure. Even this was partly supplanted when, in 1860, the Manchester-Whaley Bridge line was extended to Buxton ; Dove Holes Station was opened in 1862, and a branch line thrust into the quarrying district. The Rowsley to Manchester extension of the Midland railway, opened in 1864, introduced a new alignment of quarries, and when the High Peak Railway was re-laid to standard gauge in the 1870s its horses were replaced by locomotives.

Close similarities between the system of railways and that of canals and navigations should really cause no surprise. Quite apart from the matter of direct competition or of supersession, waterways both constituted the existing routes of heavy transport when railway building began and followed easy gradients which were selected by railway engineers in their turn. Perhaps the outstanding example of parallelism is the line which, taken by the Grand Junction Canal round the side of the Nene valley west of Northampton, was adopted also by the London to Birmingham Railway. The myth that the city fathers of Northampton prevented the line from passing through the town is as persistent as it is inaccurate.

The Oxford Canal, built prior to the inflation of wartime, paid strikingly high dividends on its nominal share values well into the mid-century—from 1819 until 1835, at least 32% per annum. Other remarkably successful waterways at this time were the Loughborough Navigation, paying $87\frac{1}{3}$% on nominal value and 10% on market value in 1833, and the Erewash Canal, paying 47% on nominal value and

$6\frac{2}{3}\%$ on market value in the same year, when the dividend on market value of shares in the Oxford Canal was slightly more than $5\frac{1}{3}\%$. Total sales of coal by canal from collieries in the Erewash valley rose from 254,268 tons in 1803 to 475,779 tons in 1847, when coal from the East Midlands fields was competing successfully with seaborne coal from Newcastle in the southeast of the region. Tonnage receipts on the Oxford Canal rose from £27,500 in 1797 to £77,250 in 1810 and £95,500 in 1830. Tonnage carried in 1830 was about 475,000, was still 450,000 in 1888, and was running at about 350,000 as late as 1938. However, dividends began to fall, slowly at first, when railway transport began. Tonnages on the Oxford canal were retained solely by means of price cutting, which brought dividends on nominal share values down to $8\frac{1}{2}\%$ by 1870, and reduced receipts to £24,000 in the same year. The Grand Junction Canal, built at a time of high costs, paid its peak dividends of 13% on nominal share values in 1828–31, maintaining a rate of 12% from 1832 until 1837, and then falling sharply away. But the combination of market value, nominal value, and rate of dividend should not be allowed to conceal the facts that this canal was both more effective and more prosperous than the Oxford Canal. Tonnage receipts of £176,500 in 1830 were greater than those of the Oxford Canal, and £102,000 was taken in 1905. Tonnage carried in 1905 was nearly 1,800,000, greater than the 1,200,000 of 1888 and not much more than the 1,500,000 tons of 1938. At the same time, by 1938 both the Oxford and the Grand Junction (by this time the Grand Union [1]) Canals were dealing mainly with local traffic and with short hauls. Coal and coke accounted for about half their total cargo, with building materials, foodstuffs, industrial products, and bulk liquids constituting another quarter.

Canals, railways, and the application of steam power in factories combined to transform the grain-milling industry of the Nene and Ouse valleys. J. Smith concludes that all the mill sites on the Nene below Northampton were probably in use as early as 1352; for five hundred years and more they continued to rely on water power. When the Grand Junction Canal and its link to the upper Nene opened new markets in the expanding towns of the West Midlands, early in the nineteenth century, grain was shipped upstream from the Fens. Foreign grain began to enter when railways were built. From 1845 onwards steam power began to be applied to milling, although the original sites were retained. Of 35 potential sites on the Nene below Northampton, only 5 were not used for grain-milling in 1870, and two

[1] The Grand Union Canal was formed by the amalgamation of the Loughborough and Leicester Navigations, the Birmingham and Warwick Junction, Warwick and Birmingham, Warwick and Napton, Grand Junction, and Regent's Canals.

of these had paper-mills. Similar developments occurred on the Great Ouse (Pl. 11).

During the last century and a half the coal-mining industry of the East Midlands has experienced surges of development alternating with stagnation and depression. Short-term fluctuations referable to the business cycle are integrated in the record of mining with longer-term happenings which indicate five distinct phases since 1800 (Table 49, Fig. 55). A first phase of increase raised output to about 2½ million tons a year by 1850; a second, of more rapid increase, by about 400,000 tons a year, lasted until about 1890 and brought annual production to 18 million tons; the third phase, of increase by about 700,000 tons a year, culminated in the production of 30 million tons in

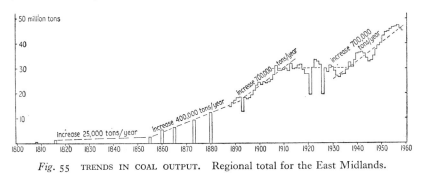

Fig. 55 TRENDS IN COAL OUTPUT. Regional total for the East Midlands.

1913. Then followed a long pause, with output varying through strikes and slumps, and a running average of 30 million tons a year barely maintained. Finally, the fifth phase of renewed increase in output by 700,000 tons a year has made annual production approach 50 million tons.

Little definite is known of the rate of extraction of coal from the exposed fields in 1800–50. Farey's estimate of 269,456 tons for 1808 seems too low, since the Erewash Canal received 321,056 tons in the following year. The pre-locomotive railway from Pinxton to Mansfield carried a quarter of a million tons in 1819–26. But two great potential markets for East Midland coal were either inaccessible or non-existent until the railway age. The entry of locomotive railways gave the East Midland collieries a share—which canals had not been able to secure —in the domestic market of London, while railway construction and the engineering which accompanied it increased demands on furnaces, iron-mills, and collieries.

The fairly steady increase in demand between 1855 and 1885 was due only in part to the increase in iron manufacture. Output of blast furnaces in Derbyshire corresponded in 1840 to the small demand of

129,000 tons of coal for use in smelting. If the proportion of coal used to pig iron produced had remained constant, the Derbyshire furnaces would have taken less than half a million tons of coal in 1855, out of 2 million tons raised. Smelting accounts for but a fraction of the total sales of 15 million tons of coal in 1890.

Glover's Directory of 1829 lists 108 active mines (Fig. 56): 6 in rocks older than Coal Measures, 92 on the exposed Derby and Nottingham-shire field, one apparently in concealed measures, and 9 for Leicester-shire. The possible sinking through the Permian conflicts with the usual statement that Shireoaks Colliery (1854–9) first penetrated the cover. Glover may have omitted collieries on the southern field but in Leicestershire county, but in any event his grand total differs little from the 109 previously recorded from Farey for about 1810. Annual production per colliery averaged about 17,500 tons by 1830.

Serial numbering, as opposed to the present naming, obscures precisely which seams the collieries of the early nineteenth century were exploiting (see Figure 3, which omits seams below the Coal Measures). Most of the coking coals lie in seams below the Deep Hard, principally in the Blackshale, Threequarters, Tupton, and Piper seams of the Derbyshire succession. When smelting with coke spread through the iron industry, mining in the axial part of the exposed field of Derbyshire received a new stimulus. Distribution of mines in 1869 differed little from that of 1829 (Fig. 57), except for numerous additions in the lower Erewash valley and for increased density throughout the field. By 1869 the number of active mines on the exposed field was 131, with one still operating in rocks older than Coal Measures, 10 on the concealed field of Nottinghamshire, 15 on the exposed field of Leicestershire, and 5 working concealed measures nearby. Average annual production per mine was 52,500 tons. The Erewash valley alone was dispatching a million tons a year by rail and canal. Com-bined employment in the iron manufacture and coal mining of Derby-shire first exceeded employment either in agriculture or in textile trades at about the same time. Before 1880 coal mining was the county's leading industrial occupation. But the main increase in coal output had still to come, aided by the sinking of new shafts in the hidden field. A string of mines lay four miles east of the upper boundary of the exposed coalfield by 1905, with Manton colliery beyond Worksop eight miles distant. The rather slow eastward dip of the concealed seams ensured that the deepest pits of 1905, with two exceptions, encountered the Coal Measures little below sea level.

Data for 1925 allow collieries to be compared in respect of numbers of employees (Fig. 58). Although these numbers indicate comparative production only roughly, they leave no doubt that the largest mines

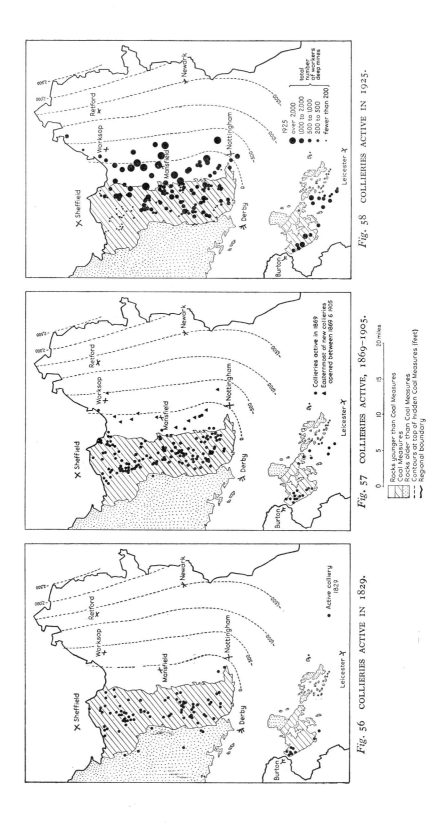

Fig. 56 COLLIERIES ACTIVE IN 1829.

Fig. 57 COLLIERIES ACTIVE, 1869–1905.

Fig. 58 COLLIERIES ACTIVE IN 1925.

Fig. 56

• Active colliery
  1829

Fig. 57

• Collieries active in 1869
▲ Easternmost of new collieries
  opened between 1869 & 1905

0	5	10	15	20 miles

Rocks younger than Coal Measures
Coal Measures
Rocks older than Coal Measures
– – – Contours at top of hidden Coal Measures (feet)
Regional boundary

Fig. 58

total
number
of workers
deep mines

1925
● over 2,000
● 1,000 to 2,000
● 500 to 1,000
• 200 to 500
• fewer than 200

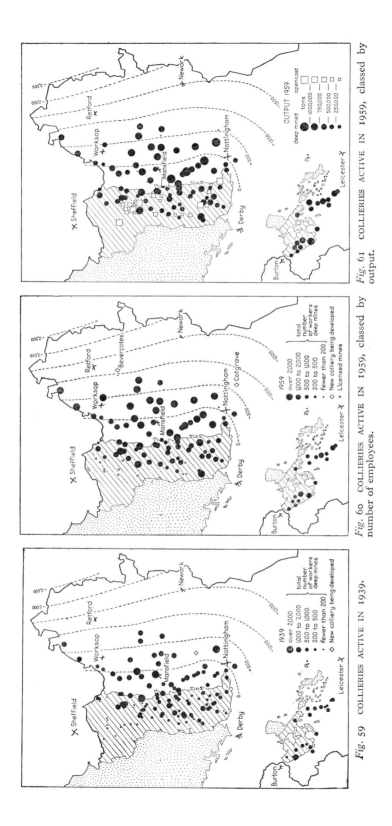

Fig. 61 COLLIERIES ACTIVE IN 1959, classed by output.

Fig. 60 COLLIERIES ACTIVE IN 1959, classed by number of employees.

Fig. 59 COLLIERIES ACTIVE IN 1939.

were, as one would expect, concentrated on the concealed measures, while a compact group of 22 mines in the northwest, around Chesterfield and Dronfield, were without exception small. This is one of the first-developed portions of the exposed field, with its flat-lying seams quite freely accessible and heavily drawn upon by ironworks. The troubles of the mining industry in the inter-war period reduced the total of active mines on the exposed Derby and Nottinghamshire field from 122 in 1925 to 91 in 1939 (Fig. 59); half the small mines in the northwest ceased work. One mine closed but three opened on the hidden field in Nottinghamshire during the same period, while three additional mines came into work on the exposed field of Leicestershire.

Closures because of exhaustion, and winding of coal from some pairs of collieries up single shafts, reduced the number of National Coal Board collieries to 43 by 1959 (Fig. 60). Fourteen licensed collieries, one of them opencast, were also active in that year, giving a total of 56 deep mines on the Derby and Nottinghamshire field. The Leicestershire field had 10 (including one licensed mine) on the exposed field, and 8 working concealed measures. Comparison between the maps for 1939 and 1959, where collieries are classed by numbers of workers, suggests a distinct eastward movement of deep mining across the exposed field of Derby and Nottinghamshire and a further movement from the exposed on to the hidden coalfield (Pl. 37).

Since data for 1925 and 1939 are grouped by colliery companies, output per mine or per worker cannot be precisely stated for these years. The lists omit tonnages for some collieries, while approximate tonnages are alone determinable for some others, on the assumption that output within a company was proportional to numbers employed. Nevertheless, the data suggest median numbers of employees per colliery of 590 in 1925, 610 in 1939, and 830 in 1959. Median output for 1939 was 320,000 tons, for collieries listing tonnages, while in 1959 it was 480,000.

Figure 61, showing collieries by tonnage produced in 1959, makes clear the broad distinction between the large collieries of the hidden Nottinghamshire field and the medium-sized collieries of the exposed field to the west. Except for licensed mines and opencast workings, the northwestern part of the exposed field is abandoned. Nevertheless, considerable reserves still exist in the exposed field as a whole. Some of its largest deep mines raise coking coal (Fig. 64). While perceptibly more than half the output of deep-mined coal is supplied by collieries on the hidden field, opencast workings on the exposed field yielded more than 10 million tons in 1959.

An exclusive assumption that large collieries on the hidden field are the most productive, in terms of output per worker or output per

174

worker underground, is unjustified. Nor did it apply in 1939, when, although some of the deepest mines averaged 800 tons per worker below ground, some of the lowest rates of production were recorded by mines of the same type. Productivity in both years ranged considerably from one colliery to another. Exceptionally for the present day, however, both the Derby and Nottinghamshire field and the Leicestershire field are profitable : their profit of £18½ million in 1959 nearly equalled the national profit of £19 million. Low-cost working and high mechanisation have long typified both fields : 99% of East Midland coal was cut by machinery in 1959, 99·5% machine-conveyed, 55% mechanically cleaned, and 49·5% power-loaded.

The East Midland coalfields now head the national list of producing groups (Figs. 62 and 63). Peak output in the Northumberland and Durham, South Wales, and Scottish fields preceded the First World War ; peaks reached in about 1935 and 1940-5 have not enabled the Yorkshire coalfield to maintain a lead over the East Midlands. Between 1890 and 1960 the East Midland fields more than doubled their proportional share in national output. Future prospects are better than those of any other fields, although developments will be influenced in detail by underground geology. Estimated reserves within existing colliery-takes amount to some 6,275 million tons, but not all are necessarily workable. Opencast working is steadily reducing the coal left in the exposed fields. Hidden seams near Nottingham rise to encounter the unconformity at the base of the Permo-Trias, where flooding is a great potential danger. Principal current developments include the new colliery at Cotgrave under construction (1961) south-east of Nottingham, and that at Bevercotes near Retford, which began work in January 1961. Bevercotes is planned to produce 1¼ million tons a year from the Top Hard, Deep Soft, and Parkgate seams. Recent developments on the Leicestershire field are concentrated in the southeast, but borings show a concealed extension to the west, between Netherseal and Burton upon Trent.

Coal from all seams in the Leicestershire field, and from most seams in the Derby and Nottinghamshire field, is unsuitable for making metallurgical coke. Mines which are now raising coal of coking quality lie grouped round Mansfield, with extensions towards Chesterfield and Alfreton ; coking plants are located south and southeast of Chesterfield, at Stanton, and on the Northampton Sand ironfield at Corby (Fig. 64). High-grade steam coal in the Derby and Nottinghamshire field comes from the Top Hard and Deep Hard seams, while the Waterloo, Deep Soft, and Tupton seams chiefly provide house coal. The Leicestershire field produces general-purpose coal of rather low grade, but has the compensating advantage of thick and close-spaced seams.

Power stations take more than half the combined output of the two fields, and will increase both their demand for tonnage and their share in the output. As E. M. Rawstron observes, the large (and expanding) stations on the Trent are well placed to secure abundant supplies of water, and to obtain low-cost coal by quite short hauls (Fig. 64). They alone seem enough to guarantee a working future for the East Midland coalfields (Pl. 47).

Apart from metal works and from the collieries themselves, four

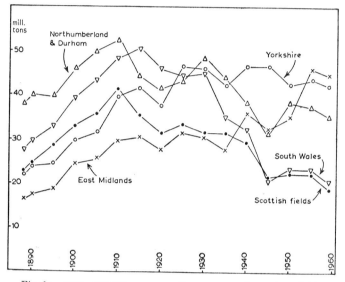

Fig. 62   COAL OUTPUT : comparative tonnages for various fields.

chief types of building accompanied the development of mining and its eastward spread into Nottinghamshire. Additional housing distended previously-established settlements ; small groups of miners' houses appeared ; some nuclei of settlement entangled themselves in spreading and formless towns ; and large, compact colliery villages arose. Both exposed coalfields at first sight appear disorderly in respect of settlement pattern, partly because of piecemeal construction and abandonment of collieries, metal works, and houses, and partly because of the small terraced rows mentioned above. Such rows are well represented by the back-to-back houses at Arkwright Town, where a fragment of some nineteenth-century industrial town seems, as it were, deposited in the countryside. Mansfield and Worksop illustrate settlements distended through the development of mining. Among the specially built colliery villages, Bolsover Model Village dates from 1891–4 and Creswell from 1896. Style of architecture in villages of this type ranges from cheap and depressing to solid and acceptable. Formless towns constitute a transition from small groups of terrace houses to distended settlements of early original date. Some have achieved town status merely by force of numbers living in a small district, without developing an effective urban centre, but others include at least an original village nucleus. This group includes Swadlincote, where metal-working, quarrying, and mining subsidence have all contributed to oppose compact and orderly growth.

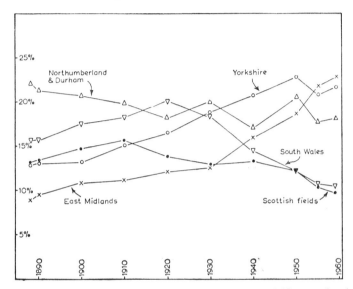

Fig. 63   COAL OUTPUT : percentage contributions of various fields to national total.

Blast furnaces in Derbyshire produced 32,000 tons of pig iron in 1840—an output forty times as great as that of 1720, but still modest. It was in about 1840, despite the onset of a sharp commercial depression, that Derbyshire began to increase its output rapidly (Fig. 65, Tables 50, 51) ; as the percentages reveal, this was part of the swift rise of the national smelting industry.   In the early 1850s, when their output rose above 100,000 tons of pig a year, the Derbyshire furnaces still depended on ore from the Coal Measures, some 350,000 to 400,000 tons of which were raised annually between 1855 and 1870.

The Coal-Measure ores occur as irregular rows of nodules in shale, mainly between the Silkstone and Top Hard Coals. Their iron content of 22% to 31% compares unfavourably with that of much Jurassic ore, conflicting with the belief that Coal-Measure ores are typically rich. Although coal and iron could be shifted by pre-locomotive railways and by canal, the furnaces were initially located with reference to ores which

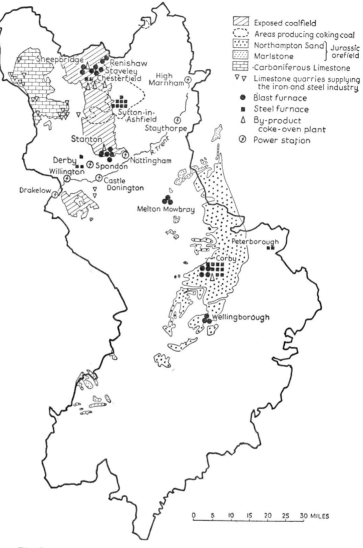

Legend:
- Exposed coalfield
- Areas producing coking coal
- Northampton Sand } Jurassic
- Marlstone } orefield
- Carboniferous Limestone
- ▽ ▽ Limestone quarries supplying the iron-and steel industry
- ● Blast furnace
- ■ Steel furnace
- △ By-product coke-oven plant
- ⊘ Power station

0 5 10 15 20 25 30 MILES

Fig. 64   SOME ELEMENTS IN THE INDUSTRIAL GEOGRAPHY OF 1960.

anticlinal folding of the rocks, and downcutting by rivers, brought close to the surface of the ground. Iron-manufacturing concerns in the early nineteenth century, typically owning coalmines and the bell-pits in which ore was dug, grouped themselves in and near Belper, Ripley-Alfreton, and Chesterfield. In 1869 there were 17 furnaces in the Rother valley, with one other (out of blast) northwest of Chester-field at Unstone; smelting had receded from Belper to the 6 furnaces at Denby and Morley Park between Belper and Heanor; the Alfreton-

178

Ripley neighbourhood, served by railway and canal through the col between the Erewash and Derwent valleys, had 11, while 3 at West Hallam and 5 at Stanton represented the southward extension of smelting along the lower Erewash (Table 52). Puddling and rolling in the Derbyshire of 1869 were concentrated at Alfreton, Chesterfield (including Sheepbridge), and Derby.

Use of local ores diminished rapidly from 1875 onwards, until their extraction became merely incidental to coal mining. Some iron-working firms obtained rights in the developing Jurassic orefields,

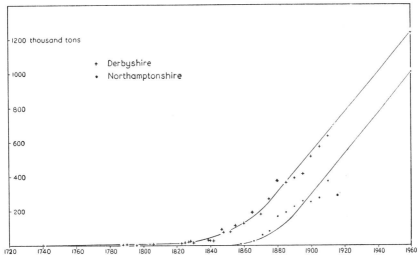

Fig. 65   TRENDS IN THE OUTPUT OF PIG IRON by furnaces in Derbyshire (with Stanton Ironworks, Notts.) and on the Northamptonshire orefield.   Highly generalised.

which became to some extent annexes of the Derbyshire smelting industry. Nevertheless, these orefields witnessed in the second half of the nineteenth century experiments reminiscent of the earlier half, eventually acquiring well-established furnaces of their own. The con-trasted histories of the three fields (located in Figure 64) result partly from their situation with respect to consuming plants, partly from the accidents of industrial record, partly from the physical characteristics of the terrains, and partly—especially in recent years—from large-scale planning. All three fields correspond to shallow depositional basins, characteristic of the Jurassic sedimentary environment, where ore-beds thicken and the iron content rises. All the ores are phosphoric, suitable only for basic processes. They were useless for steel-making until the Thomas-Gilchrist process was developed in 1878, and were for many years charged into furnaces which exclusively produced pig iron of forge and foundry qualities.

179

The development of the Northampton Sand field up to 1930 has been traced in some detail by S. H. Beaver, who notes that the first consignments of ore were unfavourably received by Staffordshire smelters. Quarrying started near Blisworth, where the Grand Union Canal provided a route of transport. Subsequent to experiments with a cold-blast furnace, smelting began at Wellingborough in 1853; the first plants were located at and near Wellingborough and Kettering, or else in the southwestern part of the orefield (Table 53). Extraction at first greatly outran the capacity of local works, 80% of the ore raised in 1875 being sent away, mainly to Derbyshire. Construction of the Kettering–Manston railway in 1879 revealed the Corby ore, just as the Northampton–Market Harborough line (1859) and various branches had previously given access to other localities. By the end of the century the ironworks in the southwest lay abandoned, except for that at Hunsbury Hill which lasted until 1921. In 1910, when the field produced 3 million tons of ore, its furnaces made less than 400,000 tons of pig, against the more than 600,000 tons made in Derbyshire (Table 50, Fig. 65)—and this, despite a fuel/pig ratio of about $1\frac{1}{2}/1$, which implies an ore/coke ratio of about $4\frac{1}{2}/1$. Although the first smelters were surprisingly economical in fuel, and although the ores are lean, with an iron content ranging mainly from 28% to 35%, the momentum of the Derbyshire smelting industry was obviously great. An alternative view is that that industry was located primarily with respect to coal, not to ore.

Another relevant factor—the early influence of which, however, is difficult to assess—is that the chemistry of the Jurassic ores varies, even within a single field. The Northampton Sand ore is siliceous, but its silica content varies with relationship to minor tectonic axes active during deposition, and also rises towards the margins of the sedimentary basins. Variable chemistry encourages blending, which involves transfer of ore from place to place.

Both in the Banbury and in the Leicestershire field the Marlstone ore is calcareous. Like the Northampton Sand ore it is enriched by weathering where exposed or thinly covered, but again is somewhat eroded near its northwestern outcrop boundaries. Iron content is about $24\frac{1}{2}$% in the Banbury field, and 23% to 26% in the Leicestershire field, rising to 40% at Holwell. Working started on the Banbury field in the late 1850s, but was at first spasmodic, even though extensive natural stripping and widespread absence of structural disturbances favour opencast quarries. This field seems to have been handicapped by inconvenient railway connections, and possibly also by lack of the water demanded by ironworks: the Edge Hill Plateau is a watershed, where head-valleys are dry. Some quarries were economically marginal

180

until demand for ore by South Wales increased after the Second World War. The Charwelton and Banbury quarries operated in the First World War, closed subsequently, and reopened in the Second, on each occasion supplying furnaces at Rotherham. Up to the outbreak of the Second World War annual production from this field seems not to have exceeded 200,000 tons.

Exploitation of the Marlstone field of Leicestershire began in the late 1870s, after trials of its ore at Clay Cross, in 1855, had been abandoned because of difficulties with transport. The Holwell Iron

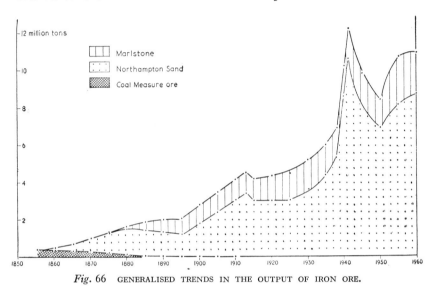

Fig. 66 GENERALISED TRENDS IN THE OUTPUT OF IRON ORE.

Company blew in its first furnace near Melton Mowbray in 1881. Quarrying rapidly spread to most parts of the field, with the aid of branch railways and mineral lines, and annual production ran at some 650,000 tons by the end of the century.

At this time the combined output of the Jurassic orefields of the East Midland region promised to level off at about 2 million tons a year; but by 1913 it rose to more than 4 million tons (Fig. 66). Mechanical diggers came increasingly into use for stripping overburden, although most of the actual quarrying of ore was still done by hand in 1920. Short-term fluctuations in the economy do not obscure the steep and remarkably similar increases in the output of pig iron, respectively in Derbyshire (with which is grouped the Stanton works of Nottinghamshire) and in Northamptonshire (Fig. 65).

Derbyshire smelters became involved with the substitution of steel for iron in the late nineteenth century. In 1888 the Butterley Company put into operation an open-hearth steelworks, achieving a small output of steel rails until it closed in 1902. The Staveley, Clay Cross, and Stanton works specialised rather than emulated, turning to the manufacture of cast-iron pipes as their chief interest. Engineering manufacture became truly elaborated only at Sheepbridge. The principal developments in steel making within the region occurred at Corby, singularly enough, in economic conditions which were anything but promising at each critical stage. The first of two furnaces at the new ironworks at Corby began work in 1910, the second following in the next year. Outbreak of war in 1914 reduced labour supply and caused extraction of ore to fall off (Table 54, Fig. 66). Charging of scrap iron into furnaces, widely practised in the war years, continued in the succeeding peace when Corby was not well placed to obtain scrap. Until the 1930s its basic pig went mainly to the West Midlands. In 1934, however, an integrated steelworks with coke ovens, blast furnaces, steel furnaces, and a tube plant came into operation; its construction had been deferred by the Great Slump, and prospects were still somewhat dubious when production started. In 1939, with rearmament going on, its converters made half a million tons of steel.

From the outset the Corby works have been large in scale. Their first blast furnaces were the biggest on the Northampton Sand field, while output of pig per furnace in 1960 was 20% above national average. With a consumption of $2\frac{1}{2}$ million tons of ore a year go enormous quarries equipped with walking draglines and served by aerial ropeways. Production of ore from the Northampton Sand field, now more than 8 million tons a year, is still however well above the combined needs of Corby, Wellingborough, and the furnaces in Derbyshire and Nottinghamshire. Production of steel, similarly, lags behind the production of pig in the region as a whole (Tables 54, 55), although the grouping of statistics obscures the position at Corby itself, where 1,147,500 tons of crude steel were made in 1960 against 895,000 tons of pig. Whereas the Northampton Sand orefield alone raised 20% of the national output of ore in 1920, over 30% in 1930, and 50% from 1940 onwards, pig-iron production in the East Midland region was about 11% of the national total in 1920, something above 20% in 1940, and distinctly below 20% in 1960 when new furnaces had begun work in South Wales. Output of crude steel is about half that at Scunthorpe; nearly all the 5% of the national total credited to the East Midlands and scattered outlying works comes, in fact, from Corby.

The siliceous Northampton Sand ore has good welding qualities, suiting it well to the production of steel tubes. Planned extensions of the Corby works are intended to raise annual capacity of pig to

1,350,000 tons and that of crude steel to 1,550,000 tons by 1965, in addition to providing for the making of steel billets wherein Corby's low costs promise great advantages. Expansion at Corby has been, and will be, accompanied by closures elsewhere. Furnaces at Kettering and at the New Cransley works nearby have gone out of blast, while the number at Melton Mowbray has fallen from 5 to 3 (Table 52). Concentration is typical also of the Derby and Nottinghamshire coalfield, where iron is now smelted only at Renishaw, Sheepbridge, Staveley, and Stanton (Fig. 64). The combined output of pig from these works is expected to decline slightly by 1965, although still remaining above the combined total for Corby, Wellingborough, and Melton Mowbray. Present trends suggest that the output of blast furnaces on the Jurassic orefields in the East Midland region will overtake that from furnaces on the exposed coalfield by 1970, in spite of a coke/iron ratio of about unity which abolishes one of the early advantages of smelting on the orefields. Against the strong tendency of smelting to be progressively concentrated must be set the tendency of certain processes of manufacture to become dispersed; examples include the casting of steel alloys at Sutton-in-Ashfield and the milling of steel tubes at Desford in Leicestershire.

Reserves of ore in the Jurassic fields are considerable (Table 56), although increasing rates of extraction suggest that working out may be complete in some fifty years' time. Mining must increase, even though 100-feet thickness of overburden can be stripped economically by walking draglines, as opposed to the 50 feet considered near the limit as late as 1950. Ore has been mined since 1933 at Holwell, while a new mine was opened in 1956 in the Northampton Sand near Oakham. North of the Welland, some 44% of proved and probable reserves are thought accessible only to mining—a fact which suggests still further mechanisation, since the iron content is but 31% and falls to $27\frac{1}{2}\%$ after necessary limestone has been added (cf. Pl. 38).

As is well known, some of the smelting plants in Staffordshire and South Wales are located less with reference to greatest economy than to policies of providing employment in early-developed industrial districts. Quite apart from this, however, there is no sign of a lessening in the dispatch of ore to distant consumers. The mixed chemistry of the Jurassic ores sets technical problems in concentration, although sintering, which raises the iron content to 35% or 40%, is increasingly practised. Preparation—the mixing of ore to promote self-fluxing and to yield slag of required constitution—is simpler. Siliceous Northampton Sand ore is blended with the local calcareous ore at Scunthorpe, which in 1960 took more than a quarter of the output from the Northampton Sand field; the Middlesbrough district took another

9%. Little of the Leicestershire Marlstone ore leaves the region, although there is much traffic from Leicestershire to Derbyshire. Nearly half the Banbury ore used in 1960 went to South Wales, and something more than a third to Staffordshire. Something more than 5% by weight of the ore used within the region is imported.

Lead mining in Derbyshire employed fewer than 1,500 workers by 1841. The industry was suffering both from the impoverishment of ore with depth and from the violent fluctuations which typify the trade in base metals generally. Despite the introduction of pumping machinery and of miners from Cornwall, lead miners were moving from the ore fields at the turn of the century, and continued to migrate during the twentieth century to the textile districts of Lancashire and Cheshire, to the collieries of Staffordshire, and to the ironstone mines of south Yorkshire. Although the numbers of lead miners actually rose in the mid-nineteenth century to 2,333 in 1861, there were but 285 in 1901 ; in the second half of the century the only large-scale working was that at Millclose Mine, near Matlock. Nearly all other workings had been abandoned, commonly at the levels of the great soughs, where sinkings to greater depths would have been outrageously expensive.

Rising prices of lead promoted some re-openings in the early twentieth century, while the Snelston Mine, near Ashbourne, recommenced as a copper producer in 1909 after lying idle for thirty-six years. During the Korean War, in 1952, the Riber leadmine near Matlock renewed its operations, reaching an output of 100 tons of metal a year by 1958.

Fluorite was a waste mineral until the very end of the nineteenth century, but suddenly became valuable as a flux in steel making and in the smelting of base metals. Derbyshire provided 34,000 tons in 1905 ; half the output of 37,000 tons in 1910 came from old minedumps. After declining to 8,000 tons a year in the depressed 1930s, annual production rose to 52,000 tons in the Second World War ; Derbyshire shared in the nationally increased output between 1950 and 1960.

In 1841, when the iron trade was on the threshold of its ascent, Derbyshire employed only 79 workers in limestone quarries and burners. In 1861 there were 1,057 ; by 1901, when the quarrying district in the general vicinity of Buxton had been entered by locomotive railways, there were nearly 3,500. The metal and chemical industries, agriculture, and roadmaking all make heavy current demands on the working quarries, which are for the most part rail-served (Pl. 39).

Brick making and associated ceramic industries in the East Midlands reflect especially clearly the complex influences which affect production.

The clay industry of the Leicestershire coalfield produces a quarter of the national output of salt-glazed pipeware, relying especially on the Derby Fireclay with its 35% content of aluminium. Most clayworks lie in the western basin, brick making alone being concentrated in the east. Problems include those of short runs, wherein the industry resembles the production of fashion wear by the leatherworks of Leicester.

A series of brickworks operated by the National Coal Board constitute successors of the many former small plants on the exposed coalfield of Derby and Nottinghamshire, or represent a not uncommon ultimate stage of coal mining. Minute concerns scattered through the villages of the region have mostly ceased production. Production of standard types of brick in huge runs is highly concentrated in the Oxford-Clay belt, where the clay is well suited to the cheap semi-dry process of manufacture—a process, however, which demands large outlay of capital—and where the carbon content of the raw material reduces costs of firing. About a quarter of the national output of bricks is made here. P. R. Healey and E. M. Rawstron state that all the works, from those developed near Peterborough from 1890 onwards to the Stewarthy plant built in 1925, relied originally on rail transport. Coal still comes in by rail, but at least half the product is distributed by road.

Large-scale mineral working of the present day includes extraction of sand and gravel, mainly from floodplains, valley fills, and low river terraces, although outwash is extensively worked in places. Wet gravel-working is associated at the former ordnance factory, near Retford, with industrial location of one distinctive post-war kind. The site was chosen in 1949 for the fabrication of pre-cast concrete, not merely with reference to reserves of ballast, but chiefly because it offered buildings, water, electricity, and railway sidings ; clinker comes from power stations at Sheffield, Rotherham, and Doncaster. The leading products are large building blocks, pre-stressed beams, and tensioned units.

Other visually remarkable mining activity goes on at Shipton-on-Cherwell and at the scarp-foot in the general vicinity of Luton, where Great Oolite and Chalk respectively are quarried by cement works ; but perhaps the most engaging form of extraction belongs to the little oilfields of the Trent valley, where walking beams nod slowly at the surrounding farmland. Of 262 producing oil-wells in the country in 1960, 241 lay in the East Midlands—101 of them at Dukes Wood, 40 at Kelham Hills, 36 at Egmanton, and 31 at Eakring. Output is maintained at about 80,000 tons a year with the aid of new drilling and of water-injection.

The engineering industry of the East Midlands records a whole complex of trends in development. In part it succeeds directly from medieval ironwork, as has been described for the exposed coalfield. In Nottingham and Leicester it developed principally in association with the hosiery industry, although at Leicester particularly it has now achieved considerable independence from textile manufacture : production of machinery in Leicester, already vigorous before the Second World War, was greatly stimulated in the war years and is today a great employer. Cycle manufacture at Nottingham, also a prominent industry, represents that class of production for which no particular locating factor can be adduced, whereas the railway engineering of Derby and Wolverton are more readily explicable in terms of company policies. Bletchley benefits from present-day schemes of dispersal from London. Two factors in the location of aluminium milling at Banbury were a situation about midway between London and Birmingham, and labour available in a depressed agricultural area when the plant opened in 1931 ; the Banbury works obtains ingots from Canada and supplies rolled strip and extruded bars to London, Birmingham, and Coventry. Northampton, with its production of bearings, also illustrates the invasion of provincial towns by modern engineering.

The extent to which car manufacture developed from mechanical engineering, including the making of agricultural machinery, remains obscure. The automobile industry displays a typically twentieth-century structure in its reliance upon assembly of components from separate factories. Oxford, Bedford, and Luton are all heavily committed to this industry ; the first Morris car at the Cowley plant was produced in 1912, while the Cowley, Osberton, and Abingdon works now combine to produce about a quarter of the country's output of automobiles. Whereas Bedford and Luton seem to derive nothing but benefit from their industries, however, Oxford finds much discomfort in supplying retail services to workers at Cowley, and the university inclines to regard the swift rise of local industry with a certain distaste (Pl. 42).

CHAPTER II

REGIONAL POPULATION AND GROWTH OF TOWNS

WELL below a million in 1801, the population of the East Midland region exceeded $3\frac{1}{2}$ million by 1951 and approached 4 million by 1961. Results of parish-by-parish analysis of the censuses of 1801, 1851, 1901, and 1951 appear in Tables 57–61 and Figures 67–79 ; Figures 80 and 81 express some of the changes between the 1951 census and that of 1961, for which parish data are not available at the time of writing. For the sake of standardisation and of convenience in comparison the boundaries used in mapping are those of 1951 ; parish totals have been re-grouped accordingly for earlier censuses. But whereas no objections to re-grouping arise in distribution maps, density maps for the early censuses are liable to moderate the innermost densities of the greatest towns. Against this, however, the re-grouped data make possible a comparison between one census and another in terms of density : the series of maps of percentage density change by-pass, to a large extent, the effects of numerous minor alterations in parish boundaries.

Both the distribution map and the density map for 1801 (Figs. 67, 71) testify to a notably even spread of population at the beginning of the nineteenth century. Except for Oxford, the towns in the southern half of the region were all much of a size, and Oxford itself was small by present standards. Higher-than-average densities, but still rural densities, typified the exposed coalfields in the lower Soar valley in the northern half of the region, with an unusually thick scatter of small towns but with Leicester and Nottingham alone prominent by their size. Lower-than-average densities brought parts of the High Peak, Sherwood, and the Leicestershire Wolds into the sparse-rural class of density, but in this northern division, as in the southern, most of the total area belonged to the class of rural density proper.

Matters changed perceptibly by 1851 (Figs. 68, 72, 75). A general increase in numbers throughout the region during the fifty years almost obliterated, for the time being, the sparse-rural class of density. Distribution thickened on the exposed coalfields and in the middle Trent valley, where small towns and large villages earned separate representation on the distribution map, and where numbers of parishes passed into the transitional group of density. The greatest percentage increases occurred either here or along the eastern and southeastern borders of the region, where checks to migration were in force.

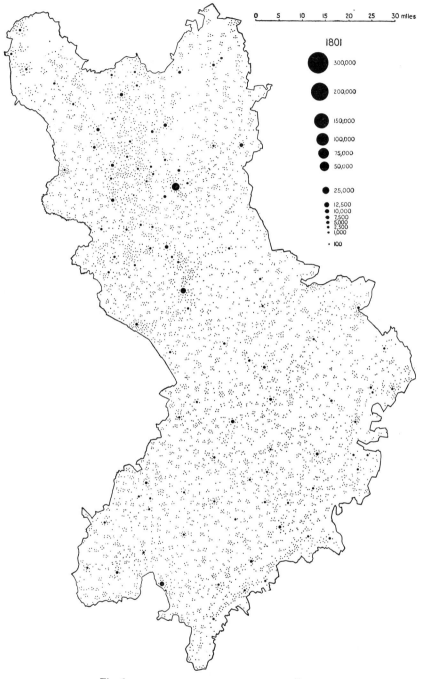

Fig. 67   DISTRIBUTION OF POPULATION, 1801.

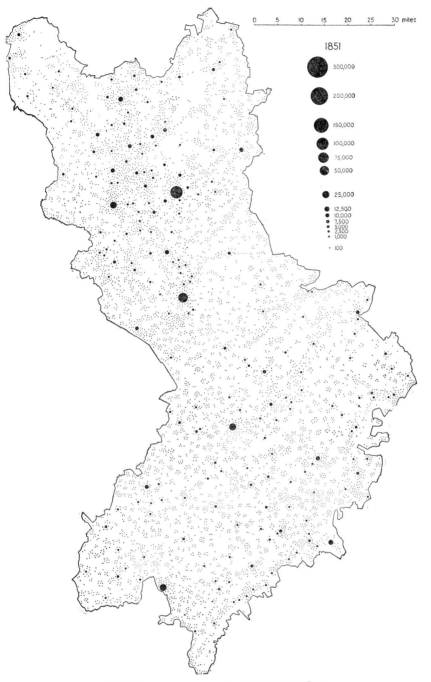

1851

300,000

200,000

150,000

100,000

75,000

50,000

25,000

12,500
10,000
7,500
5,000
2,500
1,000

• 100

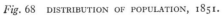

Fig. 68   DISTRIBUTION OF POPULATION, 1851.

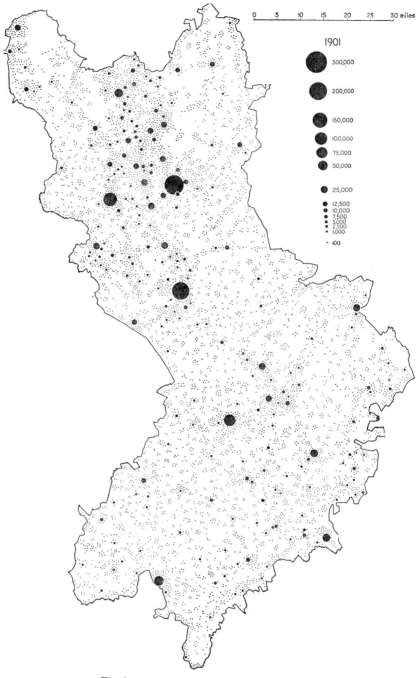

Fig. 69 DISTRIBUTION OF POPULATION, 1901.

190

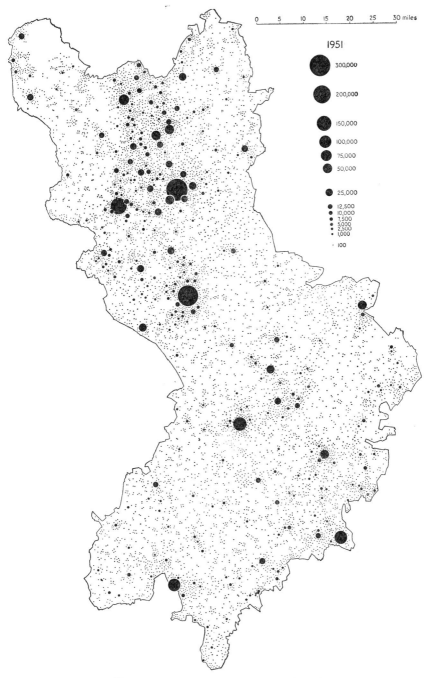

Fig. 70 DISTRIBUTION OF POPULATION, 1951.

191

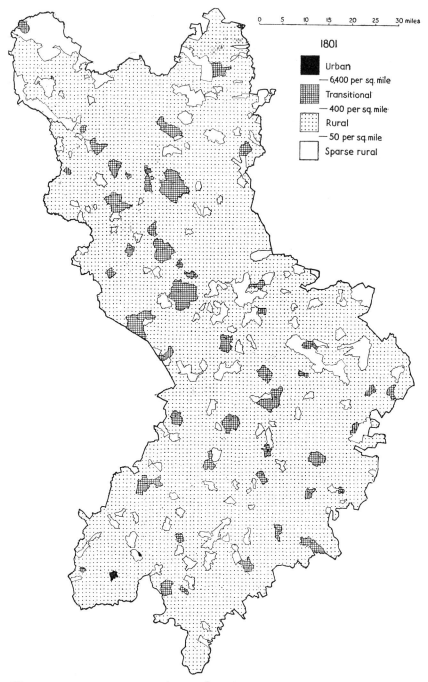

1801

■ Urban
— 6,400 per sq. mile
▦ Transitional
— 400 per sq. mile
▨ Rural
— 50 per sq. mile
□ Sparse rural

Fig. 71   POPULATION DENSITY, 1801 ; adjusted to the administrative boundaries of 1951.

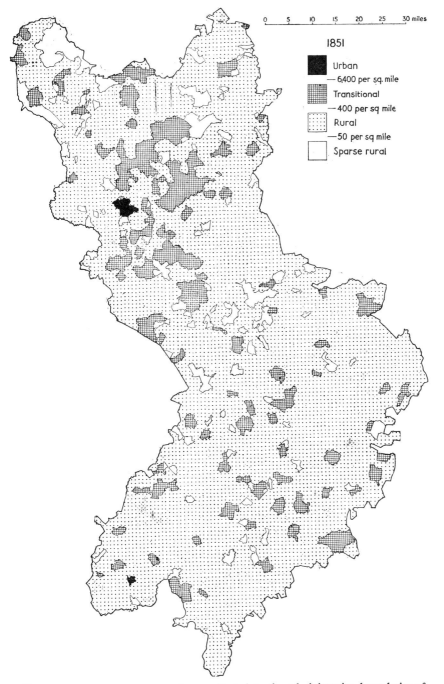

1851

■ Urban
— 6,400 per sq. mile
▦ Transitional
— 400 per sq mile
⠿ Rural
— 50 per sq mile
☐ Sparse rural

0   5   10   15   20   25   30 miles

Fig. 72 POPULATION DENSITY, 1851 ; adjusted to the administrative boundaries of 1951.

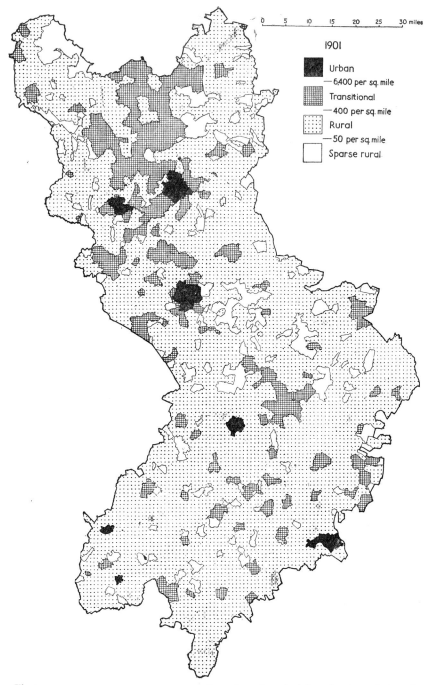

Fig. 73 POPULATION DENSITY, 1901 ; adjusted to the administrative boundaries of 1951.

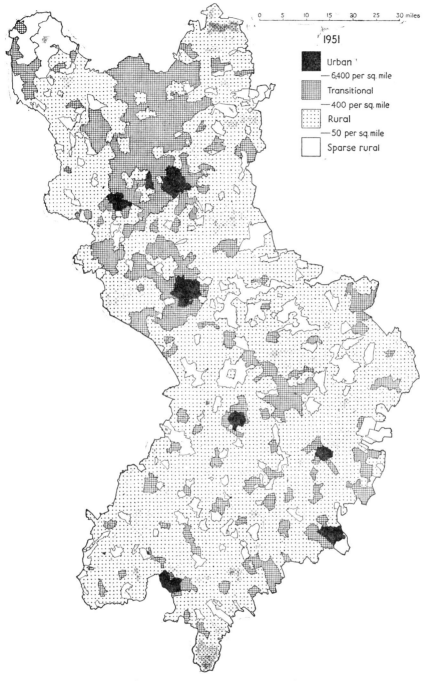

Fig. 74 POPULATION DENSITY, 1951.

195

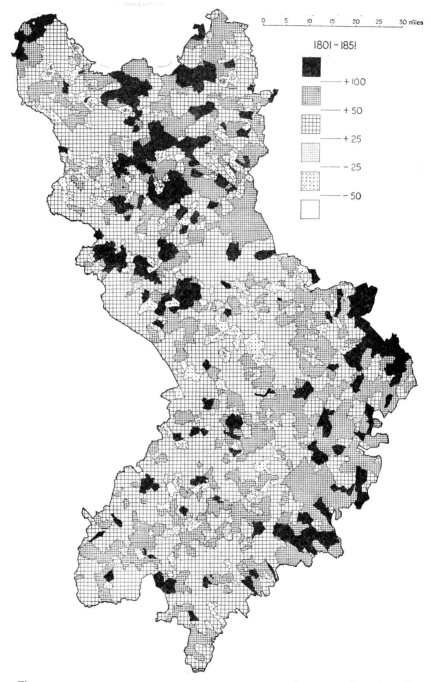

Fig. 75 PERCENTAGE CHANGE IN POPULATION DENSITY, 1801–51 ; adjusted to the administrative boundaries of 1951.

196

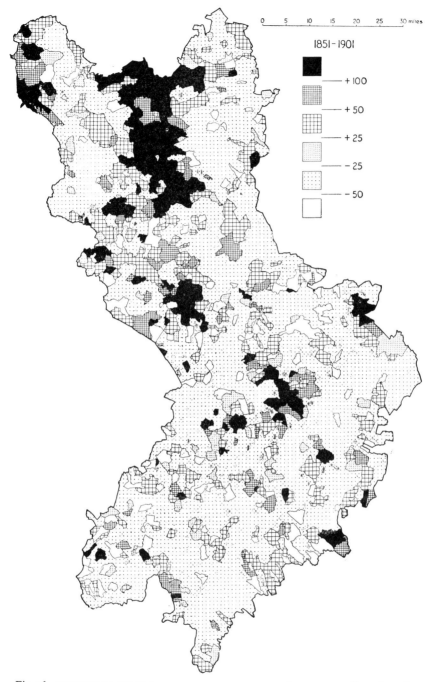

Fig. 76 PERCENTAGE CHANGE IN POPULATION DENSITY, 1851–1901 ; adjusted to the administrative boundaries of 1951.

197

14

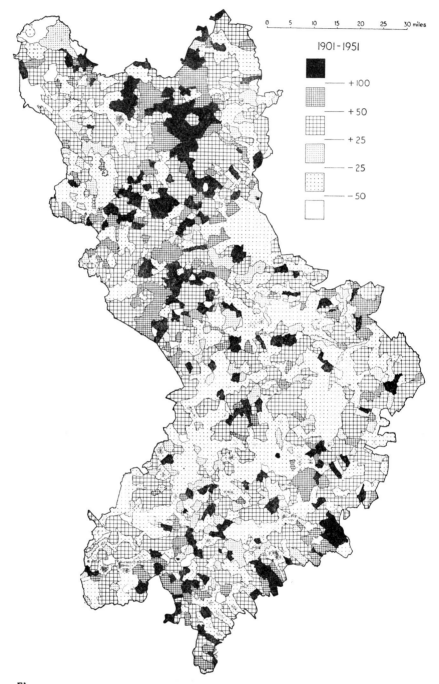

Fig. 77 PERCENTAGE CHANGE IN POPULATION DENSITY, 1901–51 ; adjusted to the administrative boundaries of 1951.

198

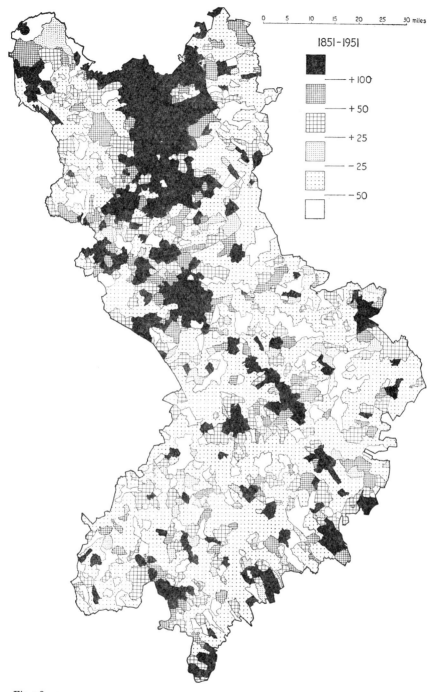

Fig. 78 PERCENTAGE CHANGE IN POPULATION DENSITY, 1851–1951 ; adjusted to the administrative boundaries of 1951.

199

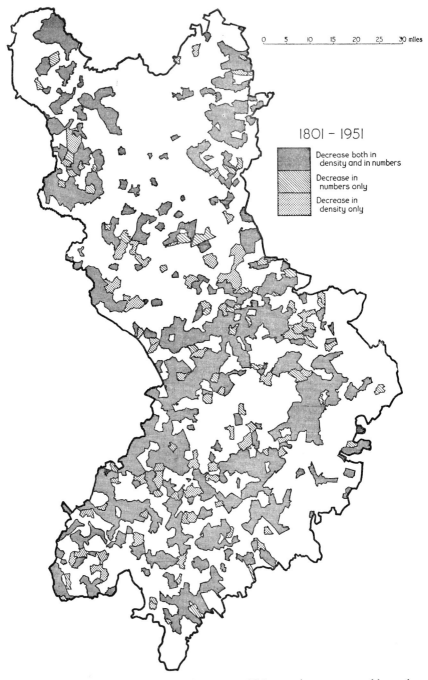

Fig. 79 DECREASE IN POPULATION, 1801–1951. This map is not comparable to the four maps immediately preceding.

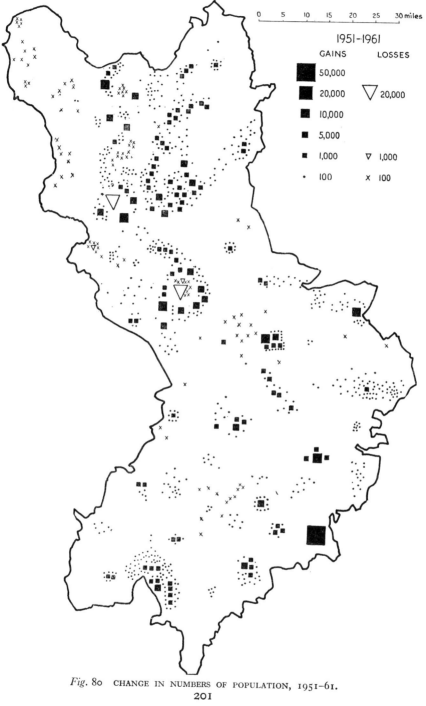

Fig. 80 CHANGE IN NUMBERS OF POPULATION, 1951–61.

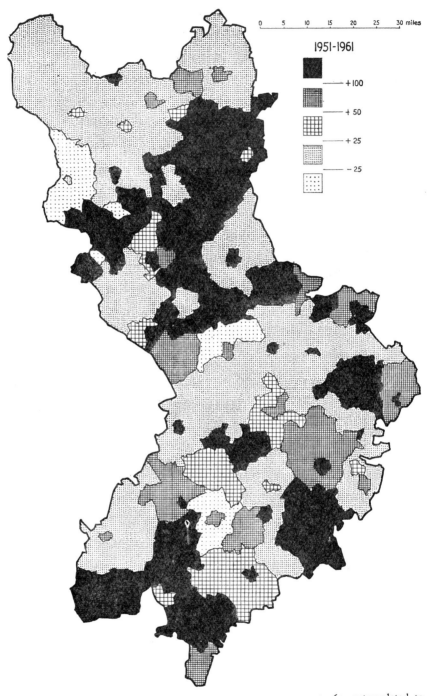

1951–1961

— + 100

— + 50

— + 25

— - 25

Fig. 81   PERCENTAGE CHANGE IN DENSITY OF POPULATION, 1951–61, extrapolated to
rates for a 50-year interval.

202

R. F. Peel and A. Constant provide examples of immobility of population in studies of local marriages in this area.

By 1901 the division between country and town was clear and deep; the great urban centres were by this time parasitic on the countryside rather than symbiotic with it. Oxford, Luton, Bedford, and Northampton had all far outrun possible rivals, but a whole new concentration of people had appeared in the Ise valley to the east of Northampton (Fig. 69). Combined stimuli operated here—railways, leather manufacture, quarrying, and smelting. Migration was considerable: C. D. Morley relates that Northampton's share of the county population rose from 6% to 29% in the 150 years 1801–1951, while that of the Ise valley rose almost as fast, from 6% to 26%. Northampton gained 10,000 migrants in 1801–41 when the rest of the county lost 24,000, and the Ise valley experienced its greatest decade of in-movement at the end of the nineteenth century. By 1901, also, the concentrations of people on the coalfields and in the Soar and middle Trent valleys were noticeably greater than in 1851. Large patches of transitional density amid rural expanses gave way to an irregular sprawl of transitional density with rural enclaves, and with urban blocks at Derby, Leicester, and Nottingham (Fig. 73). The map of percentage changes in density between 1851 and 1901 (Fig. 76) amplifies the story: rural parts mostly suffered a distinct loss of population during these fifty years, while the outstanding gains occurred in the Ise valley, in Leicester and its near neighbourhood, and on or near the Derby and Nottinghamshire coalfields. The total of population constituting the rural class of density was less in 1901 than in 1851, or indeed than in 1801 (Tables 57–9).

During the period 1901–51 the losing trend in rural southern parts of the region was patchily reversed (Fig. 77); much of the north continued to gain, although gains were far less regularly distributed than in the preceding fifty years, and concentrated on the concealed rather than on the exposed coalfield. With the largest towns slackening their pace of growth, lesser centres increased significantly in numbers, individual size, and aggregate population (Fig. 70). The coal-mining districts and the Soar valley became almost solidly transitional in class of density, while an additional urban patch appeared on the Erewash at Ilkeston (Fig. 74).

A. G. Powell, discussing population changes between 1931 and 1951 in Derbyshire, Nottinghamshire, and Leicestershire, records a number of migratory trends. Outward movement from Derby and Nottinghamshire towns heavily affected surrounding parishes, with continued industrial growth in the lower Erewash valley and with dormitories for Nottingham and Derby expanding; Beighton parish, in the north of the region, acquired dormitory housing for Sheffield. Wartime decentralisation, persisting for example in the metal and hosiery industries of Matlock and Belper, also required new dwellings, as did cement works between Hope and Bradwell. People displaced from Derwent and Hope Woodlands by the filling of Ladybower Reservoir were rehoused mainly in Bamford. Harworth, Firbeck, and Manton collieries on the hidden field all demanded additional miners, whereas much of the exposed coalfield lost by migration, especially where occupations were least varied. The pattern of migration in Nottinghamshire almost precisely reversed the pattern of natural increase, recalling eighteenth-century conditions in Nottingham town. In Leicestershire both Lutterworth and Market Harborough gained some industry during the war ; disused airfields at Bitteswell and Bruntingthorpe became sites of aero- and auto-engineering.

Figure 78 reflects the net demographic advantages of the coalfields and of the Leicester district in the century from 1851 to 1951, and re-emphasises the irregular distribution of gains and losses in the southern half of the region during the same interval. Figure 79 differs from the other maps of change : it relates solely to net losses between 1801 and 1951, indicating loss both in numbers and in density, and representing the surest losses by its heaviest tinting. Comparison of this Figure with Figure 34 reveals that the areas of population loss between 1801 and 1951 correspond very closely indeed with the areas where sites of depopulation lie most thickly scattered. For whatever reason, and in highly contrasted contexts, these portions of the East Midland region have proved chronically and severely vulnerable to loss of population.

The diagrams in Figure 82 show the grouping of change in parishes belonging to the rural and sparse rural classes of density, by fifty-year periods ; in effect they summarise the trends of population outside the region's towns. A few parishes in each interval recorded large percentage increases in association for instance with new mining, new quarrying, or with new industrialisation and peopling within the near reach of a large town. Such instances apart, the modal trend between 1801 and 1851 was an increase in numbers by about 25%. Few rural parishes lost population : natural increase far more than offset the still-slight townward drift. In 1851–1901 the trend was reversed to a modal loss of about 25%. Although in 1901–51 the rate of loss slackened, more rural parishes lost population than gained, with the peak rate of loss at 5%.

In the absence of data for single parishes, preliminary findings at the 1961 census provide the basis of two maps : Figure 80 locates gains and losses of population between 1951 and 1961, while Figure 81 shows percentage trends in the same period. Because the 1961 data for rural areas apply to districts, as opposed to parishes, both maps are somewhat generalised, although a very high fraction of numerical gains and losses is in fact accurately located. Trends of change, extrapolated to a fifty-year interval, make Figure 81 comparable to previous maps of the same kind.

Absolute decline in numbers between 1951 and 1961 occurred in the surroundings of Buckingham, Market Harborough, and Ashbourne,

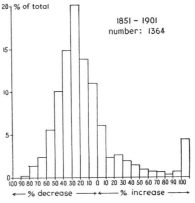

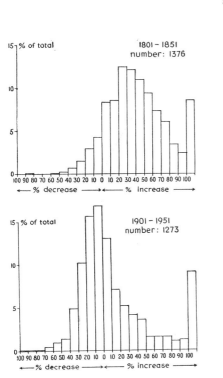

Fig. 82 PERCENTAGE CHANGE IN POPU-
LATIONS OF EAST MIDLAND PARISHES
which at the beginning of each 50-year
interval belonged to the class of rural
density.

and in the High Peak, but the greatest losses of all resulted from movement outward from the centres of Derby and Leicester. The greatest gains affected the environs of Oxford, the town and environs of Luton, the town of Corby, the Soar valley around Leicester, the middle Trent valley, and parts of the hidden coalfield. In considerable part, of course, the increases at Luton and near Oxford are associated in some direct or indirect way with automobile manufacture, while those at Corby have to do wholly with smelting and steel-making. Gaining urban-district status by 1939, with its 2,000 new workers' houses and some thousands of mainly Scottish immigrants, Corby officially became a New Town after the Second World War. The first corporation house of 1952 initiated a population increase which raised numbers to some 36,000 by 1961. Dormitory settlement and increasing industrialisation affect the middle Trent, where the artificial-fibre plant at Spondon is a great employer of textile workers, and where Beeston's electrical engineering and chemical production require a net daily in-movement.

In all probability the axial function of the Trent valley influences the location of increase near Derby and Nottingham, as does that of the Soar near Leicester. Nevertheless it can be argued that where lessening rates of increase, or actual decline of numbers affect the central parts of large towns, complementary rapid increases nearby principally affect the side towards London. The greatest and most rapid increases between 1951 and 1961, on the borders of Leicester and Northampton, occurred on the southern side. Because of the location of its motor works Oxford is perhaps not fairly relevant here, although it too seems to be promoting the greatest increases precisely where access to London is most free, that is, on the east and north.

Comparison of Figure 81 with Figure 79 shows a striking displacement away from the exposed coalfields of the most rapid tendency of increase. The totals involved do not however warrant an additional map of distribution. If the trends of 1951–61 continued for another forty years, they would still leave much of the exposed Derby and Nottinghamshire coalfield more thickly peopled than the hidden field, and would fail to produce dense peopling in parts of Sherwood, most of the Keuper belt, and along the lower Trent. They would ensure very dense distribution on the middle Trent and in much of the Soar valley, with a whole new group of distended settlements adjoining Leicester on its southern periphery. Corby's future population cannot reasonably be extrapolated from 1951–61; of other towns in the southern half of the region, Luton alone as yet promises to grow really large.

Figure 83, where occupational groups are illustrated by counties for the years 1851, 1901, and 1951, clearly illustrates changes in the social and economic structure of the region. The classifications by employment are not strictly compatible from one census to another; it is for this reason that workers in transport and communication, in commerce, and in clerical, administrative, financial, professional, and technical posts are not separately shown for 1851, and that commercial and clerical employment are not separated for 1901. However, the main increases in all these groups, both proportional and numerical, occurred between 1901 and 1951, so that the diagrams succeed in showing most of the principal trends.

All counties record a marked proportional decrease in agricultural employment during the century. In the three northern counties and in Northamptonshire this decrease occurred mainly before 1901 ; elsewhere the proportional trend is steadily downwards throughout the period. In Derbyshire and Nottinghamshire, losses to agriculture between 1851 and 1951 were roughly compensated by increases in mining and metal working, which did in fact absorb many countrymen. Metal working and engineering increased their proportional demands on labour, and still more their absolute demands (Table 62), in each fifty-year interval. Trends of employment in the making of textiles, garments, and leather vary from county to county, according to the varying success of particular industries. In 1851, when framework knitting prevailed, hosiery manufacture took half the workers in this group in Nottinghamshire, and more than three-quarters of those in Leicestershire, while straw plaiting required about half those in Bedfordshire, and lace making about two-thirds of those in Buckinghamshire. Deep involvement with leather working appears throughout the Northamptonshire record, whereas Leicestershire quite markedly reduced its proportion of workers in this industry between 1901 and 1951.

Except for Rutland the graphs all show an increase in employment in personal service between 1851 and 1901, while all counties experienced a decrease between 1901 and 1951. The changes correspond broadly to changes in society—to the rise of the nineteenth-century middle class (in the widest sense of the term), which demanded large numbers of domestic servants. To those drawn off the land, domestic service was the main alternative to manufacturing work in towns ; in some counties it took more people than did the main groups of industrial employment. Personal service at the present time would be far less noticeable in the records than it is, without the considerable substitution of domestic servants by workers in the restaurant trade.

The whole balance of distribution among the chief categories of employment changed between 1901 and 1951 with the great increase of commercial and clerical posts, and with the less marked increase in administration, finance, the professions, and technical work. The increases were partly proportional, corresponding to mechanisation in industry, but mainly absolute (Table 62), corresponding to the elaboration of business, a rise in the standard of living, and the great expansion of retail trading with which mechanisation and improved living standard were both linked. Aside from the special characteristics of single counties, the trends illustrated by Figure 83 are common to the whole nation, and, indeed, largely common to western society in general. They suggest that replacements of clerks by computers, and the rise of self-service retail shopping, may lead to a reduction in the relevant

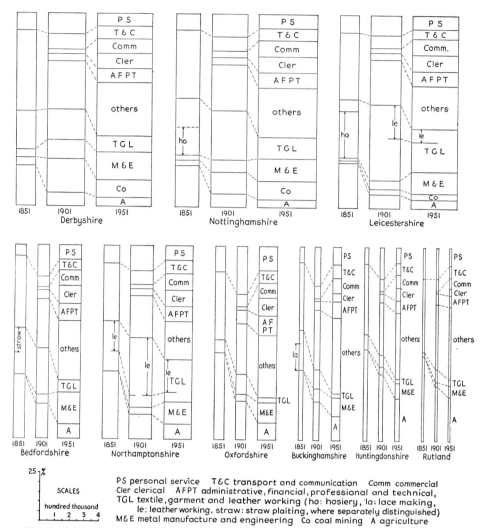

PS personal service   T&C transport and communication   Comm commercial
Cler clerical   AFPT administrative, financial, professional and technical,
TGL textile, garment and leather working (ho: hosiery, la: lace making,
le: leather working, straw: straw plaiting, where separately distinguished)
M&E metal manufacture and engineering   Co coal mining   A agriculture

1851 total gainfully occupied (all ages)   1901 occupied population (10 yrs. and over)   1951 occupied population

Fig. 83   EMPLOYMENT, BY COUNTIES, IN 1851, 1901, 1951. Width of bars proportional
to county totals. Census data for 1851 and 1901 re-grouped. Totals for Oxfordshire
have been reduced as follows : 1951 by subtraction of Henley M.B. and Henley R.D. ;
1851 and 1901 by reduction to 93·5 % of total for county. Totals for Buckinghamshire
have been reduced as follows : 1951 by subtraction of Slough M.B., Beaconsfield,
Chesham, Eton, High Wycombe, and Marlow U.D.s ; Amersham, Eton, and
Wycombe R.D.s ; 1851 and 1901 by arbitrary reduction based on comparisons with
adjacent counties.

208

categories of employment as great as that which has already affected personal service.

Although each of its towns is unique in some or other respect, the East Midland region contributes nothing special to the history of urban growth in nineteenth-century England. Three-quarters of the regional population in 1801 lived in parishes of rural or sparse-rural density; the transitional and urban classes accounted for that proportion by 1901 (Table 61). Because the data relate to administrative boundaries as existing in 1951, the main increase in the urban density class seems to have occurred in the twentieth century, and the greatest proportional rise in the transitional density class to lie between 1801 and 1851. When boundary changes are ignored, as by the generalised trends shown in Figure 84, the nineteenth century as a whole appears as the main period of growth for most towns. The onset of steep increase in numbers was usually sudden; an equally abrupt loss of impetus set in by 1900 (Table 63).

Even among the ten cases illustrated in Figure 84, however, variations on the theme of nineteenth-century growth appear. The populations of Nottingham and Leicester increased considerably during the eighteenth century. J. D. Chambers calculates that natural increase made no contribution to the 75% increase at Nottingham during the first half of the eighteenth century, when the town, like so many others, was a squalid killer, replacing with migrants its losses by disease. Leicester also received many immigrants during this period; Derby, Oxford, and Northampton seem likely to have benefited in similar fashion.

Oxford, Luton, and Bedford illustrate the effects of breaks in the trend of increase. In the mid-nineteenth century, almost precisely when an abrupt increase at Luton made the town more populous than the steadily growing Bedford, Oxford experienced a decade of near-stagnation. Bedford failed to maintain its previous rate of increase in the period 1905-40, falling in consequence well behind Luton, which up to the 1961 census showed no sign of slackening its growth; continuing to increase at the rate recorded by some other towns in the nineteenth century, Luton has surpassed Oxford and Northampton, and is on the point of surpassing Derby.

Buckingham, Huntingdon, and Oakham began the nineteenth century with modest totals of population and with modest rates of increase. If these rates had been maintained throughout the century, Buckingham and Huntingdon would each have contained some 8,000 inhabitants by 1900, and Oakham some 6,000. As it was, Huntingdon and Oakham became stagnant in the mid-century, and Buckingham entered ninety years of decline. Renewed increase in the mid-twentieth century leaves

209

all three far less populous than the seven other towns illustrated in Figure 84. Buckingham, early losing some of its functions to Aylesbury, is a special case, but Huntingdon and Oakham show that status of county headquarters is not enough to guarantee expansion (cf. Pl. 41).

To some extent the loss of resident population from the centres of Leicester and Derby reflects a making over of the innermost districts, but in part it also reflects saturation. Even at Nottingham the addition of population totals for Arnold, West Bridgford, Beeston and Staple-

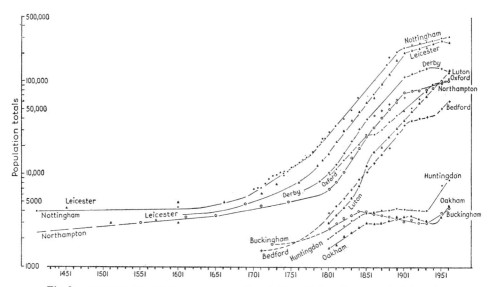

Fig. 84 GROWTH OF SELECTED TOWNS. Population totals relate to administrative boundaries existing in the years plotted. Trends are generalised, omitting short-term effects of boundary changes. Populations are on logarithmic scale. Totals prior to 1801 are from various sources, those from 1801 onwards from census returns except for mid-year estimates of 1939.

ford, and Carlton would not restore the nineteenth-century upward trend of numbers. Furthermore, although Nottingham is today continuous with these adjacent towns, they were physically separate during most or all of the nineteenth century, with populations of their own which Figure 84 does not record. The lessened rate of growth shown for Nottingham since about 1890 is therefore actual. Similarly, the addition of Wigston and Oadby to Leicester fails to offset the lessened rate of increase in the present century. Since Derby, Oxford, and Northampton all have plenty of room to expand, one must conclude that their apparent tendency to achieve stable totals of population is also real.

Nineteenth-century growth of towns involved lasting and profound changes in marketing and distribution. Much eighteenth-century trading took place on the 312 days of fairs held at 120 places. Numbers of days do not necessarily indicate the ranking of a particular place as a marketing centre for livestock and produce, for some fairs were notoriously decayed; but the 12 days at Market Bosworth, 11 at Chapel-en-le-Frith, 7 each at Ashbourne, Buckingham, and Higham Ferrers, belong to a period when these towns had far more significance in commerce than they have today. Wagon and cart services, radiating from most towns of any size, brought parts at least of the countryside within the urban fields of the time. By the mid-nineteenth century, just prior to the railway age, much of the region possessed carrier services which clearly delimited the areas of distribution from particular centres. P. R. Odell demonstrates in a detailed study of Leicestershire that the county town served a compact area some 10 to 15 miles across. Smaller but no less compact areas of distribution surrounded Ashby de la Zouch, Loughborough, Melton Mowbray, Market Harborough, Lutterworth, and Hinckley.

Nevertheless, the urban fields of a hundred or even of two hundred years ago foreshadowed the known complexities of today. Carrier services radiating from Banbury in 1769 demarcate a rough circle, with the town in the centre, whereas the area from which butchers visited the Banbury markets was distinctly eccentric. Although the length of carrier services had increased by 1850, not the whole of the surrounding district was necessarily in contact with commercial activity in general and with town life in particular.

Elaboration of the railway network facilitated and prompted considerable shifts in population, and contributed to the growing influence of nineteenth-century towns. At its maximum extent the net left scarcely any part of the region more than 5 miles from a passenger station, and no more than small scattered areas more than $2\frac{1}{2}$ miles distant. By 1961, however, whole blocks of country lay beyond $2\frac{1}{2}$ miles from the nearest active station—a probably significant limit, in view of the spacing of the stations themselves. As might be expected, closures affect either the most rural parts, with the least dense populations, or else the older-developed portions of the Derbyshire coalfield which record persistent emigration (Fig. 85).

The well-known types of map which represent limits of circulation of local newspapers, or which state accessibility in terms of local bus services, frequently imply false assumptions. Local newspapers demonstrably tend to establish limits of circulation in which lie towns with distinctive lives of their own. Because some towns fail to offer certain services, maximum accessibility by bus (Fig. 86) does not satisfactorily define urban fields. On the hypothesis that the provision of services

Fig. 85 THE RAILWAY NET. Where stations are shown without tracks, the stations are abandoned or demolished, and the tracks have been removed. Closures recorded up to early 1962.

Fig. 86 AREAS OF MAXIMUM ACCESSIBILITY BY BUS in the late 1940s. Boundaries mark limits of equal accessibility. After the *Planning Map.* See also the next two Figures.

15

varies in extent and complexity with size of town, breaks in the serial graph of population (Fig. 87) can be used to classify the towns of the East Midlands. Subjective criteria suggest that more than one of the breaks is in fact significant—that, where a jump occurs in the population series, or where the graph suddenly steepens, a sudden elaboration of urban character sets in. It is obviously desirable that the matter should be carefully investigated. Meanwhile, the view that towns of the lowest rank cannot properly be said to exercise the minimal range

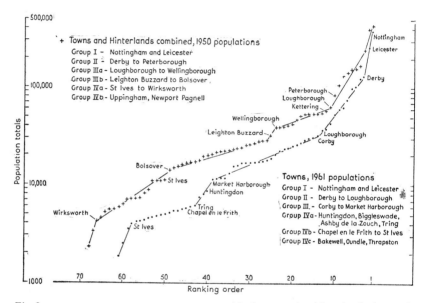

Fig. 87   RANKING OF EAST MIDLAND TOWNS, and of towns plus hinterlands, by totals of population.   See also the next Figure.

of urban functions implies some such pattern as that in Figure 88, where the smallest towns lie mainly on hinterland boundaries of their larger neighbours. This map probably represents urban catchments more accurately than does Figure 86.

But the redistribution of hinterlands in Figure 88 is still not enough. K. C. Edwards and F. A. Wells record overlapping hinterlands for the Chesterfield district, where towns ranging widely in size are close-set, and where the service areas of Clay Cross, Staveley, Eckington, and Killamarsh lie wholly or largely within the service area of Chesterfield itself. D. C. D. Pocock shows for Corby that, as one would expect, individual services relate to hinterlands of varying size, shape, and extent, even within the range of service provided by towns of modest size.

Mere listing of functions or structures is much inferior to complex

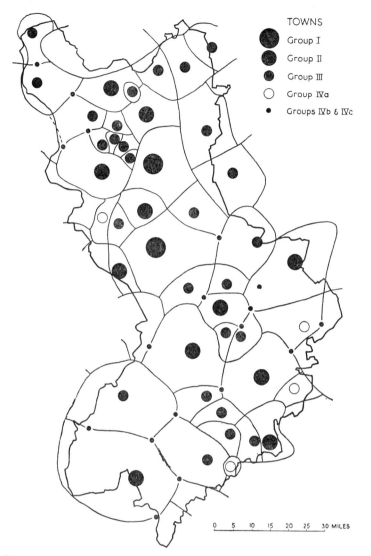

TOWNS

● Group I
● Group II
● Group III
○ Group IVa
• Groups IVb & IVc

0 5 10 15 20 25 30 MILES

Fig. 88 A POSSIBLE REGROUPING OF TOWN HINTERLANDS, based on the ranking, and the breaks in ranking, indicated by the preceding Figure.

analysis which relies on computers. C. A. Moser and W. Scott have made a signal beginning with the application of multivariate analysis to the sociology of British towns exceeding 50,000 in population. Nine examples come from the East Midland region. Oxford and Bedford belong to the class of mainly professional and administrative centres, despite the establishment of car-making at both, but presumably, at Oxford, by virtue of the town's special history of university centre.

Peterborough and Northampton represent mainly commercial centres with some industry, while Derby and Chesterfield (chiefly engineering) and Leicester and Nottingham (chiefly textiles) are mainly industrial. Corby must resemble Scunthorpe, which Moser and Scott include under the heading of recently developed metal-manufacturing towns, while Luton falls into the mixed group of generally suburban type. Although the results of analysis may appear to go little beyond the obvious, they depend in fact upon bulks of data, and upon rigorous treatment, which merely verbal statements cannot accomplish.

Frequent, although not universal, elements of the early towns of the East Midland region include castles, town walls, and river crossings. Northampton, superseding the Iron-Age Hunsbury, and Huntingdon, replacing the Roman Godmanchester, exemplify change of site from one side of the river to the other ; a similar shift may have taken place from an Iron-Age Grimsbury to the present Banbury. Until the eighteenth century and even later, some towns had grown very little beyond their old walls, if indeed the space within the walls was yet wholly built-up. The plan of Oxford taken by Ralph Agas in 1578 shows very low density of building within the town, and none but the slightest radial growth along outgoing roads. Oxford still had little by way of suburb in 1800 : the first main wave of expansion rose in the second half of the nineteenth century, when university Fellows were permitted to marry, and housing spread on the north. Between Speed's survey of 1610 and that by Noble and Butlin in 1746, Northampton did little to build over its walled enclosure, although it possessed an early suburban process on the south, on the London road. Bedford similarly acquired a small complementary settlement on the far side of the Ouse bridge, but late-eighteenth-century Derby extended westward and southward along overland roads rather than eastward across St Mary's Bridge over the Derwent.

Three highly contrasted towns will exemplify rates, extents, and modes of urban growth in the East Midlands : Buckingham, Chesterfield, and Nottingham. Buckingham and Nottingham stand at the extremes of the range of original county headquarters, the one long stagnant until very recent times, the other the largest town of the region. Chesterfield illustrates growth associated principally with mining and heavy industry.

Buckingham in the late eighteenth century, although tiny by any urban standards, nevertheless displayed the results of expansion (Fig. 89). The plan of its former castle walls appeared distinctly in the loop of road which, enclosing the castle mound, occupied the neck of a valley-meander on the Ouse ; the site powerfully resembles those of Shrewsbury and Durham. The marketplace lay immediately outside

Fig. 90 BUCKINGHAM IN 1950.

Fig. 89 BUCKINGHAM IN 1788.

¼ mile

¼ mile

0

0

217

the line of the walls on the northeast, where the broad incoming road was well built up and partly built over. The map for 1950 (Fig. 90) adds the railway, a suburb across the river on the London side, and the beginnings of residential expansion of the housing-estate kind, but most of the fabric of present-day Buckingham still occupies medieval building-sites.

Chesterfield has a long history as market town and a record of metallurgy going back to the Middle Ages. Its population reached 4,000 in the late eighteenth century, but rapid growth did not set in until the North Midland Railway came to open up the coalfield. By the mid-nineteenth century Chesterfield was still compact: its heavily built-up core, surrounding All Saints Church but by this time including also the marketplace, was fringed by less dense building which left room for welfare institutions and the new Town Hall. This fringing belt, called in Figure 91 the *inner integument*, was congested only to the south of the core.

Two axes of industry and transport limited and guided the spread of Chesterfield in the second half of the nineteenth century. The Rother valley, immediately below the old town on the east, contained mines, factories, railways, and the Chesterfield Canal which remained in use until the Norwood tunnel collapsed because of mining subsidence in 1907. The tributary Hipper valley, coming in from the west, made an angle in which the old Chesterfield occupied a site resembling that of Derby; the Hipper valley, like the Rother valley, was early industrialised, and experienced much industrial expansion during the nineteenth century. Residential building at Chesterfield between 1850 and 1914 produced brick-and-slate terraces of the standard nineteenth-century type; but whereas such building is elsewhere compactly concentrated (for instance, in parts of Northampton and Derby), only the northwest quadrant bordering the inner integument of Chesterfield acquired a continuous band. Partly, no doubt, because the ironworks of the time were by no means centrally located, scattered blocks of terrace arose elsewhere, and not invariably along radial roads. Hasland, beyond the railways on the southeast, is a case in point. These scattered blocks lie midway along a series, which at one end includes wholesale urban spread, while the single incongruous rows of terrace on the coalfield lie at the other.

That miscellaneous class grouped in Figure 91 as *other building* includes some nineteenth-century housing, originally suburban or rural, and in part expensive in its day. Also in this class come former outlying villages and hamlets which Chesterfield has absorbed, and patches of mixed building which include minor shopping centres and small factories. The specifically identified classes, however, account for most

218

of the total fabric of the town, while estate housing of the twentieth-century kind accounts for a large fraction of the total area. Its extent has increased since 1950, to which year Figure 91 applies. Because of earlier building it is impossible for the new estates to constitute a continuous belt, although they naturally tend to be concentrated round

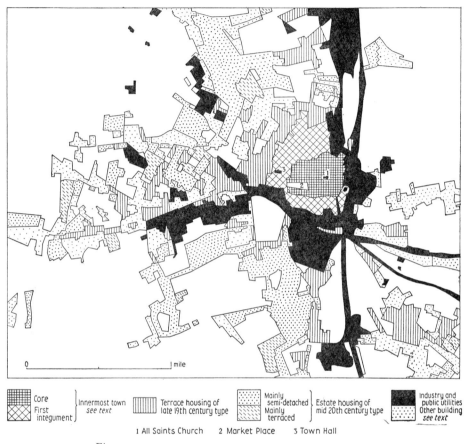

O _____| mile

Core	Innermost town	Terrace housing of	Mainly	Estate housing of	Industry and
First	see text	late 19th century type	semi-detached	mid 20th century type	public utilities
integument			Mainly		Other building
			terraced		see text

1 All Saints Church   2 Market Place   3 Town Hall

Fig. 91 ELEMENTS IN THE MORPHOLOGY OF CHESTERFIELD.

the edges of the formerly built-up parts. New estates have their clearest field south of the Hipper, where they are swiftly filling in the southern angle between Hipper and Rother, but difficult access appears to obstruct development beyond the Rother to the northeast.

Nottingham underwent very little physical expansion indeed between Norman times and the mid-nineteenth century. The Norman town included—or rather, perhaps, abutted on—the smaller and earlier-founded English town. Civil government of the two towns was long separate, although the greater size of the Norman site, and the Norman castle at the southwest, admitted no doubt about which was predominant. Both towns had walls along their west, north, and east sides, with bluffs descending to the floodplain of the Trent on the south (Fig. 92).

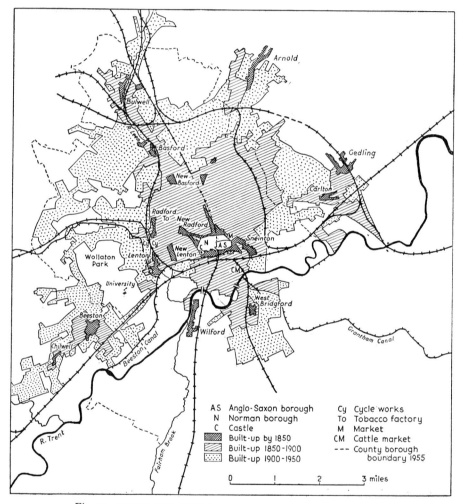

Fig. 92 EXTENT AND DIRECTION OF THE SPREAD OF NOTTINGHAM.

The map of 1744 by Badder and Peat shows extremely little suburban development outside the Norman enclosure, and buildings by no means congested on the inside. The broad marketplace of the time lay in the northwest of the former Norman town, entered by Bar Gate from the Derby road. Immigration and natural increase during the late eighteenth and the early nineteenth century combined, however, to promote a rapid increase in population, and house-lined alleys developed between the existing roads. The Plan of Nottingham in 1831 by Staveley and Wood shows the town still surrounded by Lammas Land, the Meadows, and the Duke of Newcastle's park. The legal bounds, enclosing 876 acres, may have remained unchanged since 1600 or earlier. Two enclosures in 1839 slightly enlarged the town to 928 acres and reduced the commons from 1,120 to 1,068 acres ; but their effect was negligible in comparison with the need of the time. In the early 1840s Nottingham had more than 50,000 inhabitants, of whom 40,000 lived in 8,000 back-to-back houses. To an almost complete lack of public sanitation corresponded an appalling death-rate.

Although most of the open land then surrounding Nottingham was privately owned, it functioned in practice mainly as public open space or as intensively worked garden land. The chief obstacle to extension of the town boundaries consisted in the commons, where the burgesses successfully opposed the issue of enclosure at the elections of 1787 and 1835. But in 1845 the commons were absorbed, more than doubling the area of the town. Development plans completed by 1865 allotted some 400 separate blocks to 400 owners ; as many separate developments occurred in consequence, guided by old patterns of field boundaries and footpaths. Under the Extension Act of 1877 the borough absorbed the industrialised suburbs of Basford, Bulwell, Sneinton, Radford, and Lenton (Fig. 92), increasing in area from 1,996 to 10,935 acres. Terrace-housing of the Victorian model extended swiftly across the two northern quadrants of the enlarged borough, while 17,000 corporation houses were built in the period 1919–39. Additional building since 1945 has also been concentrated mainly in the west and north, although some of the most recent developments affect land south of the Trent. Arnold and Carlton, with urban district status and physically contiguous with Nottingham, appear to set limits to growth towards the northeast. Hucknall on the north, also an urban district, is not yet wholly entangled with the outskirts of its large neighbour. West Bridgford, on the far bank of the Trent on the south, and again an urban district, has not prevented the absorption by Nottingham of the parish of Clifton on its western side.

I. G. Weekley gives the name *over-running* to the process by which Nottingham spread to, round, and past the centres of population which lay formerly on its periphery. Their physical ingestion was certainly rapid—far too rapid to allow anything but an haphazard development of retail and other service facilities. Only with the building of planned municipal housing estates during the twentieth century did planned service centres arise. Nevertheless, Nottingham achieved some kind of integration, if merely by sheer force of size. Taken as a whole, it possesses a distinctly centralised net of bus routes. Its industries tend to be distinctly grouped in certain localities. Thus, lace manufacture is strongly concentrated in the ancient borough; bleaching works, dyeworks, and leather factories string themselves along the valley of the Leen, while metal working and engineering occupy the lower Leen valley and the Trent valley immediately south of the main complex of railway premises. Hosiery factories and textile factories generally are somewhat more scattered, but even they concentrate principally in one of three types of locality : in or very close to the old borough, about a mile from the town centre along main roads to the north and northwest, or in a loose scatter in and east of Basford and New Basford. Gasworks, as one might expect, lie in the Leen valley and on the low ground near the Trent, which also contains Wilford power station. The sharp descent to the alluvial trough of the Trent is accurately defined by the lower reaches of the Nottingham Canal, which effectively divides the core of the town from railway premises, engineering works, and the cattle market.

Despite its rapid and late expansion, Nottingham strongly resembles many towns of slower growth in combining elements of radial and concentric designs. The most noticeable concentric portions of the road system occur on the west-northwest-north, where Western Boulevard lies beyond the Leen. Farther out still lies Beeston, which, as D. M. Smith maintains, constitutes an industrial satellite rather than a suburb of Nottingham. Whereas West Bridgford, Carlton, Arnold, and Hucknall experience net daily out-movements of workers, Beeston records a net daily in-movement. Although Beeston took advantage of the partial dispersal of lace manufacture from Nottingham, both in 1831–45 in the period of congestion prior to the enclosure of the commons, and again in the 1870s and 1880s when strengthening unions were forcing up wages in the borough, its main interest today is in electrical engineering and in the chemical trades. In its heavy involvement in a limited range of industry it contrasts strongly with present-day Nottingham, where the last hundred years have produced a marked change towards an even distribution of employment among the principal industries. In this, as in other ways, Nottingham displays metropolitan characteristics.

It is scarcely possible to discuss Nottingham without referring to the manufacture of tobacco, cycles, and pharmaceutical chemicals. The relevant firms, in something like their present modes of organisation, came into being in the 1870s and 1880s. To this extent they were typical products of the later nineteenth century. In all three instances, however, historical accident had much to do with the actual foundation.

Among them they have contributed signally to techniques of mass production, mass marketing, and branding. No particular factors of location seem to have affected them, although they accord well with the industrial scene of Nottingham in general, where emphasis falls on small products and light trades. Indeed, despite its sprawl of Victorian brick, Nottingham generally attains an effect of airy spaciousness which would greatly enhance many other towns of the East Midland region (Pls. 44, 45, 46).

CHAPTER 12

CONCLUSION

Two themes constantly recur in the foregoing text : the transitions of climate and agriculture from west to east across the region, and the agricultural, industrial, and demographic contrasts between north and south. If subdivision could be justified or appeared desirable, these changes and contrasts would suggest the first lines of promising investigation. Much, however, depends on context and on terms of reference. At the end of the penetration phase of the Saxon entry a frontier ran north–south across the region. In Defoe's time the chief regional contrast was that between southern England and England ' North by Trent ' (Defoe). There is justification today for placing Derbyshire, Nottinghamshire, and Leicester with part of its county in industrial North England, although in the absence of quantitative data on accents of speech and on social habits the demarcation of south from north must remain a matter of subjective judgment.

Subdivision into units of modest size, for such limited purposes as the definition of service areas of towns, or the discussion of spatial variation of dominant types of employment, poses no insoluble problems. Regional grouping and regional subdivision of the general-purpose type, however, are even less satisfactory in the East Midlands than in most other parts of England. E. W. Gilbert's examination of groupings at higher than county level show that, already in 1939, boundaries of statistical, administrative, private-purpose, and military groupings rarely coincided. But it does not necessarily follow that multi-purpose groupings are desirable, except within the ranges of functions discharged by a single type of authority. And it certainly does not follow that regional devolution and regional capitals, of the order of magnitude recommended by C. B. Fawcett, have any prospect of taking effect. Suggestions of this kind may perhaps be measured by Gilbert's proposal of Oxford as an alternative national capital. The wish to foster a new local regional patriotism is probably discordant with the strong contemporary trend towards loyalty to an organisation rather than to a place.

Furthermore, the whole scheme of provincial subdivision has been overtaken by the propensity of metropolitan concentrations to establish distant colonies. Parts of the south (notably, perhaps, Aylesbury and Luton) have been brought within the range of commuting to London, by means of suburban railways. Bedford also is connected to London by railway services classed technically as suburban, while London Transport's long-distance coaches cross the regional boundary at more than one point. But, in addition to these circumstances, which result from piecemeal extension, both London and Birmingham have colonial interests deep inside the East Midlands. Overspill schemes of the L.C.C. already influence Bletchley in particular, while Daventry is the proposed recipient of overspill from Birmingham; its eventual population is forecast at 25,000.

Long-term and long-distance planning of this order must involve urban growth in the still predominantly rural southern parts of the East Midland region. Checks to building are however incorporated in the relevant county plans by the designation of areas of great natural beauty, while most existing farmland is expected to remain in agricultural use. For instance, the county plan for Northamptonshire provides for no major increase of industrial capacity, except at Corby, and for no considerable urban extension elsewhere, except at Wellingborough. But the new factories already established at Bletchley, aligned not on the railway but on the main road, stand, with the London-to-Birmingham motorway, in earnest of future developments. The motorway immediately promoted rapid coach service to London from accessible parts of Northamptonshire, Bedfordshire, and Buckinghamshire (Pl. 48).

Planning in general, like zoning of land for categories of use, cannot prove effective unless numbers of population are forecast accurately. The persistent southward drift of people in England suggests that, unless movement is guided or controlled, forecasts will be falsified by actualities. Oxford, already adjoined by large industrial sites, and facing agonising choices of road-building, is attempting to encircle itself with a protective green belt. But here, as with London and Birmingham, the establishment of a green belt seems to involve out-movement to greater distances than would otherwise be required: the Oxford plan envisages an outspill of 10,000 people from the town proper. At the other end of the region, Chesterfield may need 8,000 new dwellings, for which the existing town offers little room; but parts of its northern environs already lie within, or not far beyond, commuting distance from Sheffield.

Plans for most large towns in the region involve the construction, or completion, of ring-roads and radial roads, with the general effect of providing one inner and at least one outer ring. Although they derive in part from roads just inside or just outside town walls, and in part from the already overrun by-passes of the 1930s, complete ring-roads are still not usual in the urban geography of the East Midlands. In their association with other planned improvements they exemplify a

Fig. 93   ADMINISTRATIVE HIERARCHY OF THE EAST MIDLAND REGION.
Boundary changes incorporated up to 1955.

signal characteristic of the Act of 1947, itself the culmination of lengthy trends—that is, the concept of wholesale, albeit phased, construction and renewal, as opposed for example to the piecemeal clearance of slums. The written statements of the several plans show that every town of any size contains numbers of houses which, in various states of disrepair, poor sanitation, or intolerable inconvenience, ought to go. But, with housing, services, shops, industries, and roads all considered in relation to one another, changes become possible which planning maps do not always reveal. Impartial records of project or accomplishment do not illustrate the visual effect of rebuilding to modern design and with modern materials, such as is notably changing parts of Bedford. Although the antique layout of many a town centre can scarcely now be recast, dramatic and welcome changes in fabric and appearance progress rapidly (Pl. 43).

In the administrative context, certain drastic changes are in prospect. The Local Government Commission reporting in 1961—dealing, incidentally, with Leicestershire, Rutland, Northamptonshire, the Soke of Peterborough, Bedfordshire, Huntingdonshire, Cambridgeshire, and the Isle of Ely under the heading *East Midlands*—proposed the merging of Rutland with Leicestershire and the merging of Huntingdonshire with the Soke of Peterborough (Fig. 93). Lesser adjustments recommended in county boundaries would transfer Linslade from Buckinghamshire to Bedfordshire, uniting it with Leighton Buzzard, would straighten the irregular junction of Huntingdonshire with Cambridgeshire, and would transfer Thorney and its surroundings from the Isle of Ely to the Soke of Peterborough–Huntingdonshire. Extensions would restore a roughly circular outline to an enlarged Northampton, while extensions of a more modest kind at Leicester would leave Wigston and Oadby on the southeast as separate urban districts, comparable in location and status to Arnold and Carlton on the bounds of Nottingham.

Naturally enough, proposals to merge or to down-grade arouse fierce local opposition, particularly in Rutland. For all its modest size, Buckingham is left as a municipal borough, perhaps out of respect for its high early status. On the principle that a population of 100,000 is a working minimum for a county borough, and in view of continuing expansion, Luton is suggested for elevation to county borough status and for considerable extension of boundaries. If the various proposals, or some substantial part of them, be carried into effect, some of the existing anomalies of administrative distributions will vanish. Not all will go, however. Not even a group of commissioners acting on the principle of size, and ready to suggest fundamental changes, can bring themselves to sweep away all traces of the arrangements of the distant past.

TABLES
REFERENCES

Table 1

Generalised stratigraphical succession of the Carboniferous Limestone in the Matlock, Eyam, and Castleton Districts (adapted from Shirley)

Edale Shales		Thickness in feet
Nunlow Limestone	grey to very dark grey, passing laterally into lighter, brachiopod-rich lenses (Reef Knolls)	0—160
Castleton Limestones	light-coloured limestone of Reef Knoll type. Thickness very variable, up to about	200
Strong unconformity		
Limestones	dark grey in lower part, passing up into lighter, fine-grained or calcite mudstones; chert common	280 approx.
Grey limestones	becoming lighter and more massive upward	0—180
Slight unconformity		
Limestones	generally light and fine-grained, occasional thickening into brachiopod-rich lenses on the north	
Limestones	grey to dark grey, partly dolomitised, seen to	30

Table 2

Principal grits, with approximate thicknesses, in the Millstone Grit Series on the east flank of the Derbyshire Dome (after Black)

Coal Measures	Thickness in feet
Rough Rock Grit	100
shales and variable thin grits	
Chatsworth Grit	up to 250
shales	
Upper Kinderscout Grit	80–300
shales	
Lower Kinderscout Grit	0–200
shales and variable thin grits	
Edale Shales	up to 700
Unconformity	
Carboniferous Limestone	

Table 3

Lithological subdivisions of the Permo-Trias of Nottinghamshire south of Worksop

Keuper Marl
Keuper Sandstone ⎱ Keuper facies
Keuper Basement Beds ⎰
Bunter Pebble Beds
Lower Bunter ⎱ Bunter facies
Apparent unconformity ⎰
Middle Marl
Lower Magnesian Limestone ⎱ Permian facies
Marl Slate ⎰
Breccia

Table 4

Charnian rocks of Charnwood Forest

Brand Series	3	Swithland Slates
	2	Conglomerate, grits, and quartzites
	1	Hanging Rock Conglomerates
Maplewell Series	4	Woodhouse and Bradgate Beds (tuffs, grits, hornstones)
	3	Slate-agglomerate
	2	Beacon Hill Beds (agglomerates, tuffs, hornstones)
	1	Felsitic Agglomerate
Blackbrook Series	1	Blackbrook Beds (grits, hornstones, tuffs)

Rocks of later but uncertain age

Basic dykes, some certainly post-Coal Measures

Monzonitic intrusions of Croft, Enderby, etc.; ? possibly related to Mountsorrel rocks, ? possibly post-Cambrian

Mountsorrel Granodiorite; ? possibly Caledonian

Syenites, possibly emplaced during the main Charnian folding

Table 5

Summary of the Jurassic succession in the East Midland region, with generalised thicknesses (feet) for selected areas (various sources)

	West Oxfordshire	North Oxfordshire	East Oxfordshire and Central Buckinghamshire	Northamptonshire Ironstone field, south part	Leicestershire—Rutland
Purbeck Beds: limestones and sandstones			up to 15		
Portland Beds: limestones and sandstones			0–100		
Kimmeridge Clay			100–180		
Corallian: limestones			0–90		
Oxford Clay			335–400		
Cornbrash: limestones	9–12		8–10	0–8	5–15
Great Oolite Series: mainly limestones, with clays	120–150		105–140	40–90	65–95
Inferior Oolite Series: limestones, sandstones	25–45	17	0–35	0–145	30–150
Upper Lias Clay	30–80	40	0–15	up to 185	80–200
Middle Lias: limestones, sandstones, silts	30–100	50	10–15	90	60–120
Lower Lias: clays, with argillaceous limestones in lower part	440	600	160–230	500	650–750
Rhaetic: limestones, shales	33			22	15–40

Table 6

Generalised succession in the south of the Northamptonshire Ironstone Field (adapted from Hollingworth and Taylor)

Oxford Clay and Kellaways Beds

		Thickness in feet	
Cornbrash	rubbly to massive limestone	0–8	
Great Oolite Clay		10–20	Great Oolite Series
Great Oolite Limestone		15–25	
Upper Estuarine Series	clays and limestones	15–25	
Lincolnshire Limestone		0–80	Inferior Oolite Series
Lower Estuarine Series	silts, sands, clays	0–25	
Northampton Sand	ferruginous sandstones (in part commercial ore), flaggy limestones	0–40	

Upper Lias

Table 7

Generalised succession of the Inferior and Great Oolite Series about the Evenlode (adapted from Arkell)

Cornbrash

		Thickness in feet	
Forest Marble	flaggy limestones, passing laterally to clays	10–40	
White Limestone		30–50	
Hampen Marly Beds	marls, with limestone bands	20–30	Great Oolite Series
Taynton Stone	flaggy limestone and freestone	15–25	
Stonesfield Slate	fissile limestone passing laterally into upper part of	0–6 (lenticular)	
Sharp's Hill Beds	clays with thin limestones, passing laterally at the base into top of	0–25	
Chipping Norton Limestone	variable limestone, massive in places	12–35	Inferior Oolite Series
Clypeus Grit	massive to rubbly limestone	25–35	

Upper Lias

Table 8

A tentative correlation of pleistocene sequences in the East Midland Region—combining the results of various authors

General and North European sequences	East Anglian sequence	Vale of Moreton and Stour valley	Evenlode valley and Oxford district	Cherwell valley	Nene valley	Trent valley
Post glacial		large channels filled: partial re-clearance at times	large channels filled: partial re-clearance at times	lake deposits of Cothill	large channels filled: partial re-clearance at times	large channels filled: partial re-clearance at times
		last complete clearance of large channels				
Last Glacial [Weichsel]		No. 1 Terrace	solifluxion	alluvial pebbly clay	? 10-ft. Terrace	? Floodplain Terr.
			cold gravels of Flood Plain Terr.	slight erosion		erosion
		No. 2 Terrace		soliffuxion		? Beeston Terrace
				erosion		
			soliffuxion			
Last Interglacial [Eem]		Nos. 3 and 4 Terraces	upper gravels of Summertown-Radley Terrace	Begbroke Stage flats Summertown-Radley Terrace gravel	? 25-ft. Terrace	? Lower Hilton Terrace
				erosion		

Stratigraphic correlation chart (rotated table):

Stage	No. 5 Terrace	base of Summertown-Radley Terrace	? 45-50-ft. Terrace	Upper Hilton Terrace
Penultimate Glacial [Saale] — Gipping Glaciation	Lake Harrison II, overspilling at 430 ft. — Chalky Boulder Clay Wolvercote Terr. outwash, Moreton Drift — Lake Harrison I, overspilling at 415 ft. — Paxford Gravel / erosion / Campden Tunnel drift	overspill from Lake Harrison II at 410 ft — outwash & solifluxion in Wolvercote Ter. — ? overspill; erosion — Wolvercote Channel: solifluxion silts, sands and peat, lower gravel	Chalky Boulder Clay and associated outwash	Chalky and Middle Pennine Boulder Clay and associated outwash
Hoxnian Interglacial	Northern Drift	river grading to Wolvercote Channel level — erosion — Hanborough Terrace, river grading to Hanborough Terr. — erosion	? mid-glacial gravels? — Northern Drift	
Penultimate Interglacial [Holstein]		Northern Drift — Freeland Terrace / Coombe Terrace / Northern Drift	Northern Drift	
Antepenultimate Glacial [Elster] — Lowestoft advance } Lowestoft Glaciation / Cromer advance		Northern Drift	Northern Drift — ? pre-glacial gravels	Skegby outwash — Early Pennine boulder-clay

235

Table 9

Mean monthly temperatures, mean monthly maxima and minima, and mean monthly ranges, for selected stations, °F; length of growing season in days (g.s.)

		Jan	Feb	Mar	Apr	May	June	July	Aug	Sept	Oct	Nov	Dec	Year	g.s.
Buxton 1,007 ft. (1926–50)	mean	36·1	36·2	39·2	43·3	48·7	54·2	57·7	56·9	53·0	46·9	40·9	37·4	45·9	202
	max.	40·2	40·6	45·1	49·7	56·2	61·6	64·4	63·5	59·1	52·0	45·2	41·2	51·6	
	min.	32·0	31·8	33·4	36·9	41·1	46·8	51·0	50·3	46·9	41·7	36·7	33·5	40·2	
	range	8·2	8·8	11·7	12·8	15·1	14·8	13·4	13·2	12·2	10·3	8·5	7·7	11·4	
Belper 203 ft. (1921–50)	mean	38·3	38·6	42·1	46·5	52·1	57·6	61·3	60·2	56·1	49·2	42·8	39·3	48·7	238
	max.	43·8	44·4	49·7	54·8	61·4	67·1	70·2	69·1	64·4	56·6	48·9	44·5	56·2	
	min.	32·7	32·8	34·6	38·1	42·9	48·1	52·4	51·4	47·8	41·8	36·7	34·2	41·1	
	range	11·1	11·6	15·1	16·7	18·5	19·0	17·8	17·7	16·7	14·8	12·2	10·3	15·1	
Mansfield 357 ft. (1926–50)	mean	38·0	38·4	42·0	46·3	51·9	57·5	61·3	60·2	56·3	49·4	42·6	38·7	48·6	232
	max.	42·7	43·6	48·8	53·9	60·5	66·2	69·7	68·4	63·5	55·5	47·5	43·5	55·3	
	min.	33·4	33·3	35·2	38·8	43·2	48·8	52·9	52·1	49·0	43·2	37·7	33·8	41·9	
	range	9·3	10·3	13·6	15·1	17·3	17·6	16·8	16·3	14·5	12·3	9·8	9·7	13·4	
Sutton Bonington 157 ft. (1924–50)	mean	38·4	38·9	42·2	46·7	52·0	57·6	61·6	60·5	56·3	49·6	43·0	39·4	48·9	241
	max.	43·7	44·7	49·8	54·9	61·1	67·0	70·5	69·4	64·5	56·8	48·7	44·4	56·3	
	min.	33·0	33·2	34·7	38·5	42·9	48·1	52·7	51·5	48·2	42·5	37·3	34·5	41·4	
	range	10·7	11·5	15·1	16·4	18·2	18·9	17·8	17·9	16·3	14·3	11·4	9·9	14·9	
Northampton 258 ft. (1933–57)	mean	38·7	39·3	43·1	48·8	54·2	60·0	63·3	63·0	58·0	50·8	44·6	40·6	50·4	255
	max.	—	—	—	—	—	—	—	—	—	—	—	—	—	
	min.	—	—	—	—	—	—	—	—	—	—	—	—	—	
	range	—	—	—	—	—	—	—	—	—	—	—	—	—	
Oxford 208 ft. (1921–50)	mean	39·5	40·1	43·6	48·0	53·5	59·1	62·8	62·1	57·9	50·8	44·1	40·3	50·1	259
	max.	44·6	45·7	51·1	56·0	62·3	68·1	71·4	70·6	65·9	57·9	49·7	45·1	57·4	
	min.	34·5	34·4	36·1	40·0	44·7	50·2	54·2	53·5	49·9	43·7	38·4	35·5	42·9	
	range	10·1	11·3	15·0	16·0	17·6	17·9	17·2	17·1	16·0	14·2	11·3	9·6	14·5	
Luton 381 ft. (1921–50)	mean	38·4	38·7	42·1	46·5	52·1	57·7	61·7	61·0	56·9	49·8	43·0	39·0	48·9	236
	max.	43·5	44·1	49·6	54·5	61·2	66·9	70·5	69·8	65·2	56·9	48·5	43·9	56·2	
	min.	33·2	33·3	34·6	38·4	43·0	48·5	52·8	52·2	48·7	42·8	37·5	34·2	41·6	
	range	10·3	10·8	15·0	16·1	18·2	18·4	17·7	17·6	16·5	14·1	11·0	9·7	14·6	
Cambridge 41 ft. (1921–50)	mean	38·9	39·5	42·9	47·5	53·1	58·8	62·6	61·8	57·6	50·4	43·5	39·5	49·7	245
	max.	44·3	45·7	51·1	56·2	62·7	68·4	72·1	71·3	66·5	58·2	49·5	44·5	57·6	
	min.	33·5	33·4	34·6	38·7	43·5	49·1	53·1	52·3	48·8	42·6	37·6	34·5	41·8	
	range	10·8	12·3	16·5	17·5	19·2	19·3	19·0	19·0	16·7	15·6	11·9	10·0	15·8	

Table 10
Apparent temperature/height gradients between selected pairs of stations

Pairs of stations (higher one first)	Difference in height, feet	Diff. in mean temp., °F			Mean temp. grad., °F/300 ft.		
		Annual	Jan	July	Annual	Jan	July
Buxton/Belper	804	2·8	2·2	2·6	1·05	0·9	1·3
Mansfield/Belper	154	0·1	0·3	0·0	0·2	0·6	0·0
Luton/Cambridge	340	0·8	0·5	0·9	0·7	0·4	0·8
Luton/Oxford	73	1·2	1·1	1·1	2·1	1·9	1·9

Table 11
Absolute maximum and absolute minimum temperatures at selected stations

	Jan	Feb	Mar	Apr	May	June	July	Aug	Sept	Oct	Nov	Dec
Absolute maxima												
Buxton 1896–1954	56	59	68	73	81	84	88	88	86	77	63	60
Belvoir Castle 1896–1913	57	62	69	75	84	86	90	95	92	79	63	59
Oxford 1881–1950	58	64	72	81	87	90	93	95	92	81	66	59
Absolute minima for same periods												
Buxton	−1	−11	1	8	19	30	31	33	28	18	12	4
Belvoir Castle	7	9	13	10	26	31	35	34	29	23	15	10
Oxford	6	3	12	23	29	34	41	38	31	23	16	8

Table 12
Mean monthly numbers of days with ground frost at selected stations

	Jan	Feb	Mar	Apr	May	June	July	Aug	Sept	Oct	Nov	Dec	Year
Sheffield (period not stated)	15	12	10	5	1	1	0	0	1	3	6	11	65
Belvoir Castle, 1908–1930	16	16	15	12	4	1	0	0	1	7	14	14	100
Oxford, 1881–1950	15	15	14	9	3	0	0	0	1	6	11	13	87

237

Table 13
Mean monthly hours of bright sunshine at selected stations

	Jan	Feb	Mar	Apr	May	June	July	Aug	Sept	Oct	Nov	Dec	Year
Buxton 1921–1950	22	42	89	120	161	176	154	145	111	76	36	14	1146
Belvoir Castle 1881–1915	54	74	111	150	203	197	193	186	145	104	67	45	1529
Oxford 1881–1950	52	69	114	151	191	196	186	176	138	100	61	46	1480

Table 14
Mean monthly number of rain-days at selected stations

	Jan	Feb	Mar	Apr	May	June	July	Aug	Sept	Oct	Nov	Dec	Year
Buxton 1881–1918	19	18	19	16	16	14	16	19	15	19	19	21	211
Belvoir Castle 1881–1915	19	16	18	16	15	12	15	17	15	20	22	20	205
Oxford (period not stated)	17	14	14	14	13	12	14	13	13	16	16	18	174

Table 15
Mean monthly number of days with lying snow at 9 a.m. at selected stations

	Jan	Feb	Mar	Apr	May	June	July	Aug	Sept	Oct	Nov	Dec	Year
Buxton (period not stated)	8	8	8	3	1	0	0	0	0	1	3	6	38
Belvoir Castle 1913–1930	2·5	1·6	1·4	0·4	0	0	0	0	0	0	0·3	0·9	7·1
Oxford (period not stated)	4	4	4	0·9	0·1	0	0	0	0	0·1	1	3	17

Table 16
Mean monthly number of days with thunder at selected stations

	Jan	Feb	Mar	Apr	May	June	July	Aug	Sept	Oct	Nov	Dec	Year
Buxton (period not stated)	0·2	0·3	0·2	0·9	2	2	2	2	1	0·3	0·2	0·2	11·5
Belvoir Castle 1896–1930	0·1	0·3	0·7	1·4	3·2	3·9	4·0	3·9	1·3	0·8	0·2	1·0	19·9
Oxford (period not stated)	0·1	0·1	0·3	0·8	2	2	2	2	0·9	0·4	0·0	0·1	11·0

Table 17

Stations supplying records of precipitation which have been standardised for use in constructing dispersion diagrams and graphs of monthly means. Column A: Standardised yearly total in inches; Column B: percentage of standardised annual total falling in April-September inclusive. The stations are numbered to correspond with Figure 19.

Name of station	Height ft. O.D.	Grid ref.	Period for which standardised	A	B
Pennine Division					
1 Buxton (Portobello Bar)	924	SK032712	25 yrs, 1933–57	52·76	46·91
2 Howden Dam	845	SK168924	25 yrs, 1932–56	49·25	42·30
3 Hope (Cement Works)	580	SK168822	25 yrs, 1932–56	40·24	41·15
4 Lower Burbage	924	SK259804	25 yrs, 1932–56	37·36	43·79
5 Clay Cross (Press Reservoirs)	810	SK355658	25 yrs, 1932–56	31·42	46·05
6 Matlock (Wolds Reservoir)	ca. 670	SK310610	25 yrs, 1934–58	31·00	47·00
Central Division					
7 Mansfield (Carr Bank)	357	SK541601	25 yrs, 1932–56	27·66	47·15
8 Rodsley Pumping Station	415	SK197413	25 yrs, 1932–56	31·31	46·89
9 Stanton-by-bridge Waterworks	144	SK375272	26 yrs, 1933–58	26·12	47·78
10 Sneinton Pumping Station, Nottingham	83	SK595393	25 yrs, 1932–56	24·34	50·58
11 Nanpantan Reservoir	269	SK508172	25 yrs, 1932–56	27·96	47·47
12 White Lodge, Melton Mowbray	237	SK756187	25 yrs, 1932–56	25·83	49·33
13 Uppingham [1]	534	SP 865999	25 yrs, 1915–39	26·90	50·59
Southern Division					
14 Northampton (General Hospital)	258	SP754606	25 yrs. 1933–57	25·48	49·45
15 Wellingborough (Swanspool)	187	SP890685	25 yrs. 1932–56	24·97	48·94
16 St Ives [1]	25	TL313713	25 yrs. 1932–56	22·72	51·50
17 Sandy [1]	152	TL164492	25 yrs. 1932–56	23·34	50·81
18 Oxford (Radcliffe) [1]	208	SP411036	25 yrs. 1932–56	25·50	48·16

[1] Records for four stations are defective in *British Rainfall*, and published records for nearby stations have been used to make up the 25-year series, as follows—Uppingham: records for 1915–18 defective, records from Stamford used; St Ives: records for 1943–5 defective, records from Whittlesea Mere used; Sandy: records for 1932–5 defective, records from Shefford used; Oxford: records for 1932–5 defective, records for Wootton used.

Table 18

Selected monthly totals of precipitation at Buxton and Nottingham; extreme high and low totals, and crude means, for calendar months; standardised means and most probable totals for 30-day months in a 25-year period; standardised (25-year) limits for dispersion diagrams, 30-day months

		Jan	Feb	Mar	Apr	May	June	July	Aug	Sept	Oct	Nov	Dec
Buxton (Portobello Bar) 1933–57	Extreme high totals (calendar months)	12·32	9·10	8·17	5·17	5·34	9·14	10·99	12·52	12·70	11·11	12·65	8·35
	Top of upper quartile	9·15	8·65	6·40	5·82	5·52	7·28	10·35	10·13	10·80	11·00	11·73	9·10
	Top of interquartile band	5·78	4·88	3·89	3·78	3·48	4·58	6·32	5·55	6·13	6·41	7·10	5·94
	Mean	4·84	3·91	3·22	3·21	2·91	3·84	5·18	4·41	4·78	5·14	5·52	5·01
	Median	4·55	3·50	3·05	2·97	2·71	3·57	4·76	3·97	4·33	4·67	5·30	4·70
	Most probable total	4·30	3·36	2·86	2·89	2·65	3·50	4·57	3·79	4·20	4·50	4·68	4·52
	Base of interquartile band	3·44	2·36	2·18	2·35	2·08	2·77	3·55	2·56	2·90	3·26	3·15	3·73
	Base of lower quartile	1·99	0·74	1·08	1·45	1·16	1·60	1·74	0·65	0·80	1·21	0·60	2·32
	Extreme low totals (calendar months)	1·46	0·38	0·88	0·60	0·59	0·82	1·80	0·71	0·77	1·22	0·80	0·56
	Crude means (calendar months)	4·82	3·75	3·26	3·05	2·91	3·96	5·24	4·52	4·68	5·28	5·48	5·00
Snenton Pumping Station, Nottingham 1932–56	Extreme high totals (calendar months)	4·25	4·19	4·47	2·82	5·99	3·60	5·45	5·62	5·26	4·60	5·64	3·99
	Top of upper quartile	4·50	4·28	3·70	3·30	4·28	4·45	5·28	5·66	4·20	4·58	5·62	3·76
	Top of interquartile band	2·63	2·33	2·03	2·10	2·47	2·43	2·97	3·10	2·30	2·66	3·18	2·18
	Mean	2·13	1·79	1·57	1·75	1·95	1·89	2·34	2·35	1·80	2·16	2·50	1·73
	Median	1·94	1·57	1·37	1·64	1·76	1·65	2·11	2·13	1·60	1·94	2·24	1·56
	Base of interquartile band	1·35	0·96	0·87	1·25	1·21	1·02	1·36	1·31	1·00	1·36	1·48	1·07
	Base of lower quartile	0·55	0·11	0·15	0·70	0·41	0·15	0·36	0·19	0·20	0·53	0·40	0·39
	Extreme low totals (calendar months)	0·81	0·33	0·16	0·08	0·36	0·47	0·32	0·16	0·37	0·28	0·19	0·19
	Crude means (calendar months)	2·13	1·66	1·53	1·62	2·05	1·98	2·30	2·37	1·77	2·16	2·40	1·74

Table 19

Standardised monthly mean totals of precipitation, in inches, reduced to 30-day months, for selected stations

	Jan	Feb	Mar	Apr	May	June	July	Aug	Sept	Oct	Nov	Dec
Buxton (Portobello Bar)	4·84	3·91	3·22	3·21	2·91	3·84	5·18	4·41	4·78	5·14	5·52	5·01
Hope	4·23	3·70	2·50	2·54	2·52	2·41	3·16	2·72	2·94	4·03	4·71	4·24
Matlock	2·80	2·45	1·89	1·87	2·20	2·38	2·56	2·73	2·55	2·71	3·53	2·84
Rodsley	3·01	2·32	1·86	2·12	1·97	2·33	2·67	2·71	2·62	2·87	3·45	2·89
Sneinton	2·13	1·79	1·57	1·75	1·95	1·89	2·34	2·35	1·80	2·16	2·50	1·73
Melton Mowbray	2·27	2·04	1·75	1·80	1·93	2·02	2·45	2·36	1·96	2·32	2·60	1·93
Northampton	2·14	1·86	1·64	1·69	2·03	2·03	2·18	2·25	2·20	2·45	2·57	2·05
Oxford	2·32	1·78	1·68	1·79	2·03	1·91	1·87	2·18	2·30	2·41	2·77	2·07
Sandy	2·05	1·60	1·52	1·55	2·13	1·92	2·12	2·09	1·84	2·13	2·44	1·59
St Ives	1·93	1·59	1·59	1·60	2·02	1·83	2·04	2·27	1·72	1·90	2·28	1·59

Table 20

Means of precipitation and runoff for selected catchments, in inches (30-day months). Extreme values of runoff (calendar months) during the periods stated

		Jan	Feb	Mar	Apr	May	June	July	Aug	Sept	Oct	Nov	Dec	Cal. year
Derwent at Yorkshire Bridge (48·9 sq. miles) 1937-8 to 1953-4	rain	5·98	5·27	3·53	3·31	3·21	3·29	4·33	4·34	4·19	4·59	6·41	4·94	54·00
	runoff	5·01	4·61	3·36	2·50	1·64	1·64	1·91	2·05	2·23	3·00	4·92	4·24	37·60
	highest runoff	11·71	9·21	9·86	4·48	2·61	2·80	3·91	6·30	4·24	6·75	8·97	8·35	44·67
	lowest runoff	0·86	0·91	1·17	1·06	0·92	0·43	0·80	0·44	0·36	0·45	1·55	1·91	23·25
Nene (Brampton Branch) (89·9 sq. miles) 1940-1 to 1956-7	rain	2·07	1·83	1·79	1·49	2·23	1·95	1·98	2·65	2·29	2·31	2·93	1·90	25·41
	runoff	1·12	1·27	1·04	0·62	0·38	0·22	0·14	0·16	0·18	0·18	0·87	0·80	7·07
	highest runoff	2·94	2·55	3·98	1·78	1·04	0·67	0·26	0·40	0·45	0·37	2·58	1·92	15·63
	lowest runoff	0·31	0·23	0·17	0·22	0·13	0·07	0·07	0·06	0·07	0·10	0·11	0·15	2·98
Nene at Orton (631 sq. miles) 1940-1 to 1956-7	rain	2·07	1·81	1·73	1·39	2·18	1·95	1·93	2·55	2·14	2·14	2·75	1·79	24·81
	runoff	0·96	1·20	1·01	0·54	0·32	0·20	0·11	0·15	0·13	0·15	0·66	0·72	6·24
	highest runoff	2·01	2·06	5·14	1·68	0·84	0·51	0·19	0·53	0·36	0·28	2·33	2·76	13·84
	lowest runoff	0·20	0·17	0·18	0·16	0·10	0·03	0·04	0·03	0·04	0·07	0·07	0·10	1·24

Table 22

Calculated values of potential evapotranspiration at Buxton (1,007 ft.) (long-term average) and Northampton (1940-57); in inches, for 30-day months

		Jan	Feb	Mar	Apr	May	June	July	Aug	Sept	Oct	Nov	Dec	Cal. year
Buxton	mean	0·34	0·42	0·79	1·49	2·53	3·45	3·82	3·40	2·53	1·51	0·78	0·43	21·80
Northampton	mean	0·42	0·51	1·13	1·98	3·09	4·01	4·55	4·06	2·87	1·76	0·95	0·61	26·13
	highest	0·81	0·96	1·73	2·35	3·45	4·80	5·02	4·90	3·25	2·20	1·20	0·96	27·83
	lowest	0·00	0·00	0·64	1·50	2·52	3·30	4·10	3·40	2·30	1·60	0·75	0·14	25·20

Table 21 on p. 242

241

Table 21

Mean annual values of precipitation, runoff, water loss, and apparent soil-moisture depletion/recharge for selected catchments

Basin	Recording station	Catchment area sq. miles	Period	Mean annual values, in inches				
				Rainfall	Runoff	Recorded water loss	Calculated water loss	Apparent soil-moisture depletion/recharge
Derwent	Yorkshire Bridge	48·9	17 years 1940–1 to 1956–7 (water years)	54·47	38·51	15·96	—	—
Nene	Orton	631·0	as above	24·81	6·24	18·57	—	—
Nene (Harpers Brook)	Old Mill Bridge	26·9	17 years 1940–56	24·40	6·70	17·70	16·55	1·15
Nene (Kislingbury Branch)	Upton	86·1	as above	25·70	7·13	18·57	16·55	1·92
	Dodford	41·3	11 years 1946–56	26·52	6·60	19·92	17·25	2·67
Nene (Brampton Branch)	St Andrew's Mill	89·9	as above	26·13	7·25	18·88	16·97	1·91
			17 years 1940–56	25·56	7·26	18·30	16·59	1·71

Note. The calculated water loss has been obtained by summing monthly values of precipitation or evapotranspiration, whichever was the greater for any month; the apparent value of soil-moisture depletion/recharge is the difference between recorded and calculated water losses.

Table 23

Soils developed on solid formations and on Clay-with-Flints in the southwest of the region (adapted from Clarke)

Parent Material	Profile drainage	Soil	Series name: Type	Phases
Clay-with-Flints	free	brownearth of high base status	Winchester Medium Loam	shallow
	imperfect	gleyed brownearth	Christmas Common Heavy Loam	deep
Upper Chalk	excessive	Chalk rendzina	Icknield Light Loam	shallow
Lower Chalk	free	Chalk rendzina	Wantage Medium Loam	shallow
Upper Greensand	free	brownearth of high base status	Ardington Sandy Medium Loam	shallow, deep
Oxford Clay, Kimmeridge Clay	imperfect	brownearth of high base status	Gosford Heavy Loam (Oxford Clay); Denchworth Heavy Clay Loam (Kimmeridge Clay)	shallow, deep
	impeded	gleyed brownearth, gleyed meadow soil		
Calcareous Grit Corallian Limestone	excessive	brownearth (sands)	Frilford Loamy Coarse Sand	deep
	free	heavy rendzinas	Marcham Coarse Sandy Loam	eroded, shallow
Cornbrash	free	red and brown rendzinas	Blenheim Light Loam, Blenheim Medium Loam	eroded, shallow, deep
Forest Marble, Great Oolite limestone	free	red, brown, and black rendzinas	Sherborne Light Loam	eroded
			Sherborne Medium Loam	shallow
	imperfect		Sourbrash Heavy Loam	deep
Inferior sand Oolite	excessive	podsol; podsol as arable	Tadmarton Light Sand	deep
limestone	excessive	red and brown rendzinas	Sherborne Light Loam	eroded
			Sherborne Medium Loam	shallow
Upper Lias Clay	free	brownearth of high base status	Hornton Red Clay	deep
Middle Lias Marlstone	free	brownearth of high base status	Banbury Red Loams	eroded, shallow, deep
Lower Lias Clay	free	brownearth of high base status	Barford Loam	deep
	impeded	gleyed meadow soil	Barford Clay	shallow

243

Table 24

Soils of a sample area of scarp and scarp-foot around Ivinghoe

Parent material	Site characteristics	Typical profile	Name
Clay-with-Flints overlying Chalk at 15 to 72 ins.	outlying spurs and valley sides with moderate drainage	flinty, acid clay loam overlying yellow-red plastic clay with large flints	Winchester Series
Upper and Middle Chalk, white Lower Chalk	rolling land with rapid internal drainage	very dark greyish brown to pale brown chalky loam overlying disintegrating Chalk	Icknield Series
	scarps and valley sides, often exceeding 12° of slope		Icknield Steepland Complex
grey Chalk or Chalk Marl (Lower Chalk)	undulating, gently rolling, well-drained to moderately well-drained	grey calcareous silty clay loam to silty clay with olive-grey subsoil, passing into disintegrating marly Chalk at 12–24 ins	Wantage Series
Chalk Marl, with Chalky, flinty Coombe deposits and Tael gravel	level to gently undulating land, with moderate to imperfect drainage	(variants) grey calcareous silty clay loam to clay overlying olive-grey to nearly white marly subsoil with rusty mottling (Burwell Series); grey, calcareous flinty clay loam to clay overlying pale brown to olive-grey flinty marly subsoil with rusty mottling and layers of flint and Chalk gravel; Chalk Marl at 12–48 ins	Halton (Burwell-Gubblecote) Complex

Parent material		Topography and drainage	Soil profile	Series
Upper Greensand glauconitic	grey, fine sandy, micaceous malm	gently undulating to rolling land, moderately well-drained	dark grey non-calcareous fine sandy clay loam overlying dark grey-green sandy clay-becoming greener and often calcareous with depth	Ardington Series
		gently undulating to rolling land, with moderate to imperfect drainage	dark grey, non-calcareous clay loam to clay, with appreciable very fine sand, overlying olive-grey stiff, slightly fine sandy non-calcareous clay with some very faint mottling; soft malm at 18–30 ins	Cheddington Series
re-worked Gault		gently undulating to rolling land, with slow internal drainage	very dark greyish-brown, near-neutral, clay, to clay loam with olive, faintly mottled clay subsoil, overlying light grey calcareous clay at 15–24 ins	Wicken Series
flinty, Chalky, head or Taele gravel, decalcified at surface, overlying clay		level or very gently-sloping low-lying land, with imperfect to poor drainage, affected by a perched water-table	dark grey-brown flinty clay loam to sandy clay loam, neutral to slightly acid, with olive-brown faintly mottled subsoil. over-lying Chalk and flint gravel, or rust-mottled stony sandy clay, at 9–24 ins; Gault at 18–60 ins	Wilstone Series
re-worked Gault and Chalky, flinty Taele gravel		level or depressed low-lying land with poor or very poor natural drainage	(variants) poorly drained and very poorly drained variants of the Wilstone and Wicken Series, with local alluvial additions	Marstongate (Challow) Complex
alluvium and spring deposits derived from Chalk and associated drifts		alluvial flats and seep areas affected by a fluctuating water-table, occasionally subject to floods	variants include dark grey calcareous loam to clay loam, thick humic topsoil, and dark brown loam overlying calcareous silt or flint gravel	Waterend Complex

Small patches indicated on the map by letters are
(a) silt-clay alluvial soil
(b) largely decalcified, clayey Coombe deposits and Taele gravel overlying Chalk or Chalk Marl
(c) loams developed on Chalky Coombe deposits, downwash, and creep of Clay-with-Flints

245

17

Table 25

Estimates of population, by counties, 1086–1570

County	Domesday			1340	1377	1545	1570	Densities per sq. mile				
	Landed	Burghal	Total					1086	1340	1377	1545	1570
Derbyshire	9,982	490	10,472	51,000	36,433	47,400	51,427	9·7	48·0	33·8	44·0	48·2
Nottinghamshire	19,040	1,190	20,230	60,500	43,328	56,250	70,778	22·8	69·5	48·8	63·5	80·0
Leicestershire	23,320	1,278	24,598	71,000	50,748	61,000	67,557	28·2	83·0	58·1	75·5	64·5
Rutland	2,992	—	2,992	12,500	8,991	9,000	8,798	19·7	84·5	59·0	59·0	58·0
Northamptonshire	29,008	1,032	30,040	87,500	62,553	80,500	73,382	29·0	86·0	60·3	78·5	71·5
Huntingdonshire	8,998	1,136	10,134	29,500	21,243	27,500	25,393	24·6	72·5	50·7	66·0	61·0
Bedfordshire	13,562	420	13,982	43,000	30,982	40,250	33,611	29·1	90·5	63·4	82·5	69·0
Buckinghamshire	18,879	560	19,439	51,750	37,008	48,000	51,501	25·5	69·5	48·5	63·0	67·5
Oxfordshire	23,706	1,431	25,137	57,500	41,008	53,300	51,126	31·3	73·0	51·0	82·5	79·5
Total	149,487	7,537	157,024	464,250	332,294	423,200	433,573					

Notes. Totals for Domesday and 1377 are from Russell. Totals for 1340 assume a 30% reduction by epidemics up to 1377. Totals for 1545 for Oxfordshire and Rutland are obtained by applying Russell's 1377/1545 ratios, but his indicated total of 90,700 for Northamptonshire has been reduced, and that of 99,900 for Buckinghamshire has been rejected as impossibly high. Russell gives no 1337/1545 ratio for the remaining counties, where the value 1·3 has been applied. Totals for 1570, estimated by Rickman, are given for comparison.

Table 26

Estimates of population for selected towns 1086 to ca. 1700; early 18th-century estimates added for comparison (various sources)

Town	1086	late 13th–early 14th centuries	1361	1377	ca. 1450	ca. 1550	ca. 1650	ca. 1710
Derby	490			1,569				
Nottingham	833			2,170	ca. 3,000	? ca. 3,250	ca. 6,000	7,225
Newark	357			405				
Southwell								
Leicester	1,278	4,800 [1327]	3,840	3,152	4,375	3,550	ca. 5,000	ca. 6,000
Whissendine (Rutland)				355				
Northampton	1,032			2,216		possibly ca. 3,000	possibly ca. 3,750	possibly ca. 4,750
Peterborough				790				
Huntingdon	1,316							
Bedford	420							
Buckingham	560							possibly ca. 1,500
Oxford	1,431	4,500 [1279]		3,356		ca. 4,000		
Banbury				531				

Note. Russell gives the following additional estimates for 1377: Farndish 555; Higham Ferrers 396; Irthlingborough 307; Rothwell 360; Towcester 328 (all Northamptonshire); Adderbury 300; Bloxham 325; Burford 343; Chipping Norton 304; Thame 325; Witney 434 (all Oxfordshire). With an allowance of 30% reduction by epidemic, the typical lesser town of ca. 1340 appears to have contained 425–800 people, with 450–550 a frequent total.

247

Table 27

First recorded appearances of selected place-name elements indicative of secondary settlement (compiled from the place-name handbooks)

	A.D.	900	950	1000	1050	1100	1150	1200	1250	1300	1350	1400	1450	1500	Post-Domesday peak periods (50-year duration)
Derbyshire	—cote	1	—	—	9	1	1	5	1	7	2	—	—		
	—leah	—	—	6	34	6	6	16	32	19	3	5	11		
	—thorpe	—	—	—	6	—	3	3	6	4	—	2	—		
	Total	1	—	6	49	7	10	24	39	30	5	7	11		1260–1310
Nottinghamshire	—cote	—	—	—	4	1	2	1	1	1	—	—	—		
	—leah	—	—	—	14	1	4	6	3	—	—	1	—		
	—thorpe	—	—	—	15	1	6	6	2	1	—	—	—		
	Total	—	—	—	33	3	12	13	6	2	—	1	—		1180–1230
Northamptonshire	—cote	—	—	—	7	1	6	12	4	2	—	—	—		
	—leah	—	5	—	11	1	4	7	5	2	2	2	—		
	—thorpe	—	3	—	15	2	2	4	3	—	—	—	—		
	Total	—	8	—	33	4	12	23	12	4	2	2	—		1200–1250
Huntingdonshire	—cote	—	—	—	2	—	—	4	3	—	—	—	—		
	—leah	—	1	—	5	—	1	5	2	—	—	—	—		
	—thorpe	—	—	—	—	—	—	1	—	1	—	—	—		
	Total	—	1	—	7	—	2	9	6	—	—	—	—		1210–1260
Bedfordshire	—cote	—	1	—	2	—	1	4	2	—	—	—	—		
	—leah	—	2	—	7	1	3	6	4	1	—	1	—		
	—thorpe	—	—	—	—	1	—	—	—	—	—	—	—		
	Total	—	3	—	9	2	4	11	6	1	—	1	—		1210–1260
Buckinghamshire	—cote	—	—	—	4	—	6	8	—	—	—	—	—		
	—leah	2	—	—	12	1	5	5	2	1	—	—	—		
	Total	2	—	—	16	1	11	13	2	1	—	—	—		1180–1230
Oxfordshire	—cote	—	1	—	14	3	11	7	2	—	1	—	—		
	—leah	1	2	5	7	3	8	10	9	2	2	—	—		
	Total	1	3	5	21	6	19	17	11	2	3	—	—		1170–1220

Table 28

Percentage distribution of first post-Domesday records of selected place-name elements

		1100	1150	1200	1250	1300	1350	1400	1450	1500
—cote		6	27	41	13	10	3	—	—	
—leah	Derbyshire only	6	6	16·5	33	19·5	3	5	11	
	excluding Derbyshire	6·5	22·5	35·5	23	5·5	3·5	3·5	—	
	including Derbyshire	6	15	26·5	27·5	12	3·5	4·25	5·25	
—thorpe		7·75	23·5	27·5	23·5	9·75	—	4	—	
total of —cote —leah —thorpe	Derbyshire only	5·25	7·5	18	29·5	22·5	3·75	5·25	8·25	
	excluding Derbyshire	7·25	27	38	19·25	4·40	2·25	1·80	—	
	including Derbyshire	9	27	43	32	15·5	4	4·25	4·25	

Table 29

Numbers of medieval religious houses (based on information in Knowles and Hadcock)

County	Establishments of Benedictine and Cluniac, etc. monks; Cistercians, Carthusians, and Premonstratensians; Augustinian Canons and others			Establishments of Friars, Nuns, Hospitallers		
	rank			Friars	Nuns	Hospi-tallers ca. 1509
	1st	2nd	3rd			
Derbyshire	3 (Dale, Darley, Repton)	—	5	1	1	2
Nottinghamshire	4 (Beauvale, Mattersey, Rufford, Welbeck)	7	2	3	2	7
Leicestershire	3 (Croxton, Garendon, Leicester)	4	5	4	2	6
Rutland	—	1	1	—	—	—
Northamptonshire	4 (Northampton, Peterborough, Pipewell, Sulby)	5	8	5	5	9
Huntingdonshire	2 (Ramsey, Sawtrey)	3	1	2	1	—
Bedfordshire	3 (Chicksands, Warden, Woburn)	3	4	2	3	6
Buckinghamshire	3 (Biddlesden, Lavendon, Notley)	3	6	1	—	1
Oxfordshire	6 (Bruern, Dorchester, Eynsham, Osney, Rewley, Thame)	7	9	6	4	6
Totals	28	33	41	24	18	37

Table 30

Estimates of ratio of urban to rural populations, 1086 and 1377, based on Russell's estimates of totals

Town	Town population as % of county population	
	1086	1377
Derby	3·7	4·3
Nottingham	4·4	5·0
Leicester	5·2	7·6
Northampton	3·4	3·6
Oxford	5·7	8·1
total of five towns as % of total for five counties	4·6	5·8
% in burghal group at 1086, nine counties	4·5	—
% in 21 towns at 1377, nine counties	—	7·0

Table 31

Prosperity index, by counties, 1341 to 1693

Assessment, grant, levy, etc.	1341	1453	1503	1636	1641	1649	1660	1672	1690	1693
Derbyshire	49	39	40	64	40	48	58	57	55	52
Nottinghamshire	69	79	75	80	55	58	73	72	103	74
Leicestershire	72	81	84	106	72	76	96	92	73	97
Rutland	129	128	122	101	104	115	120	108	131	83
Northamptonshire	96	101	94	115	74	80	108	97	92	108
Huntingdonshire	113	106	107	105	147	160	107	118	95	94
Bedfordshire	133	123	129	122	141	145	130	131	106	131
Buckinghamshire	87	81	82	117	138	119	111	121	110	144
Oxfordshire	146	128	122	101	104	115	120	108	131	83

Note: The indices are derived from ratios cited by Thorold Rogers for value/area at the wool tax (1341), grant of archers (1453), tax assessment (1503), Ship Money valuation (1636), and tax assessments of 16 Car. I (1641), 1649 (mean of two series), 1660 (proposed assessment), 1672, and 1693. The indices for 1690 are derived from the ratio of hearths/houses, as given in the hearth books, but have been subjected to spreading. Regional mean index = 100 throughout.

250

Table 32

Rates of population increase (calculated from estimates of population by Russell and Rickman)

	1377–1545	1377–1570	1570–1600	1600–1630	1630–1670	1670–1700	1700–1750	1750–1801
Derbyshire	—	1·4	1·5	1·05	0·98	1·4	0·94	1·5
Nottinghamshire	—	1·6	1·2	1·1	1·15	0·81	1·05	1·55
Leicestershire	—	1·3	1·02	1·1	0·96	1·1	1·25	1·3
Rutland	1·0	0·98	1·45	1·02	1·02	1·15	0·81	1·3
Northamptonshire	1·45	1·2	1·35	1·1	0·93	1·1	1·05	1·1
Huntingdonshire	—	1·2	1·15	1·15	1·0	0·93	1·02	1·15
Bedfordshire	—	1·1	1·3	1·25	0·91	1·05	1·1	1·05
Buckinghamshire	2·7	1·4	1·15	1·15	0·91	1·15	1·2	1·35
Oxfordshire	1·63	1·25	1·45	1·1	0·93	1·15	1·1	1·15

Table 33

Percentage distribution of crops on some Leicestershire holdings

	Year	Wheat	Rye	Barley	Oats	Peas and beans	Totals	
							Winter corn	Spring corn
By weight on Leicester Abbey lands (after Hilton)	1363	21·5	1·5	57	3	17	23	77
	1393	14	5	40	9	32	19	81
	1399	14	6	45	7	28	20	80
	1401	11·5	5·5	44·5	6	32·5	17	83
	1470	14·5	5		6	30	19·5	78·5
By area on groups of farms (after Hoskins)	1500–31 fifteen farms 378½ acres sown	13·8	5	37·6	0·4	43·2	18·8	81·2
	1588 fourteen farms 343 acres sown	8·6	8·6	35·8	8·5	38·5	17·2	82·8
	1588 350½ acres sown	8·5	4	38·5	9·5	40·5	12·5	87·5

Note. The Leicester Abbey lands included some tenures outside the county.

Table 34

Estimates of county populations, 1570 to 1781, with census totals for 1801

	1570	1600	1630	1670	1690	1700	1750	1781	1801
Derbyshire	51,427	77,639	82,507	81,252	99,776	115,564	108,251	119,500	161,142
Nottinghamshire	70,778	86,092	92,759	106,026	71,272	86,315	91,353	92,300	140,350
Leicestershire	67,557	69,543	75,554	73,186	81,792	80,210	98,488	116,500	130,081
Rutland	8,798	12,876	13,127	13,398	14,654	15,616	12,618	12,300	16,356
Northamptonshire	73,382	100,604	108,498	101,056	107,616	113,670	120,180	88,000	131,757
Huntingdonshire	25,393	29,624	34,024	34,144	34,852	31,966	32,516	32,650	37,568
Bedfordshire	33,611	44,429	54,902	49,928	48,680	53,706	59,542	53,900	63,393
Buckinghamshire	51,501	59,743	69,153	62,976	74,752	73,325	87,821	90,700	107,444
Oxfordshire	51,126	74,103	80,043	74,321	78,508	85,159	95,886	92,400	109,620
Total	433,573	560,089	610,954	596,287	611,902	655,531	706,655	698,250	897,711

Notes. Estimates for 1570, 1600, 1630, 1670, 1700, and 1750 are by Rickman (1841 Census). Estimates for 1690 are from hearth book totals, at the suggested value of 4 people per house, given by Rogers. Estimates for 1781 are from records of window tax, at the suggested value of 8½ per returned house, given by Macpherson. Outstanding discrepancies are: low 1690 total for Nottinghamshire; low 1781 totals for Northamptonshire, Bedfordshire, and Oxfordshire.

Table 35

Comparison between growths of agricultural and industrial villages in the Trent basin 1674–1801 (after Chambers)

Trent Basin	Average pop. 1674	% increase 1674–1743	Average pop. 1743	% increase 1743–1746	Average pop. 1764	% increase 1764–1801	Average pop. 1801
62 agricultural villages	166	12·7	187	6·4	199	38·7	276
40 industrialised villages	230	47·8	340	35·9	462	96·5	908

Nottinghamshire	Average pop. 1740–1750	% increase 1740–50 to 1801	Average pop. 1801
34 agricultural villages	220	54	340
26 industrialised villages	435	152	1,140

Table 36

Selected examples of distinctive, or unusual, combinations of materials in rural domestic architecture

Combination		Locality	Grid reference
Walling	Roofing		
Carboniferous Limestone	gritstone slabs	Foolow	$4^{19}_{3}76$
Carboniferous Limestone	slates	Taddington	$4^{14}_{3}71$
Carboniferous Limestone	flat tiles	Parwich	$4^{18}_{3}54$
Carboniferous Limestone with cornering and lintels of Millstone Grit	flat tiles	Middleton	$4^{27}_{3}56$
Carboniferous Limestone with cornering and lintels of Millstone Grit	gritstone slabs	Ashford	$4^{19}_{3}69$
Millstone Grit	gritstone slabs	Bamford	$4^{20}_{3}83$
Millstone Grit	flat tiles	Idridgehay	$4^{28}_{3}48$
Magnesian Limestone	pantiles	Nether Langwith	$4^{53}_{3}70$
brick	pantiles	North Leverton	$4^{78}_{3}82$
brick	flat [Woodville]	Kirk Langley	$4^{29}_{3}39$
Charnian rock	slate, thatch	Newtown Linford	$4^{52}_{3}10$
sandstone (? from Coal Measures) in terraced houses	flat tiles	Moira	$4^{31}_{3}15$
red brick	blue slates	Arnesby	$4^{61}_{2}92$
		Yelvertoft	$4^{59}_{2}75$
Lower Lias (remnantal)	——	Walton on the Wolds	$4^{80}_{3}25$
Marlstone	thatch	Newnham	$4^{58}_{2}59$
Marlstone	pantiles	Wymondham	$4^{85}_{3}18$
Marlstone	stone slabs	Oakham	$4^{86}_{3}08$
Marlstone	slates	Epwell	$4^{35}_{2}40$
Northampton Sand	thatch	Harlestone	$4^{70}_{2}64$
Northampton Sand	pantile	Harrowden	$4^{88}_{2}71$
Northampton Sand, cornerings of red brick	slates	Orton	$4^{80}_{2}79$
oolite	thatch	Geddington	$4^{89}_{2}83$
oolite	stone slabs	Glympton	$4^{42}_{2}21$
		Upper Benefield	$4^{98}_{2}89$
oolite	pantiles	Islip	$4^{98}_{2}79$
oolite	flat tiles	Higham Ferrers	$4^{96}_{2}68$
oolite	slate	Whittlebury	$4^{69}_{2}44$
oolite and Marlstone	——	Duns Tew	$4^{45}_{2}28$
oolite and Northampton Sand	——	Burton Latimer	$4^{90}_{2}75$
oolite, raised by brick	slate, after thatch	Great Linford	$4^{86}_{2}42$
red brick	thatch	Quainton	$4^{74}_{2}20$
timber frames, brick fillings	thatch	Stewkley	$4^{85}_{2}26$
		Stewkley North End	$4^{84}_{2}26$
timber frames, brick fillings	flat tile	Haddenham	$4^{74}_{2}08$
timber frame, filling of cob below and lath-and-plaster above	thatch	Claycoton (one, abandoned)	$4^{59}_{2}77$

253

Table 36 (*continued*)

Combination		Locality	Grid reference
Walling	Roofing		
cob	thatch	Walcote	$_456_283$
		Haddenham	$_474_208$
cob	flat tile	Haddenham	$_474_208$
lath-and-plaster	thatch	Thurleigh	$_505_258$
lath-and-plaster	flat tile	Tempsford	$_516_253$
wattle-and-daub	——	Wrestlingworth	$_525_247$
stone, brick, and cob	thatch	Winwick	$_462_273$
cob, with brick cornerings and flint-faced end walls	thatch	Chinnor	$_475_201$
yellow brick	slate	Ramsey	$_528_285$
yellow brick	flat tile	Kimbolton	$_510_267$
clapboard	flat tile	Potton	$_522_249$
red brick with stone footings	pantiles in hipped roofs	Yaxley	$_518_292$
Barns			
clapboard	pantiles	Houghton Conquest	$_505_241$
board	stone slabs	Northmoor	$_442_203$
board	heavy thatch	East Claydon	$_473_225$
mud	thatch	Guilsborough	$_467_273$
Minor mud walling		West Haddon	$_463_271$

Table 37

Land use in six East Midland counties in the early nineteenth century (based on the second series of Reports to the Board of Agriculture)

County	Percentage		
	Tillage	Improved grassland	Other land
Derbyshire	19	56	25
Leicestershire	30	62 (16 rotation grass)	8
Northamptonshire	$35\frac{1}{4}$	$58\frac{1}{2}$	$6\frac{1}{4}$
Buckinghamshire (part of)	$40\frac{1}{2}$	57 ($18\frac{1}{2}$ meadow, 38 pasture)	$2\frac{1}{2}$
Rutland	47	49 (11 meadow, 38 pasture)	4
Huntingdonshire	62	$29\frac{3}{4}$ ($10\frac{1}{2}$ meadow, $19\frac{1}{4}$ pasture)	$8\frac{1}{4}$

Table 38

Number of knitting frames, according to contemporary estimates and counts

Date	National total	Three Midland counties total	Midland total as % of national total	Leicestershire total	*Leicester (town) total	Nottinghamshire total	*Nottingham (town) total	Derbyshire total	*Derby (town) total
1660	—	—	—	50	—	100	—	—	—
1664	650	140	21½	—	—	—	—	—	—
1669	660	ca. 260	39½	—	—	ca. 100	2	nil	—
1714	8,000	3,400	42½	—	600	—	400	—	50
1727	8,000	4,650	58	—	500	—	400	—	—
1739	—	—	—	—	—	3,000	1,200	—	—
1753	13,200	9,700	73½	—	1,000	—	1,500	—	200
1782	20,000	17,350	87	—	—	—	—	—	—
1789	—	—	—	—	—	—	—	1,350	—
1812	30,000	ca. 25,000	83	11,183	1,600	9,259	—	4,700	400
1832–3	33,000	28,500	86½	—	—	10,500	—	—	—
1844–5	44,484	44,040	98½	20,311	4,140	16,482	5,412	6,536	759

* Included in total in previous column.

Note. Slight discrepancies in the last line are due to oversights in reporting, and to uncertainties about totals of very small groups of scattered frames.

Table 39

Iron furnaces in Derbyshire 1806 (adapted from Farey)

1 Northern Group			2 Southern Group		
Place	Number	Annual tons pig	Place	Number	Annual tons pig
Chesterfield	5	2,400	Alfreton (Somercotes)	1	1,450
Duckmanton	2	900			
Hasland	1	723	Butterley	2	1,766
Renishaw	2	975	Morley Park	1	700
Staveley	1	596			
Wingerworth	2	819			

Table 40 Percentage distribution of all land among tillage (T), rotation grass (R), and permanent grass (P);

		1866	1870	1875	1880	1885	1890	1895	1900	1905
Derbyshire	T	18·1	17·3	16	14·4	12·4	12	10·9	10·5	9·6
	R	5 ·	6·8	5·2	4·4	4	4	3·8	3·8	3·7
	P	47·2	50	55·4	59·4	62	63	62	61·4	61·4
	F	70·3	74·1	76·6	78·2	78·4	79	76·7	75·7	74·7
Nottinghamshire	T	43·1	44·5	44·6	42·8	38·6	36·2	33·5	34·4	32·8
	R	9·5	10·5	10	11	11·7	11·6	11	10·3	9·9
	P	26·7	28·9	29·7	32·3	36·3	38·9	38·6	39	40·2
	F	79·3	83·9	84·3	86·1	86·6	86·7	83·1	83·7	82·9
Leicestershire	T	27·8	31·1	28·8	25·9	22·1	20·3	18·6	18·3	16·4
	R	4·5	5·3	5·6	5·5	6	5·1	5	4·4	4·6
	P	50	54·4	53·4	61	64·5	67·1	69·4	70·2	71·7
	F	82·3	90·8	87·8	92·4	92·6	92·5	93·0	92·9	92·7
Rutland	T	35·6	37·9	40·5	37·4	33·8	34·6	30·4	29·3	28·3
	R	6	7·2	6·1	7·2	7	7	6	6·4	6·2
	P	36·5	41	43·2	47	50·5	52·2	53·3	52·5	55·5
	F	78·1	86·1	89·8	91·6	91·3	93·8	89·7	88·2	90·0
*Northamptonshire	T	38	38	39·4	37·9	33·2	28·8	28·4	27·4	26·3
	R	5	5·9	5	5·6	6·4	5·5	5·8	5·4	4·8
	P	40	40·8	43·4	46·3	49·1	53·8	54·5	56·5	58·5
	F	83·0	84·7	87·8	89·8	88·7	88·1	88·7	89·3	89·6
* Soke of Peterborough	T	—	—	—	—	—	—	—	—	—
	R	—	—	—	—	—	—	—	—	—
	P	—	—	—	—	—	—	—	—	—
	F	—	—	—	—	—	—	—	—	—
Oxfordshire	T	46·5	48·2	50	47·8	44·5	39·4	36·8	34·9	33·3
	R	9	9·8	9·1	9·6	10·6	9·8	10·3	10·4	9·8
	P	25·5	28·6	30·1	31·2	33·7	36·4	38·6	40·4	42·8
	F	81·0	86·6	89·2	88·6	88·8	85·6	85·7	85·7	85·9
Buckinghamshire	T	38·0	39·2	39·5	37·3	34·3	33·5	28·0	26·2	24·2
	R	6·1	7·1	5·9	6·6	6·9	6·5	6·7	6·6	6·2
	P	36·7	39·4	41·5	43·1	46·5	49	49·5	51	53·1
	F	80·8	85·7	86·9	87·0	87·7	89·0	84·2	83·8	83·5
Bedfordshire	T	52·7	55·3	55·4	53·6	50·6	48·3	45·0	43·4	43·4
	R	6·3	6·7	5·7	6·9	7·7	7·1	7·5	9	7·1
	P	23	24·4	25·3	27·1	29·7	32·8	33·8	34·7	36·4
	F	82·0	86·4	86·4	87·6	88·0	88·2	86·3	87·1	86·9
Huntingdonshire	T	56	58·3	59·1	57·7	54·7	50·3	44·3	44·7	45·7
	R	5·1	5·6	6	7·5	8·5	8·1	8·8	8·6	6·3
	P	22·7	23·7	25·4	26·4	28·6	33·3	36·6	36·2	36·6
	F	83·8	87·6	90·5	91·6	91·8	91·7	89·7	89·4	88·6

* The Soke of Peterborough was included in Northamptonshire till 1915.

percentage of all land in improved farmland (F)

	1910	1915	1920	1925	1930	1935	1940	1945	1950	1955	1958
T	9·9	9·8	13·1	10·4	9·5	9	12·9	19·2	17·4	14·5	13·7
R	2·8	2·5	3·5	3	2·9	3	2·2	7·4	7·2	7·9	9·1
P	63·1	62	56	58·3	58·1	57·5	51·5	40·6	40·2	42·8	41·3
F	75·8	74·3	72·6	71·7	70·5	69·5	66·6	67·2	64·8	65·2	64·1
T	32·2	32·4	35·2	31·2	29·6	28·2	30·1	38·2	38·8	38·2	38
R	9·1	7·9	8·2	8·6	7·5	6·7	6	9·2	10	11·4	12
P	40·9	41·5	38·2	40	37·3	41·6	38·4	27·2	26·3	25	24·4
F	82·2	81·8	81·6	79·8	74·4	76·5	74·5	74·6	75·1	74·6	74·4
T	15·1	14·7	19·4	13·1	11·5	10·2	15·6	35·0	29·6	25·8	24·9
R	3·8	3·5	4·6	4·4	3·6	3·7	2·4	10·3	11·2	12	12·6
P	70·4	71	63·6	68·5	70·5	70·5	66·2	37·8	42·5	45·2	45·5
F	89·3	89·2	87·6	86·0	85·6	84·4	84·2	83·1	83·3	83·0	83·0
T	27·3	27·7	30·6	25·9	24·1	21·8	25·0	43	44·1	40·5	38·6
R	6·1	5	5·4	6·7	5·6	4·2	4·5	11	8·9	11	11·8
P	56·3	56·5	54·4	58·7	61·3	62	57·7	33	34·1	35·4	34·8
F	89·7	89·2	90·4	91·3	91·0	88·0	87·2	87·0	87·1	86·9	85·2
T	25·9	24·8	26·9	23·2	18·1	16·6	20·7	37·5	34·8	30·4	31·4
R	4·8	3·8	4·4	5·2	4·2	4	3·4	13·8	13·4	13·9	14
P	59·4	62	56·1	59·2	64·4	65·5	61·1	32·2	36·2	39·3	38
F	90·1	90·6	87·4	87·6	86·7	86·1	85·2	83·5	84·4	83·6	83·4
T	—	44·8	46·7	43·9	42·5	41	42·5	53·5	55·3	52	53·4
R	—	5·5	6	6·1	53	4·7	4·3	9·2	7·5	9	10·2
P	—	33	32·6	29·7	32·2	34·8	32·7	17·9	17·9	17·7	16·9
F	—	83·3	85·3	79·7	80·0	80·5	79·5	80·6	80·7	78·7	80·5
T	33·7	34·6	36·5	29·3	25·6	23·8	26·7	39	36·5	32·4	33·8
R	8·3	7·8	7·2	9·1	8	7·7	6·1	12·1	13·3	15·4	14·9
P	44	44·5	41·5	45·2	48·8	50	48·2	33·2	30·6	32·2	31·4
F	86·0	86·9	85·2	83·6	82·4	81·5	81·0	84·3	80·4	80·0	80·1
T	23·7	22·9	25·4	19·2	13·4	13·1	16·3	32·8	28·8	24·9	19·3
R	4·8	4·1	4·3	4·5	3·5	3·1	2·4	12	11·3	11·5	16·4
P	54·4	55·5	53·4	54·7	58·8	60	57·1	31·1	36·2	39·8	39·4
F	82·9	82·5	83·1	78·4	75·7	76·2	75·8	75·9	76·3	76·2	75·1
T	42·5	42·6	44·7	40·2	36·7	35·0	39·2	52·6	52	49·8	50·6
R	6·4	5·2	6·3	6·5	5·5	4·6	4·2	8·6	7·8	8·2	7·3
P	36·4	36·8	33·4	36·2	39·9	43·8	36·6	18·5	20·2	21	20·3
F	85·3	84·6	84·4	82·9	82·1	83·4	80·0	79·7	80·0	79·0	78·2
T	46·2	47·5	49·9	47·3	43·9	44·3	46·4	57·3	60·8	59·4	60·8
R	6·3	5·1	6·3	5·8	6·3	5·3	5	8·5	6·7	7·4	7·2
P	36·9	37·7	33·1	33·8	35·1	35·8	33·5	18	17·8	18·3	17·1
F	89·4	90·3	89·3	86·9	85·3	85·4	84·9	83·8	85·3	85·1	85·1

Table 41   Percentage distribution of farmland among tillage (T), rotation grass (R), and permanent grass (P)

		1866	1870	1875	1880	1885	1890	1895	1900	1905
Derbyshire	T	26	23·25	21	18·5	16	15	14	14	13
	R	7	9·25	6·75	5·5	5	5	5	5	5
	P	67	67·5	72·25	76	79	80	81	81	82
Nottinghamshire	T	54·5	53	53	49·75	44·5	41·75	40·25	41	39·5
	R	12	12·5	12	12·75	13·5	13·25	13·25	12·25	12
	P	33·5	34·5	35	37·5	42	45	46·5	46·75	48·5
Leicestershire	T	34	34	33·5	28	24	22	20	19·75	17·5
	R	5·5	6	6·25	6	6·5	5·5	5·5	4·75	5
	P	60·5	60	60·25	66	69·5	72·5	74·5	75·5	77·5
Rutland	T	45·5	44	45	41	37	37	34	33·25	31·5
	R	7·5	8·5	7	7·75	7·75	7·5	6·75	7·25	6·75
	P	47	47·5	48	51·25	55·25	55·5	59·25	59·5	61·75
*Northamptonshire	T	46	45	45	42	37·5	32·75	32	30·5	29·25
	R	6	7	5·75	6·25	7·25	6·25	6·5	6	5·5
	P	48	48	49·25	51·75	55·25	61	61·5	63·5	65·25
*Soke of Peterborough	T	—	—	—	—	—	—	—	—	—
	R	—	—	—	—	—	—	—	—	—
	P	—	—	—	—	—	—	—	—	—
Oxfordshire	T	57·5	55·5	56	54	50	46	43	40·75	38·75
	R	11	11·5	10	11	12	11·5	12	12	11·5
	P	31·5	33	34	35	38	42·5	45	47·25	49·75
Buckinghamshire	T	47	45·5	45·5	43	39	37·5	33·25	31·25	29
	R	7·5	8·5	6·75	7·5	8	7·5	8	8	7·5
	P	45·5	46	47·75	49·5	53	55	58·75	60·75	63·5
Bedfordshire	T	64·25	64	64	61	57·5	54·75	52	50	50
	R	7·75	7·75	6·5	8	8·75	8	8·75	10	8
	P	28	28·25	29·5	31	33·75	37·25	39·25	40	42
Huntingdonshire	T	67	66·5	65·5	63	59·5	55	49·5	50	51·5
	R	6	6·5	6·5	8	9·25	9	9·75	9·5	7
	P	27	27	28	29	31·25	36	40·75	40·5	41·5

* The Soke of Peterborough was included in Northamptonshire until 1915.

	1910	1915	1920	1925	1930	1935	1940	1945	1950	1955	1958
T	13	13	18	14·5	13·5	13	19·5	28·5	27	22	21·5
R	3·75	3·5	5	4	4	4·25	3·25	11	11	12	14
P	83·25	83·5	77	81·5	82·5	82·75	77·25	60·5	62	66	64·5
T	39	39·5	43·25	39·5	40	37	40·5	51	51·75	51·25	51
R	11	9·75	10	10·5	10	8·75	8	12·5	13·25	15·25	16
P	50	50·75	46·75	50	50	54·25	51·5	36·5	35	33·5	33
T	17	16·5	22·25	15·25	13·5	12	18·5	42	35·5	31·5	30
R	4	4	5	5	4	4·5	3	12·5	13·5	14·5	15
P	79	79·5	72·75	79·75	82·5	83·5	78·5	45·5	51	54	55
T	30·5	31	34	28·25	26·5	25	28·5	49·5	50·5	46·5	45·5
R	6·75	5·5	6	7·25	6	5	5	12·5	10·25	12·5	14
P	62·75	63·5	60	64·5	67·5	70	66·5	38	39·25	41	40·5
T	28·75	27·25	30·75	26·5	20·75	19·5	24·25	45	41·25	36·25	37·5
R	5·25	4·25	5	6	5	4·5	4	16·5	15·75	16·75	17
P	66	68·5	64·25	67·5	74·25	76	71·75	38·5	43	47	45·5
T	—	54	54·75	55	53	51	53·5	66·5	68·5	66	66·5
R	—	6·5	7	7·5	6·75	6	5·5	11·5	9·25	11·5	12·5
P	—	39·5	38·25	37·5	40·25	43	41	22	22·25	22·5	21
T	39	40	42·75	35	31	29	32·75	46·25	45·5	40·5	42
R	9·75	9	8·5	11	9·5	9·5	7·75	14·25	16·5	19·25	18·75
P	51·25	51	48·75	54	59·5	61·5	59·5	39·5	38	40·25	39·25
T	28·5	27·75	30·5	24·5	17·75	17	21·5	43	37·75	32·75	25·5
R	5·75	5	5·25	5·75	4·5	4	3·25	16	14·75	15	22
P	65·75	67·25	64·25	69·75	77·75	79	75·25	41	47·5	52·25	52·5
T	50	50·5	53	48·5	44·75	42	49	66	65	63	65
R	7·5	6	7·5	8	6·75	5·5	5·25	11	9·75	10·5	9
P	42·5	43·5	39·5	43·5	48·5	52·5	45·75	23	25·25	26·5	26
T	51·75	52·5	56	54·5	51·5	52	54·5	68·5	71·25	70	71·5
R	7	5·75	7	6·5	7·5	6	6	10	7·75	8·5	8·5
P	41·25	41·75	37	39	41	42	39·5	21·5	21	21·5	20

Table 42 on p. 262

Table 43 Livestock. Thousand head of cattle (Ca), cows in milk or calf (Cmc), and sheep (Sh). Totals of in milk from 1910 onwards

		1866	1870	1875	1880	1885	1890	1895	1900	1905
Derbyshire	Ca	113·6	125·9	142·7	134·8	155·3	143·2	136·1	143·6	141·8
	Cmc	—	—	—	64·3	73·9	71·2	68·8	70·7	72·5
	Sh	176·1	250·0	261·5	228·4	204·9	202·9	177·0	171·4	133·0
Nottinghamshire	Ca	68·5	72·1	79·3	77·6	88·3	82·0	81·2	86·1	85·9
	Cmc	—	—	—	23·8	28·6	28·5	26·8	28·4	28·6
	Sh	245·5	288·9	284·9	258·1	230·0	231·4	221·6	196·7	168·0
Leicestershire	Ca	89·3	119·6	136·8	126·9	149·7	140·9	131·7	141·9	144·6
	Cmc	—	—	—	33·0	42·3	40·4	38·7	40·7	42·3
	Sh	290·6	455·6	453·5	357·8	322·6	344·6	304·6	321·0	297·6
Rutland	Ca	11·7	14·8	17·7	17·4	19·8	19·8	17·5	19·1	19·4
	Cmc	—	—	—	3·3	4·3	4·0	3·4	3·5	3·7
	Sh	75·8	106·1	105·7	95·7	81·3	86·4	82·8	84·8	73·9
*Northamptonshire	Ca	76·5	100·0	118·0	113·0	129·9	130·1	119·7	126·3	132·4
	Cmc	—	—	—	25·0	29·5	30·8	27·4	29·8	32·1
	Sh	435·8	540·7	553·1	457·4	452·6	429·1	409·0	403·4	375·6
*Soke of Peterborough	Ca	—	—	—	—	—	—	—	—	—
	Cmc	—	—	—	—	—	—	—	—	—
	Sh	—	—	—	—	—	—	—	—	—
Oxfordshire	Ca	43·6	46·8	54·9	51·2	60·1	56·4	53·4	61·9	67·7
	Cmc	—	—	—	17·3	20·2	20·4	19·2	20·7	22·1
	Sh	333·3	358·0	356·4	279·2	299·2	266·6	241·7	230·3	206·1
Buckinghamshire	Ca	52·7	60·7	68·8	68·2	76·9	69·9	66·2	75·2	79·1
	Cmc	—	—	—	28·2	31·7	30·5	28·6	31·3	33·1
	Sh	263·0	305·1	292·4	195·8	230·2	213·5	192·6	195·6	178·7
Bedfordshire	Ca	25·9	28·2	34·3	31·6	37·5	33·5	30·0	34·8	34·1
	Cmc	—	—	—	10·8	12·2	12·2	11·1	11·9	12·3
	Sh	180·3	182·0	178·7	152·1	151·8	122·0	96·3	104·8	89·0
Huntingdonshire	Ca	19·8	22·3	26·3	28·3	30·1	32·0	28·0	30·7	28·8
	Cmc	—	—	—	7·5	7·3	7·9	7·1	7·6	7·0
	Sh	117·8	151·6	156·0	155·1	131·1	118·2	101·1	96·5	79·3
TOTAL	Ca	501·6	590·4	678·8	649·0	747·6	707·8	663·8	719·6	733·8
	Cmc	—	—	—	213·2	250·0	245·9	261·1	249·6	253·7
	Sh	2,118·2	2,638·0	2,642·2	2,179·6	2,103·7	2,014·7	1,826·7	1,804·5	1,601·2

* The Soke of Peterborough was included in Northamptonshire until 1915.

cows in milk are included in preceding totals of cattle; the category excludes cows in calf but not

	1910	1915	1920	1925	1930	1935	1940	1945	1950	1955	1958
Ca	146·7	152·1	142·2	152·2	146·5	167·4	168·2	186·2	191·4	187·5	178·1
Cmc	60·9	61·1	60·9	63·5	62·6	68·6	69·6	68·4	68·8	70·5	68·9
Sh	165·2	140·7	101·4	118·0	126·9	120·6	147·8	98·0	99·9	132·8	163·2
Ca	90·1	90·4	84·4	97·7	83·9	97·1	99·4	107·5	115·4	111·4	108·6
Cmc	22·1	21·6	21·4	24·8	23·5	25·9	26·7	26·5	28·8	26·9	26·5
Sh	210·5	160·5	111·5	151·2	129·2	123·2	142·9	64·9	67·1	88·9	109·3
Ca	148·9	152·2	139·1	158·4	144·7	156·0	164·6	154·4	176·5	168·3	171·6
Cmc	33·4	34·0	34·9	40·0	37·2	41·6	42·1	42·1	46·1	43·9	44·4
Sh	345·7	263·9	195·2	243·2	240·6	225·8	266·6	106·2	150·4	192·5	232·3
Ca	20·1	20·3	18·8	22·1	19·7	20·6	21·4	19·9	21·0	20·5	22·0
Cmc	2·4	2·4	.2·2	2·9	2·7	2·9	2·8	2·7	2·7	2·5	2·6
Sh	90·6	70·9	61·2	68·0	62·7	55·7	62·8	39·9	42·6	51·5	58·9
Ca	138·5	131·7	122·5	138·5	125·1	135·0	144·6	142·1	160·7	149·2	152·0
Cmc	20·7	19·6	19·2	23·6	23·3	25·7	26·3	25·9	27·4	25·2	26·4
Sh	422·7	325·2	228·2	312·4	303·5	310·8	368·9	205·8	252·8	289·6	232·6
Ca	—	7·1	6·3	6·7	6·5	7·4	7·5	7·0	7·3	7·0	7·4
Cmc	—	1·4	1·4	1·5	1·5	1·7	1·9	1·7	1·9	1·8	1·7
Sh	—	20·6	16·5	17·0	14·8	15·4	15·6	8·6	8·4	10·4	12·4
Ca	82·3	72·9	62·8	75·9	69·4	83·7	92·8	93·6	112·6	112·3	110·4
Cmc	24·6	15·7	15·6	19·5	19·7	23·7	24·2	23·9	26·3	27·1	27·8
Sh	204·8	178·6	120·7	155·4	134·6	128·3	159·3	80·1	80·9	115·0	140·5
Ca	71·1	84·3	77·3	88·7	80·4	91·7	101·9	101·3	119·3	118·5	117·8
Cmc	16·2	23·8	22·3	26·2	25·4	29·4	29·4	28·8	30·0	29·0	29·7
Sh	231·1	165·9	125·1	160·7	155·2	157·7	198·6	85·2	110·0	142·3	181·3
Ca	37·6	36·9	33·4	39·4	37·6	40·4	45·9	44·7	49·5	44·4	41·6
Cmc	8·6	8·1	7·6	9·7	9·1	9·1	9·2	10·1	10·3	10·2	10·1
Sh	94·5	65·1	44·8	57·5	58·4	56·8	66·3	19·9	22·5	31·1	40·4
Ca	30·1	30·2	26·2	29·9	25·3	27·3	26·6	28·5	30·7	29·0	28·0
Cmc	4·3	4·2	4·3	5·4	5·0	5·4	5·5	5·9	6·2	5·7	5·9
Sh	87·4	61·4	35·0	45·0	41·3	39·3	45·0	15·5	17·7	24·6	31·9
Ca	765·4	778·1	713·0	869·5	739·1	826·6	872·9	875·2	984·4	948·2	1,004·1
Cmc	193·2	191·9	189·8	217·1	210·0	234·0	237·7	236·0	248·5	242·8	243·9
Sh	1,852·5	1,452·8	1,039·6	1,428·4	1,267·2	1,233·6	1,473·8	724·1	852·3	1,078·7	1,202·8

Table 42

Distribution of all land, and of farmland, among tillage (T), Rotation grass (R), and permanent grass (P), 1866–1958; combined percentages for nine counties plus the Soke of Peterborough. (F = improved farmland)

Year	Percentage of whole area in				Percentage of farmland in		
	T	R	P	F	T	R	P
1866	38·4	6·6	37·2	82·2	46·75	8·0	45·25
1870	38·25	7·25	39·0	84·5	45·25	8·5	46·25
1875	38·4	6·3	40·0	84·7	45·5	7·5	47·0
1880	36·4	7·0	43·6	87·0	42·0	8·0	50·0
1885	33·3	7·4	46·6	87·3	38·0	8·5	53·5
1890	30·8	7·0	49·2	87·0	35·5	8·0	56·5
1895	29·5	7·1	50·3	86·9	34·0	8·0	58·0
1900	27·4	6·9	51·2	85·5	32·0	8·0	60·0
1905	26·2	6·4	52·5	85·1	31·0	7·5	61·5
1910	26·6	5·2	53·3	85·1	31·25	6·0	62·75
1915	25·3	4·9	53·5	83·7	30·0	6·0	64·0
1920	28·7	5·5	49·0	83·2	34·5	6·5	59·0
1925	26·9	2·8	52·1	81·8	32·75	3·5	63·75
1930	21·4	5·0	53·8	80·2	26·75	6·25	67·0
1935	19·8	4·6	55·2	79·6	25·0	5·75	69·25
1940	28·7	3·8	51·0	83·5	34·5	4·5	61·0
1945	36·6	10·4	31·2	78·2	47·0	13·0	40·0
1950	35·7	10·3	33·0	79·0	45·0	13·0	42·0
1955	31·7	11·2	34·8	77·7	41·0	14·25	44·75
1958	31·6	11·6	34·0	77·2	41·0	15·0	44·0

Table 44

Some land use data for Bedfordshire in the early 1940s (based on the 10,000-acre samples given by C. E. Fitchett in the L.U.S. Report)

Subdivision	% arable	% grassland	arable/ grass ratio (grass=1)	head per 100 acres		dairy/ beef ratio (beef=1)	sheep/ cattle ratio (cattle=1)
				cattle	sheep		
Chalkland	42	48·5	0·9	18	21	8	1·2
Scarp-foot	53·5	38	1·4	13	20	3	1·5
Gault belt	19·5	80	0·25	31	50	3	1·5
Eastern clayland	76	22	3·4	11·5	16	1·1	1·4
Greensand (a) plateau	16	81·5	0·5	20·5	45	2	2·2
(b) ridge	51	47	1·1	13·5	17	2	1·3
Market-gardening district	80	18	4·5	4	—	1·5	0
Oxford-Clay belt	28	70	1·9	22·5	32·5	2	1·5
Northern mixed farming	51·5	44·5	1·2	15·5	29	2·5	2

Table 45

Land-use and livestock changes in the south east of the region (after, or adapted from, Coppock)

A. Some cropping data, 1931 and 1951

Subdivision	year	percentage of all land in						
		all arable	wheat	barley	oats	potatoes	vege-tables	temp. grass
Grass clay vales	1931	8·33	1·52	0·19	2·05			2·57
	1951	43·65	8·65	2·80	5·49			15·90
Vale of Aylesbury	1931	8·16	1·13	0·32	1·29			0·75
	1951	33·47	7·02	3·60	5·57			10·56
Bedfordshire market gardening	1931	44·64	3·38	0·42	3·69	10·82	18·12	5·15
	1951	73·59	12·62	7·08	3·10	11·34	22·16	6·23
Icknield, sub-edge belt, Oxfordshire	1931	63·66	12·31	12·33	9·33			15·59
	1951	80·58	11·61	31·83	5·58			17·88

B. Livestock per 10,000 acres, 1931 and 1951

		dairy cattle	beef cattle	all cattle	sheep	pigs	fowl	live-stock units
Grass clay vales	1931	669	351	2,313	8,091	560	33,559	3,148
	1951	856	714	3,548	4,341	645	26,634	3,353
Vale of Aylesbury	1931	762	1,521	3,549	7,009	587	4,593	4,283
	1951	818	1,367	4,046	6,137	588	8,700	3,900
Bedfordshire market gardening	1931	464	400	1,699	2,926	1,584	19,083	2,299
	1951	462	603	1,850	803	2,649	29,205	2,095·
Icknield, sub-edge belt, Oxfordshire	1931	320	145	847	1,959	588	11,708	1,224
	1951	377	279	1,705	836	730	51,592	1,439

Table 46
Land-use data for sample blocks of parishes

County Land-use Region of 1938 Acreage of 1938	Year	Improved farmland as % of total area	Farmland — Grassland: Ratio of grass/tillage (=1)	Ratio of perm. grass/rotation grass (rot. grass =1)	% perm. grass for grazing	% rotation grass for grazing	Tillage: % wheat, barley, oats	Chief grain % of tillage therein	Stock per 10 acres of — farmland: sheep	farmland: cattle	grassland: sheep	grassland: cattle	Ratio sheep cattle (cattle =1)
Derbyshire limestone plateau 10,400	1870	?84½	8·5	19·0	75	50	66	O. 59	6·1	2·7	6·8	3·0	2·3
	1913	93	14·5	49·0	73	42	52	O. 50	2·6	3·0	2·8	3·2	0·9
	1932	90¾	27·5	39·0	71	54	53	O. 52	2·7	3·4	2·8	3·5	0·8
	1958	82	14·5	13·5	66	39	53	O. 52	2·3	4·9	2·5	5·3	0·5
Nottinghamshire Keuper belt 8,415	1870	?87	0·7	2·0	61	56	63½	W. 36	4·6	1·7	11·1	4·1	2·7
	1913	80	1·4	4·7	69	18	60	W. 28	2·9	1·9	5·0	3·3	1·5
	1932	82	1·7	5·7	68	12	52½	W. 24	3·3	1·9	5·2	3·0	1·7
	1958	90	1·1	2·1	80	29	75½	W. 38	2·1	3·1	4·0	5·8	0·7
Northamptonshire pastoral upland 9,313	1870	93½	2·1	13·3	78	15	62½	W. 36	11·3	2·7	16·8	4·0	4·2
	1913	91	5·7	24·0	61	2	63	W. 24	6·6	3·0	7·8	3·6	2·2
	1932	93½	11·5	21·2	79	44	65	W. 30	10·3	3·0	11·1	3·2	3·5
	1958	91½	2·5	3·4	78	50	82½	W. 45	12·2	3·1	17·3	4·4	3·9
Leicestershire wolds 12,631	1870	?90	3·8	49·0	87	37	59	W. 34	9·7	2·6	12·3	3·2	3·8
	1913	?99	15·7	99·0	65	0	59	W. 70	5·8	3·1	6·1	3·3	1·9
	1932	91½	32·4	32·3	69	21	41	W } 20½ each, O }	9·8	3·6	10·1	3·7	2·7
	1958	94	2·8	3·3	71	33	75½	W. 36	7·6	3·8	10·3	5·1	2·0

Region	Year												
North Oxfordshire mixed and dairy 9,244	1870	95½	1·2	2·4	71	31	69	B,}W,} each 29	9·6	1·4	21·6	3·2	6·8
	1913	93½	2·0	4·5	66	16	73	B, 27	5·5	1·7	8·4	2·6	3·2
	1932	84	2·8	6·1	77	31	71	W, 32	5·9	2·2	7·9	2·9	2·7
	1958	82½	1·8	2·0	73	25	80½	B, 38	5·4	2·9	8·4	4·5	1·9
Central Buckinghamshire dairy 9,685	1870	87½	2·1	14·4	78	13	58	W,} 33	7·9	2·2	11·7	3·3	3·5
	1913	99	4·4	39·0	60	7	61	W } each 27	4·8	2·4	5·9	2·9	2·0
	1932	99	9·5	39·0	73	4	63½	O } each 30	9·4	2·7	10·3	3·0	3·4
	1958	93½	2·7	4·4	72	30	81	B, 23	7·7	3·5	10·5	4·7	2·2
North Bedfordshire mixed 8,565	1870	?269	0·6	3·3	81	25	56½	W, 36	8·7	0·9	23·7	2·5	9·5
	1913	84	1·4	9·0	75	27	58	W, 33	4·6	1·2	8·0	2·1	3·8
	1932	74½	1·8	5·2	70	29	60½	W, 33	5·0	1·5	7·8	2·3	3·4
	1958	77½	0·7	1·6	75	48	71	B, 34	3·4	2·0	8·4	5·0	1·7
Huntingdonshire clay upland 7,277	1870	?78½	0·6	6·7	73	32	55	W, 35	9·8	1·2	25·7	3·2	8·1
	1913	82½	1·2	5·7	81	25	56	W, 36	6·4	1·8	11·6	3·3	3·5
	1932	76½	2·0	6·7	78	28	57½	W, 45	12·5	1·6	18·7	2·3	8·1
	1958	73½	0·4	2·4	75	25	75	W, 37	3·0	1·2	10·6	4·4	2·4
South Oxfordshire dairy 7,863	1870	96	0·8	4·3	53	21	58	W, 27	10·0	1·1	22·1	2·4	9·2
	1913	90½	1·5	8·5	49	8	66	W, 27	2·9	2·0	4·8	3·2	1·5
	1932	98	2·2	11·5	60	20	57½	W, 28	4·0	2·2	5·8	3·2	1·8
	1958	89½	1·3	1·9	63	36	80	B, 40	1·7	3·1	3·1	5·6	0·5
Bedfordshire market gardening 13,175	1870	77	0·4	3·5	65	30	51½	W, 29	3·4	1·1	12·1	3·9	3·1
	1913	76½	0·2	5·2	39	24	22	W, 13	0·3	0·7	1·4	3·5	0·4
	1932	77	0·3	8·5	85	1	16	W, 9	0·2	0·8	0·7	3·0	0·2
	1958	72	0·1	5·9	76	7	29½	W, 19	0·5	0·6	3·9	4·7	0·8

Table 47
Parishes used in land-use samples for 1870, 1913, 1932, and 1958 (see Fig. 52; Table 46)

Area	Type	Parishes
Derbyshire	limestone plateau	Aldwark, Ballidon, Brassington, Parwich
Nottinghamshire	Keuper belt	Kersall, Kneesall, Norwell, Ossington
Northamptonshire	pastoral upland	Badby, Everdon, Newnham, Preston Capes
Leicestershire	wolds	Gaddesby, Twyford and Thorpe, Somerby
North Oxfordshire	mixed farming and dairying	Hook Norton, Swalcliffe, Tadmarton
Central Buckinghamshire	dairying	Stewkley, Wing
North Bedfordshire	mixed farming	Harrold, Odell, Sharnbrook
Huntingdonshire	clay upland	Brington, Catworth, Leighton
South Oxfordshire	dairying	Eynsham, Stanton Harcourt
Bedfordshire	market gardening	Biggleswade, Northill, Sandy

Table 48
Numbers of manufacturers of boots and shoes (excluding bespoke bootmakers) in Northamptonshire

	1847	1854	1864	1870	1877
Bozeat	—	—	—	1	6
Cogenhoe	—	—	—	—	1
Daventry	12	9	8	6	7
Desborough	—	—	—	2	3
Earls Barton	7	4	3	5	8
Finedon	—	1	2	—	6
Higham Ferrers	4	5	6	7	6
Irchester	—	—	—	—	1
Irthlingborough	1	3	6	5	10
Kettering	1	1	4	21	24
Long Buckby	2	1	2	3	5
Northampton	60	74	96	94	125
Raunds	1	1	—	1	4
Rothwell	—	—	—	—	2
Wellingborough	9	15	16	13	9
Wollaston	1	—	2	1	3
TOTAL	98	114	145	159	220

Table 49
Coal production in the East Midlands (compiled from various sources)

Year	Derbyshire and Nottinghamshire		Leicestershire and South Derbyshire	Regional total
	Derbyshire	Nottinghamshire		
1808	269,456			
1816	942,218	494,665	176,665	1,613,548
1841	1,500,000[1,2]			
1855	2,256,000	809,400	425,000[3]	3,590,000
1860	4,940,000		730,000	5,670,000
1865	5,691,250		965,000	6,656,250
1869	7,035,540[4]		685,630[4]	7,721,170
1873				9,500,000[1]
1875	9,000,000[1]		1,000,000[1]	10,000,000[1]
1880				12,000,000[1]
1890			1,500,000[1,5]	18,800,000[1,6]
1900		6,970,000[7]		26,000,000[1]
1906	16,567,209	11,728,000[8]		
1910			3,000,000[1,9]	31,300,000[1]
1920			3,250,000[1,10]	29,400,000[1]
1930			See note 11	32,000,000[1]
1940			See note 12	37,500,000[1]
1950				35,100,000
1955				46,100,000
1959	37,780,000		7,120,000	44,900,000

1 approximate
2 calculated from number of miners
3 439,000 in 1854
4 seven collieries on the Leicestershire and South Derbyshire field included in return for Derbyshire
5 1891 total
6 total for 1888: 16,500,000[1] tons
7 total for 1897
8 1907 total
9 1913 total: 3,175,000
10 total for 1917 and 1919: 3,595,000 and 3,171,389 tons
11 over 3,000,000 in 1927, but 2,225,000 in 1933
12 total for 1938, slightly below 3,000,000

Table 50
Output of pig iron (Leicestershire excepted) to 1916 (compiled from various sources)

Derbyshire

Year	Blast furnaces existing	Pig iron Tonnage	% national output
1720		800	4·6
1788		4,500	6·5
1790		5,600	1·7
1796		2,107	4·0
1806	17	10,338	3·1
1823	15	14,111	
1825		19,148	
1827		20,500	
1828		22,360	
1830	18	18,591	2·7
1839	14	34,372	2·7
1840		31,000	
1842		27,500	
1847	30	95,200	4·7
1848	30	78,000	
1852		89,900	3·3
1855		116,500	3·6

	Derbyshire[1]				Northamptonshire			
	Blast furnaces		Pig iron		Blast furnaces		Pig iron	
Year	Existing	In blast	Tonnage	% national output	Existing	In blast	Tonnage	% national output
1857					3			
1858							9,750	
1860			125,850	3·3				
1865			189,360	3·9				
1866		31			8	6	26,000[2]	
1869	43				10	7		
1870			179,700	3·0				
1871							60,512	0·9
1872						9		
1875	51		272,065	4·3	18		80,689	1·3
1877					20			
1880			375,000	4·6			167,544	2·2
1883					26			
1885			360,900	4·9	30		190,261	2·6
1890			387,800	4·9			225,046	2·8
1895			413,500	6·2			254,744	3·3
1900	47		516,600	6·2			247,908	2·8
1901					21			
1905			568,300	5·9			273,366	2·8
1910			638,600	6·2			367,132	3·6
1913			698,700	6·8				
1916							284,520	3·0[3]

1 Includes Nottinghamshire after the opening of the Stanton ironworks in 1864   2 Includes production from furnaces opened in Lincolnshire   3 Approximate

Table 51

Output of pig iron in the East Midland region from 1913 (includes production at Dagenham, Essex)

Year	Pig iron produced		% national output from Scunthorpe for comparison
	Tonnage	% national output	
1913	1,166,100	11·4	4·4
1918	925,426	10·4	6·2
1920	914,400	11·4	7·3
1925	1,010,900	16·1	8·7
1930	1,120,400	18·1	12·1
1935	1,440,500	22·4	13·4
1940	1,786,700	21·8	16·0
1945	1,697,300	23·8	14·6
1950	2,209,000	22·9	12·9
1955	2,341,900	18·0	15·1
1960	2·632,500	16·7	14·5

Table 52

Blast furnaces existing in the region in selected years

		1869	1938	1950	1960
Rother Valley	Chesterfield	1	—	—	—
	Clay Cross	3	2	1	—
	Renishaw	2	2	2	2
	Sheepbridge	4	2	2	2
	Staveley	4	4	4	4
	Unstone	1	—	—	—
	Wingerworth	3	—	—	—
Belper District	Denby	4	—	—	—
	Morley Park	2	—	—	—
Alfreton-Ripley District	Alfreton	3	—	—	—
	Butterley and Codnor	6	—	—	—
	Oakerthorpe	2	—	—	—
Lower Erewash Valley, etc	Stanton	5	5	5	5
	West Hallam	3	—	—	—
Northampton Sand Ironfield	Corby	—	4	4	4
	Finedon	3	—	—	—
	Heyford	3	—	—	—
	Irthlingborough	1	—	—	—
	Islip	—	4	—	—
	Kettering and Cransley	—	4	4	—
	Wellingborough	1	2	3	3
Leics. Marlstone Field	Holwell (=Asfordby, Melton Mowbray)	—	5	5	3
Total for region		51	34	30	23

Table 53

Opening and closing dates of blast-furnace plants in Northamptonshire and Leicestershire

	Location	Began producing	Finally closed
Finally closed before 1900	Wellingborough	1857	1876
	Finedon	1857	1883
	Heyford	1857	1891
	Stow	1866	1893
	Wellingborough	1868	1874
	Towcester	1875	1882
Closed in inter-war period	Irthlingborough	1867	1934
	Hunsbury Hill	1874	1921
Closed since 1945	Islip	1873	1949
	New Cransley	1877	1958
	Kettering	1878	1959
Still operating 1961	Melton Mowbray[1]	1881	—
	Wellingborough	1883	—
	Corby	1910	—

1 Also called the Holwell or Asfordby plant; expected to close in 1963

Table 54

Extraction of iron ore, tons (compiled from various sources)

Year	Jurassic orefields			Derbyshire Coal Measures
	Northampton Sand	Leicestershire Marlstone	Banbury Marlstone	
1855	74,084	See note 2	See note 3	409,000
1860	95,664[4]		6,000	376,000
1865	364,349	See note 5		350,000
1870	761,248			384,865
1875	1,086,000			218,000
1880	1,550,000	52,387[6]	8,000	150,248
1885	1,300,000[7]	310,529		18,805
1890	1,400,000[7]	609,964		23,732
1895	1,200,000[7]	598,401		5,850
1900	1,800,000[7]	630,361	193,222[8]	2,835
1905	2,300,000[7]	691,614		
1910	2,900,000[7]	560,410[9]		1,448
1915	2,950,000[7] [10]	685,137[10]	See note 10	See note 10
1920	3,000,000[7] [11]	See note 11		
1925	2,948,400	1,527,400[12]		
1930	3,716,700	1,657,800		
1935	4,311,300	1,355,200		See note 13
1940	8,762,300	1,059,500	959,300	
1945	7,759,400[14]	818,400[14]	1,138,900[14]	
1950	6,788,500	762,900	791,000	
1955	8,078,000	1,011,300	1,591,900	
1960	8,656,500[15]	793,100	1,328,400	

1 nil in 1854
2 trials with this ore at Clay Cross in 1855
3 nil in 1857
4 140,485 in 1858
5 nil in 1868
6 99,599 in 1881
7 approximate
8 166,163 in 1899
9 incomplete return

10 1913 production: Northampton Sand, 3,400,000[7]; Leicestershire Marlstone, 846, 021; Banbury Marlstone, 153,000; Derbyshire, 116
11 1917 production: Northampton Sand, 2,933,000; Banbury Marlstone, 434,435
12 1921 production of Marlstone ore, 623,300
13 1937 production of Derbyshire ore, 1,000
14 peak annual productions in Second World War: Northampton Sand, 10,635,300 in 1942 (53 weeks); Leicestershire Marlstone, 1,108,800 in 1941; Banbury Marlstone, 1,699,900 in 1943
15 Claxby ore (cretaceous) included for recent years: 200,000 in 1960

Table 55

Output of crude steel in the East Midland region from 1937 (including production at Barking, Braintree, Letchworth, Portsmouth, and Woolwich). Output from Scunthorpe is given as a % of national output for comparison

Year	Crude steel produced		Scunthorpe % national output
	Tonnage	% national output	
1937	438,400	3·6	10·0
1940	531,600	4·1	10·0
1945	557,700	4·7	9·3
1950	755,600	4·6	9·6
1955	1,000,100	5·1	10·2
1960	1,223,700	5·0	10·5

Table 56

Reserves (tons of ore) and prospects of jurassic orefields in the East Midland region (1961 estimates). Estimated life based on proved and probable reserves only, at 1960 rate of extraction

	Northampton Sand		Leicestershire Marlstone	Banbury Marlstone
	north of the Welland	south of the Welland		
Proved and probable	830,000,000	740,000,000	40,000,000	220,000,000
Possible	145,000,000	115,000,000	1,000,000	110,000,000
Life from 1960	105 yrs	90 yrs	35 yrs	65 yrs

Table 57

Distribution of population among categories of density 1801

County	Total	Urban	Transitional	Rural	Sparse rural
Derbyshire	161,567	nil	23,459	133,245	4,863
Nottinghamshire	140,350	nil	54,684	81,588	4,078
Leicestershire	130,082	nil	42,410	85,384	2,288
Rutland	16,300	nil	2,498	12,997	805
Northamptonshire	131,757	nil	24,078	103,646	4,033
Huntingdonshire	37,568	nil	6,594	28,961	2,013
Bedfordshire	63,393	nil	11,536	51,529	328
Buckinghamshire (part of)	66,086	nil	7,221	57,047	1,818
Oxfordshire (most of)	105,235	3,906	19,805	79,481	2,043
Hertfordshire (part of)	730	nil	nil	730	nil
Regional total	853,068	3,906	192,285	634,508	22,269

Table 58 Distribution of population among categories of density 1851

County	Total	Urban	Transitional	Rural	Sparse rural
Derbyshire	296,084	28,868	134,481	128,473	4,262
Nottinghamshire	270,427	nil	177,527	90,250	2,650
Leicestershire	230,308	nil	122,594	106,141	1,573
Rutland	22,983	nil	4,868	17,367	748
Northamptonshire	212,380	nil	76,100	134,499	1,781
Huntingdonshire	64,183	nil	12,045	51,891	247
Bedfordshire	124,478	nil	52,227	72,114	137
Buckinghamshire (part of)	106,246	nil	26,483	78,802	961
Oxfordshire (most of)	161,185	4,361	51,357	105,078	389
Hertfordshire (part of)	842	nil	nil	842	nil
Regional total	1,489,116	33,229	657,682	785,457	12,748

Table 59 Distribution of population among categories of density 1901

County	Total	Urban	Transitional	Rural	Sparse rural
Derbyshire	585,837	112,245	396,254	73,727	3,611
Nottinghamshire	514,459	240,486	200,582	69,278	4,113
Leicestershire	437,501	212,379	109,230	113,009	2,883
Rutland	19,709	nil	5,882	13,319	508
Northamptonshire	335,628	87,327	143,597	100,365	4,339
Huntingdonshire	54,125	nil	20,459	32,329	1,337
Bedfordshire	171,707	43,526	68,111	59,707	363
Buckinghamshire (part of)	100,653	nil	44,572	54,880	1,201
Oxfordshire (most of)	169,052	8,858	79,578	79,169	1,447
Hertfordshire (part of)	808	nil	nil	808	nil
Regional total	2,389,479	704,821	1,068,265	595,783	19,802

Table 60 Distribution of population among categories of density 1951

County	Total	Urban	Transitional	Rural	Sparse rural
Derbyshire	826,437	174,944	572,052	75,082	4,359
Nottinghamshire	841,211	306,055	457,549	74,769	2,838
Leicestershire	631,077	285,181	272,807	69,311	3,778
Rutland	20,537	nil	5,407	13,830	1,300
Northamptonshire	423,481	104,432	230,153	84,410	4,486
Huntingdonshire	69,302	nil	29,278	37,723	2,301
Bedfordshire	311,937	163,456	86,848	60,872	761
Buckinghamshire (part of)	133,818	nil	80,894	51,246	1,678
Oxfordshire (most of)	256,239	99,399	72,289	81,961	2,590
Hertfordshire (part of)	845	nil	nil	845	nil
Regional total	3,514,884	1,133,467	1,807,277	550,049	24,091

Table 61

Percentage distribution of population among categories of density: U = urban; T = transitional; R = rural and sparse rural

		1801	1851	1901	1951
Derbyshire	U	0·0	9·8	19·2	21·0
	T	14·5	45·5	67·6	69·4
	R	85·5	44·7	13·2	9·6
Nottinghamshire	U	0·0	0·0	46·7	36·4
	T	39·0	65·6	39·0	54·4
	R	61·0	34·4	14·3	9·2
Leicestershire	U	0·0	0·0	48·5	45·2
	T	32·6	53·2	25·0	43·2
	R	67·4	46·8	26·5	11·6
Rutland	U	0·0	0·0	0·0	0·0
	T	15·3	21·2	29·8	26·3
	R	84·7	78·8	70·2	73·7
Northamptonshire	U	0·0	0·0	26·0	24·6
	T	18·3	35·8	42·8	54·4
	R	81·7	64·2	31·2	21·0
Huntingdonshire	U	0·0	0·0	0·0	0·0
	T	17·6	18·8	37·8	42·2
	R	82·4	81·2	62·2	57·8
Bedfordshire	U	0·0	0·0	25·4	52·4
	T	18·2	42·0	39·6	27·8
	R	81·8	58·0	35·0	19·8
Buckinghamshire (part of)	U	0·0	0·0	0·0	0·0
	T	10·9	24·9	44·3	60·5
	R	89·1	75·1	55·7	39·5
Oxfordshire (most of)	U	3·7	2·7	5·3	38·7
	T	18·8	31·9	47·0	28·3
	R	77·5	65·4	47·7	33·0
Total for region (including two Hertfordshire parishes)	U	0·5	2·2	29·5	32·25
	T	22·5	44·2	44·7	51·4
	R	77·0	53·6	25·8	16·35

Table 62 on p. 276

274

Table 63
Populations of selected towns 1801–1961

Year	Bedford	Buckingham	Derby	Huntingdon	Leicester	Luton	Northampton	Nottingham	Oakham	Oxford	Peterborough
1801	3,948	2,605	10,832	2,016	16,953	3,095	7,020	28,801	1,620	10,514	3,924
1811	4,601	2,987	13,043	2,397	23,146	3,716	8,427	34,030	1,704	11,609	4,285
1821	5,466	3,465	17,423	2,806	30,125	4,529	10,793	40,190	2,167	14,773	5,315
1831	6,959	3,610	23,627	3,267	39,904	5,693	15,349	50,220	2,390	17,550	6,373
1841	9,178	4,054	32,741	3,507	48,167	7,748	21,242[5]	52,164	2,726	19,617	6,959
1851	11,693	4,020	40,609	3,872	60,584	12,787	26,657	57,407	3,031	27,843	8,473
1861	13,415	3,849	43,091	3,816	68,056	17,821	32,813	74,693	2,959	27,560	11,735
1871	16,850	3,703	49,810	4,243	95,220[4]	20,733	41,168	86,621	3,089	31,404	11,264
1881	19,533	3,585	58,568	4,228	122,376	26,140	51,882	186,575[6]	3,227	33,947	20,123
1891	28,023	3,364	65,360	4,346	174,624	32,401	61,012	213,877	3,566	34,754	23,671
1901	35,144	3,152	69,266²	4,261	211,579	38,926	87,021	239,743	3,502	49,336	30,872
1911	39,183	3,282	123,410	4,203	227,222	49,978	90,064	259,901	3,667	53,048	33,574
1921	41,855	3,060	131,151	4,184	234,143	60,266	90,895	262,624	3,340	67,290	39,551
1931	42,606	3,082	142,403	4,106	239,169	70,486	92,314	276,189	3,191	80,540	43,558
1939¹					263,000		96,000	279,000		96,000	
1951	53,075	3,942	141,267	7,784	285,181	110,381	104,432	306,008	3,539	98,747	53,417
1961⁷	63,317	4,337	132,325	8,812³	273,298	131,505	105,361	311,645	4,571	106,124	62,031

1 Mid-year estimates
2 114,848 after change of boundaries
3 Now includes Godmanchester
4 Large immigration noted in the census report

5 The Priory of St. Andrew was not returned before 1841, when its population was 2,293⁶
6 Great extension of boundaries since preceeding census
7 1961 totals are from the preliminary census report

Table 62   Partial analysis of employment. Structure, by counties, for 1851, 1901, and 1951. Total

County	Year	Total employed	Agriculture	Coal mining	Metal mf. & Engineering	Textile mf.	Garment mf.
Derbyshire	1851	135,366	21·4	4·0[2]	4·2	note 3	note 3
	1901	258,644	7·1	17·3	10·0	10·8	3·9
	1951	385,605	4·3	9·8	14·1	5·4	2·0
Nottinghamshire	1851	157,980	21·7	2·3	2·5	note 3	note 3
	1901	235,002	7·2	11·0	6·3	18·2[6]	5·8
	1951	398,289	3·7	10·0	11·0	6·2	4·5
Leicestershire	1851	125,600	23·0	1·3	1·6	note 3	note 3
	1901	209,180	7·2	2·9	4·5	15·57	6·3
	1951	311,674	4·8	3·1	11·4	10·3	4·8
Rutland	1851	11,387	43·7	—	—	note 3	note 3
	1901	8,471	28·2	—	2·6	0·1	3·6
	1951	9,539	23·2	—	6·1	1·0	1·4
Northamptonshire including Soke of Peterborough	1851	104,315	35·0	—	—	note 3	note 3
	1901	148,952	12·4	—	3·8	1·1	5·6
	1951	188,409	7·8	—	11·5	0·2	3·8
Huntingdonshire	1851	27,433	47·2	—	—	note 3	note 3
	1901	22,746	34·3	—	3·8	1·0	4·0
	1951	31,856	21·8	—	8·1	0·5	0·7
Bedfordshire	1851	74,059	32·8	—	—	note 3	note 3
	1901	76,642	18·0	—	5·3	2·6	20·4[8]
	1951	150,011	7·35	—	16·1	0·4	5·3
Buckinghamshire	1851	76,075[1]	35·8	—	—	note 3	note 3
	1901[9]	81,381[1]	20·0	—	6·3	2·2	4·2
	1951	57,372[1]	12·3	—	9·7	—	1·6
Oxfordshire	1801	72,028[1]	45·2	—	—	note 3	note 3
	1901	79,472[1]	20·2	—	3·5	2·4	6·8
	1951	119,438[1]	8·8	—	10·5	0·8	1·9

Note 1851 totals: gainfully occupied (all ages); 1901 totals: occupied population (10 years of age and older); 1951 totals: occupied population

1   Scaled down for 1851 and 1901, for use in plotting diagrams; reduced for 1951 by subtraction of Slough Municipal Borough, of Beaconsfield, Chesham, Eton, High Wycombe, and Marlow Urban Districts, and of Amersham, Eton, and Wycombe Rural Districts (Buckinghamshire); and of Henley Municipal Borough and Henley Rural District (Oxfordshire)

2   Also in 1851, 1·7% lead miners and 1% ironstone miners

employment, employment percentage in selected occupational groups

Leather mf.	Transport & Communications	Commerce	Clerical	Admin., Profl., Financial, Tech.	Personal service	Hosiery mf.	Lace mf.	Cotton mf.	Straw plaiting	Percentage accounted for
3·5	—	—	—	—	7·7	3·0	3·3	10·0	—	57·1
1·4	7·9	2·0	note 4	3·9	11·0	note 5	note 5	—	—	75·3
0·5	6·5	7·7	7·8	7·3	6·9	—	—	—	—	74·3
3·6	—	—	—	—	8·1	14·4	9·9	1·5	—	64·0
1·6	7·7	2·7	note 4	3·9	11·5	note 6	note 6	—	—	73·6
0·6	6·4	8·5	8·4	7·3	7·3	—	—	—	—	73·9
4·5	—	—	—	—	9·3	24·0	1·6	—	—	65·3
17·1	6·3	2·5	note 4	3·5	10·5	note 7	—	—	—	75·3
7·2	5·3	8·4	8·4	7·7	6·8	—	—	—	—	78·2
—	—	—	—	—	16·3	—	—	—	2·0	62·0
2·5	6·9	0·65	note 4	5·8	29·2	—	—	—	—	79·55
0·8	5·9	5·6	3·7	6·0	9·5	—	—	—	—	62·2
17·0	—	—	—	—	8·9	—	9·9	—	—	70·8
29·6	7·5	1·9	note 4	3·8	13·1	—	—	—	—	78·8
17·25	7·0	8·75	8·6	7·8	7·7	—	—	—	—	84·6
3·8	—	—	—	—	8·6	—	3·7	—	—	63·3
1·5	6·7	0·9	note 4	4·4	16·25	—	—	—	—	72·85
0·5	6·4	7·2	6·4	6·0	8·1	—	—	—	—	65·7
2·6	—	—	—	—	6·0	—	7·8	—	13·5	72·7
1·5	5·7	1·65	note 4	4·6	16·25	—	—	—	—	76·0
0·8	5·4	7·8	9·6	8·2	7·8	—	—	—	—	68·75
3·4	—	—	—	—	8·1	—	13·9	—	3·8	65·0
3·8	6·7	1·3	note 4	4·6	20·5	—	—	—	—	69·6
0·85	7·1	6·7	4·4	8·3	9·4	—	—	—	—	60·35
4·0	—	—	—	—	13·4	—	2·5	—	—	65·1
1·2	6·5	1·6	note 4	6·0	25·2	—	—	—	—	73·4
0·2	6·2	7·85	9·2	10·0	12·8	—	—	—	—	68·35

3 See under Hosiery, Lace, Cotton, Straw plaiting

4 Included under Commerce

5 Account for most of employment in textile manufacture

6 Lace manufacture (10·5%) and Hosiery manufacture (4·9%) account for most of employment in Textile manufacture

7 Hosiery 12·4%   8   13·8% working in straw, mostly in hat making

9 7% in furniture manufacture, etc., in this year

REFERENCES

The *Victoria County Histories* provide a wealth of background information, which varies however in scope and import with the date of its preparation. Other general works include the essays on the *Historical Geography of England before 1800*, edited by H. C. Darby; the *British Association Handbook* (1954) on the Oxford Region, edited by A. F. Martin and R. W. Steel; and the corresponding *Handbook* (1956) on Sheffield and its Region, edited by D. L. Linton. These last two items are styled *B.A. Handbooks* elsewhere. Most counties possess at least one, and some counties more than one, vigorous local society, concerned for instance with local history, local archaeology, or natural history.

CHAPTER 2

Arkell, W. J. *The Jurassic System in Great Britain* (Clarendon Press 1933)
— 'Stratigraphy and structures east of Oxford' *Quart. Journ. Geol. Soc.* **98** (1942), 187–204 ; **100** (1944), 45–60, 61–73
— *The Geology of Oxford* (Clarendon Press 1947)
Bromehead, C. E. N., Edwards, W., Wray, D. A. and Stephens, J. V. *The Country around Holmfirth and Glossop* (Memoir of the Geological Survey 1933)
Carruthers, R. G., Pocock, R. W. and Wray, D. A. *Special Reports on the Mineral Resources of Great Britain*. Vol. iv : Fluorspar (Memoir of the Geological Survey 1916)
Dewey, H. and Eastwood, T. *Special Reports on the Mineral Resources of Great Britain*. Vol. xxx : Copper Ores of the Midlands, etc. (Memoir of the Geological Survey 1925)
Dunham, K. C. *Special Reports on the Mineral Resources of Great Britain*. Vol. iv : Fluorspar (Memoir of the Geological Survey, 4th ed. 1952)
Edwards, W. *The Concealed Coalfield of Yorkshire and Nottinghamshire* (Memoir of the Geological Survey, 3rd ed. 1951)
— 'The Yorkshire-Nottinghamshire Coalfield', in *The Coalfields of Great Britain*, ed. Sir A. Trueman
Edwards, W. and Trotter, F. M. *The Pennines and Adjacent Areas* (Geological Survey, British Regional Geology series, 3rd ed. 1954)
Falcon, N. L. and Tarrant, L. H. 'The gravitational and magnetic exploration of parts of the Mesozoic-covered areas of southeast England' *Quart. Journ. Geol. Soc.* **106** (1951), 141–70
Fox-Strangways, C. *The Geology of the Country between Atherstone and Charnwood Forest* (Memoir of the Geological Survey 1900)
— *The Geology of the Country near Leicester* (Memoir of the Geological Survey 1903)
— *The Geology of the Leicestershire and South Derbyshire Coalfield* (Memoir of the Geological Survey 1907)
Gibson, W., Pocock, T. I., Wedd, C. B. and Sherlock, R. L. *The Geology of the Southern Part of the Derbyshire and Nottinghamshire Coalfield* (Memoir of the Geological Survey 1908)
Gibson, W. and Wedd, C. B. *The Geology of the Northern Part of the Derbyshire Coalfield and Bordering Tracts* (Memoir of the Geological Survey 1913)
Greig, D. C. and Mitchell, G. H. 'The western extension of the Leicestershire and Derbyshire coalfield' *Bull. Geol. Survey* **7** (1955), 38–46
Hollingworth, S. E. and Taylor, J. H. 'An outline of the geology of the Kettering district' *Proc. Geol. Assoc.* **57** (1946), 204–23
— *The Northampton Sand Ironstone : Stratigraphy, structure, and reserves* (Memoir of the Geological Survey 1951)

Hollingworth, S. E., Taylor, J. H. and Kellaway, G. A. ' Large-scale superficial structures in the Northampton ironstone field ' *Quart. Journ. Geol. Soc.* **100** (1944), 1–44

Hudson, R. G. S. and Cotton, G. ' The Carboniferous rocks of the Edale anticline, Derbyshire ' *Quart. Journ. Geol. Soc.* **101** (1945), 10–36

Kent, P. E. ' The Melton Mowbray anticline ' *Geol. Mag.* **74** (1937), 154–60
— ' A structure contour map of the surface of the buried pre-Permian rocks of England and Wales ' *Proc. Geol. Assoc.* **60** (1949), 87–104
— ' Triassic relics and the 1,000-foot surface in the southern Pennines ' *East Mid. Geog.* **8** (1957), 3–10

Lamplugh, G. W. and Gibson, W. *The Geology of the Country around Nottingham* (Memoir of the Geological Survey 1910)

Lamplugh, G. W., Gibson, W., Sherlock, R. L., and Wright, W. B. *The Geology of the Country between Newark and Nottingham* (Memoir of the Geological Survey 1908)

Lamplugh, G. W., Gibson, W., Wedd, C. B., Sherlock, R. L. and Smith, B. *The Geology of the Melton Mowbray District and Southeast Nottinghamshire* (Memoir of the Geological Survey 1909)

Lamplugh, G. W., Wedd, C. B. and Pringle, J. *Special Reports on the Mineral Resources of Great Britain.* Vol. xii : Iron Ores ; bedded ores of the Lias, Oolites, etc. (Memoir of the Geological Survey 1920)

Marshall, C. E. (ed.) *Guide to the Geology of the East Midlands* (University of Nottingham 1948)

Mitchell, G. H. ' The Leicestershire and South Derbyshire Coalfield ', in *The Coalfields of Great Britain*, ed. Sir A. Trueman

Parkinson, D. ' The stratigraphy of the Dovedale area, Derbyshire and Staffordshire ' *Quart. Journ. Geol. Soc.* **105** (1949), 265–94
— ' The Carboniferous Limestone of Treak Cliff, Derbyshire, with notes on the structure of the Castleton reef-belt ' *Proc. Geol. Assoc.* **64** (1953), 251–68

Prentice, J. E. ' The Carboniferous Limestone of the Manifold Valley region, north Staffordshire ' *Quart. Journ. Geol. Soc.* **106** (1951), 171–209

Prentice, J. E. and Sabine, P. A. ' Some superficial structures in the Cornbrash of Northamptonshire ' *Geol. Mag.* **84** (1947), 89–97

Pringle, J., Sandford, K. S. and Bayzand, J. *The Geology of the Country around Oxford* (Memoir of the Geological Survey, 2nd ed. 1926)

Sherlock, R. L. ' A correlation of some British Permo-Triassic rocks, Part I ' *Proc. Geol. Assoc.* **37** (1926), 1–72

Shirley, J. ' The Carboniferous Limestone of the Monyash-Wirksworth area, Derbyshire ' *Quart. Journ. Geol. Soc.* **114** (1958), 411–29

Shirley, J. and Horsfield, E. L. ' The structure and ore deposits of the Carboniferous Limestone of the Eyam district, Derbyshire ' *Quart. Journ. Geol. Soc.* **100** (1944), 289–308

Stephens, J. V. *Wells and Springs of Derbyshire* (Memoir of the Geological Survey 1929)

Sweeting, G. S. ' An outline of the geology of Ashover, Derbyshire ' *Proc. Geol. Assoc.* **57** (1946), 117–36

Trueman, Sir Arthur (ed.) *The Coalfields of Great Britain* (Edward Arnold 1954)

Warwick, G. T. ' The Peak District ', in *British Caving*, ed. C. H. D. Cullingford (Routledge and Kegan Paul 1953)

White, P. H. N. ' Gravity data obtained in Great Britain ' *Quart. Journ. Geol. Soc.* **104** (1948), 339–64

Whitehead, T., Anderson, W., Wilson, V. and Wray, D. A., with contributions by Dunham, K. C. *The Liassic Ironstones* (Memoir of the Geological Survey 1952)

Wills, L. J. *Concealed Coalfields* (Blackie 1956)

CHAPTER 3

Barnes, F. A. ' The Trent Eagre ' *Survey* **3**, 1–16 (University of Nottingham)
Clayton, K. M. ' The glacial chronology of part of the Middle Trent basin ' *Proc. Geol. Assoc.* **64** (1953), 198–207
— ' The denudation chronology of the Middle Trent basin ' *Trans. Inst. Brit. Geog.* **19** (1953), 25–36
— ' The geomorphology of the area around Nottingham and Derby ' *East Mid. Geog.* **3** (1955), 16–20
— ' The differentiation of the glacial drifts of the East Midlands ' *East Mid. Geog.* **7** (1957), 31–40
Curtis, L. F., and James, J. H. ' Frost-heaved soils of Barrow, Rutland ' *Proc. Geol. Assoc.* **70** (1959), 310–14
Dury, G. H. ' Some aspects of the geomorphology of part of the Jurassic belt ' Ph.D. thesis, University of London
— ' The shrinkage of Midland streams ' *Proc. Birmingham Nat. Hist. and Phil. Soc.* **18** (1953), 81–95
— ' Tests of a general theory of misfit streams ' *Trans. Inst. Brit. Geog.* **25** (1958), 105–18
Johnson, R. H. ' An examination of the drainage patterns of the eastern part of the Peak District of North Derbyshire ' *Geog. Studies* **4** (1957), 46–55
Johnson, R. H. and Rice, R. J. ' Denudation chronology of the southwest Pennine upland ' *Proc. Geol. Assoc.* **72** (1961), 21–31
Jowett, A. and Charlesworth, J. K. ' The glacial geology of the Derbyshire Dome and the western slopes of the southern Pennines ' *Quart. Journ. Geol. Soc.* **85** (1929), 307–34
Kellaway, G. A. and Taylor, J. H. ' Early stages in the physiographic evolution of a portion of the East Midlands ' *Quart. Journ. Geol. Soc.* **108** (1952), 343–73
King, C. A. M. ' The Churnet valley ' *East Mid. Geog.* **14** (1960), 33–40
Linton, D. L. ' Geomorphology [of the Sheffield region] ', in *Sheffield B.A. Handbook* (1956), 24–43
Marker, M. E. and Cooper, A. D. ' An examination of Otmoor ', *Proc. Geol. Assoc.* **72** (1961), 41–7
Posnansky, M. ' The Pleistocene succession in the Middle Trent basin ' *Proc. Geol. Assoc.* **71** (1960), 285–311
Raistrick, A. ' The correlation of glacial retreat stages across the Pennines ' *Proc. Yorks. Geol. Soc.* **22** (1934), 199–214
Waters, R. S. and Johnson, R. H. ' The terraces of the Derbyshire Derwent ' *East Mid. Geog.* **9** (1958), 3–15
West, R. G. and Donner, J. J. ' The glaciations of East Anglia and the East Midlands ' *Quart. Journ. Geol. Soc.* **112** (1956), 69–91

CHAPTER 4

Barnes, F. A. and Potter, H. R. ' A Flash Flood in western Derbyshire ' *East Mid. Geog.* **10** (1958), 3–15
Chandler, T. J. ' Surface breeze effects of Leicester's heat island ' *East Mid. Geog.* **15** (1961), 32–8
Department of Scientific and Industrial Research. *Atmospheric Pollution in Leicester* (H.M.S.O. 1945)
Derwent Valley Water Board. *The Derwent Valley Water Board's Undertaking* (1961)
Garnett, A. ' Relief, latitude, and climate : some local consequences ' *Indian Geog. Soc.* Silver Jubilee volume (1952), 128–31
— ' Climate [of the Sheffield region] ', in *Sheffield B.A. Handbook* (1956), 44–69

Gregory, S. 'Regional variations in the trend of annual rainfall over the British Isles' *Geog. Journ.* **122** (1956), 347-53

Lockyer, A. G. 'A study of water supply in Derbyshire' *East Mid. Geog.* **8** (1957), 32-44

Ministry of Housing and Local Government. River Great Ouse basin hydro-logical survey (H.M.S.O. 1960)

Smith, C. G. 'Climate [of the Oxford region]', in *Oxford B.A. Handbook* (1954), 37-49

Thornthwaite, C. W. 'An approach toward a rational classification of climate' *Geog. Review* **38** (1948), 55-94

Tinn, A. B. 'Local temperature variations in the Nottingham district' *Quart. Journ. Roy. Met. Soc.* **64** (1938), 391-405

Water Committee of the Sheffield City Council. *The Water Supply of Sheffield* (1961)

CHAPTER 5

Balme, O. E. 'Edaphic and vegetational zoning on the Carboniferous Lime-stone of the Derbyshire dales' *Journ. Ecol.* **41** (1953), 331-44

Bower, M. 'The erosion of blanket peat in the southern Pennines' *East Mid. Geog.* **13** (1960), 22-33

Brierley, J. K. 'Some preliminary observations on the ecology of pit heaps' *Journ. Ecol.* **44** (1956), 383-90

Clarke, G. R. 'Soils [of the Oxford region]', in *Oxford B.A. Handbook* (1954), 50-5

Conway, V. M. 'Ringinglow Bog, near Sheffield' *Journ. Ecol.* **34** (1947), 149-81, and **37** (1949), 148-69

— 'Stratigraphy and pollen analysis of southern Pennine blanket peats' *Journ. Ecol.* **42** (1954), 117-47

Hepburn, I. 'The vegetation of the Barnack stone quarries : a study of the vegetation of Northamptonshire Jurassic limestone' *Journ. Ecol.* **30** (1942), 57-64

Hopkinson, J. W. 'Studies on the vegetation of Nottinghamshire : I, the ecology of the Bunter Sandstone' *Journ. Ecol.* **15** (1927), 130-71

Jackson, G. and Sheldon, J. 'The vegetation of Magnesian Limestone cliffs at Markland Grips near Sheffield' *Journ. Ecol.* **37** (1949), 38-50

Moss, C. E. *Vegetation of the Peak District* (Cambridge University Press 1913)

Pearsall, W. H. 'The soil complex in relation to plant communities : II, characteristic woodland soils' *Journ. Ecol.* **26** (1938), 194-205

— 'The soil complex in relation to plant communities : III, moorlands and bogs' *Journ. Ecol.* **26** (1938), 298-315

— *Mountains and Moorlands* (Collins 1950)

Pigott, C. D. 'Vegetation [of the Sheffield region]', in *Sheffield B.A. Hand-book* (1956), 79-89

Poore, M. E. D. 'The ecology of Woodwalton Fen' *Journ. Ecol.* **44** (1956), 455-92

Scurfield, G. 'Ecological observations in southern Pennine woodlands' *Journ. Ecol.* **41** (1953), 1-12

Tansley, A. G. *The British Islands and their Vegetation* (Cambridge University Press 1953)

Warburg, E. F. 'Vegetation and flora [of the Oxford region]', in *Oxford B.A. Handbook* (1954), 56-62

Watts, A. S. 'The vegetation of the Chiltern Hills, with special reference to the beechwoods and their seral relationships' *Journ. Ecol.* **22** (1934), 220-7 and 445-507

Woodhead, T. W. 'History of the vegetation of the southern Pennines' *Journ. Ecol.* **17** (1929), 1-34

CHAPTER 6

Prehistoric and Roman

Armstrong, A. L. 'Palaeolithic, Neolithic, and Bronze Ages [in the Sheffield region]', in *Sheffield B.A. Handbook* (1956), 90–110

Bartlett, J. E. 'Iron Age and Roman period [in the Sheffield region]', in *Sheffield B.A. Handbook* (1956), 111–20

Case, H. J. 'Prehistory of the Oxford area', in *Oxford B.A. Handbook* (1954), 76–84

Childe, V. G. *Prehistoric Communities of the British Isles* (Chambers 1940)

Clark, J. G. D. *The Mesolithic Age in Britain* (Cambridge University Press 1932)

Collingwood, R. G. *Roman Britain* (2nd ed., Clarendon Press 1953)

Collingwood, R. G. and Myres, J. N. L. *Roman Britain and the English Settlements* (Clarendon Press 1936)

Crawford, O. G. S. *The Long Barrows of the Cotswolds* (Bellows 1925)

Daniel, G. E. *The Prehistoric Chamber Tombs of England and Wales* (Cambridge University Press 1950)

Grimes, W. F. 'The Jurassic Way', in *Aspects of Archaeology in Britain and Beyond*, ed. W. F. Grimes (Edwards 1950)

Margary, I. D. *Roman Roads in Britain*: vol. i, south of the Foss Way–Bristol Channel; vol. ii, north of the Foss Way–Bristol Channel (Phoenix House 1955 and 1957)

Ordnance Survey. Map of Roman Britain (3rd ed. 1956)

Piggott, S. *Neolithic Cultures of the British Isles* (Cambridge University Press 1954)

Taylor, M. V. 'The Roman period in the Oxford area', in *Oxford B.A. Handbook* (1954), 55–95

Thomas, N. *A Guide to Prehistoric England* (Batsford 1960)

Saxon and Danish colonisation, Norman period, Middle Ages

Addison, W. *English Fairs and Markets* (Batsford 1953)

Bazeley, M. L. 'The extent of the English forest in the thirteenth century' *Trans. Roy. Hist. Soc.*, New Series, **4** (1921), 140–72

Beresford, M. *The Lost Villages of England* (Lutterworth Press 1954)

Bodleian Library and Royal Geographical Society. Map of Great Britain circa A.D. 1360 (facsimile) (Oxford University Press 1958)

Camden, W. *Britannia* (Holland's translation 1637)

Cameron, K. *The Place Names of Derbyshire*, Parts I, II and III. English Place Name Society, vols. xxvii, xxviii, and xxix (Cambridge University Press 1959)

Darby, H. C. *The Domesday Geography of Eastern England* (Cambridge University Press 1952)

Darby, H. C. and Campbell, E. M. J. (ed.). *The Domesday Geography of Southeast England* (Cambridge University Press 1962)

Darby, H. C. and Maxwell, I. S. (ed.). *The Domesday Geography of Northern England* (Cambridge University Press 1962)

Darby, H. C. and Terrett, I. B. (ed.). *The Domesday Geography of Midland England* (Cambridge University Press 1954)

Ellis, Sir Henry. *A General Introduction to Domesday Book*, vol. ii (1833)

Fuller, G. J. 'Settlement in Northamptonshire between A.D. 500 and Domesday' *East Mid. Geog.* **3** (1955), 25–36

Gelling, M. *The Place Names of Oxfordshire*, Parts I and II. English Place Name Society, vols. xxiii and xxiv (Cambridge University Press 1953 and 1954)

Gover, J. E. B., Mawer, A., and Stenton, F. M. *The Place Names of Northamptonshire.* English Place Name Society, vol. x (Cambridge University Press 1933)

Gover, J. E. B., Mawer, A., and Stenton, F. M. *The Place Names of Notting-hamshire*. English Place Name Society, vol. xvii (Cambridge University Press 1940)

Hilton, R. H. *The Economic Development of some Leicestershire Estates in the Fourteenth and Fifteenth Centuries* (Oxford University Press 1947)

Hoskins, W. G. *Essays in Leicestershire History* (Liverpool University Press 1950)

Knowles, D. and Hadcock, R. N. *Medieval Religious Houses in England and Wales* (Longmans, Green 1953)

Lennard, R. *Rural England, 1086–1135* (Clarendon Press 1959)

Lipson, E. *The Economic History of England* : vol. i, The Middle Ages (10th ed., Black 1949)

Mawer, A. and Stenton, F. M. *The Place Names of Bedfordshire and Huntingdonshire*. English Place Name Society, vol. iii (Cambridge University Press 1926)

— *The Place Names of Buckinghamshire*. English Place Name Society, vol. ii (Cambridge University Press 1925)

Parsons, E. J. S. *Introduction to the Facsimile of the Gough Map* (Oxford University Press 1958)

Rogers, J. E. T. *A History of Agriculture and Prices in England and Wales*, vol. v (Clarendon Press 1887)

Russell, J. C. *British Medieval Population* (University of New Mexico Press 1948)

Salter, H. E. *Medieval Oxford* (Clarendon Press 1936)

Stenton, Sir Frank. 'The road system of medieval England' *Econ. Hist. Review* **7** (1936), 7–19

Post-medieval

Andrews, J. H. 'Defoe and the sources of his *Tour* ' *Geog. Journ.* **126** (1960), 268–77

Camden, W. *Britannia* (Gibson's revision 1722)

Chambers, J. D. *Nottinghamshire in the Eighteenth Century* (King 1932)

— 'The Vale of Trent 1670–1800' *Econ. Hist. Review*, Supplement No. 3 (Cambridge University Press)

Defoe, Daniel *Tour Through England and Wales*

Eyre, S. R. 'The upward limit of enclosure on the East Moor of North Derbyshire' *Trans. Inst. Brit. Geographers* **24** (1957), 61–74

Leland, John *Itinerary ca.1535–43*, ed. Lucy Toulmin-Smith (Bell 1906–10)

Lennard, R. 'Rural Northamptonshire under the Commonwealth', in *Oxford Studies in Social and Legal History*, vol. v, ed. P. Vinogradoff (Clarendon Press 1916)

Miege, G. *The Present State of England* (1701)

Morton, John *The Natural History of Northamptonshire* (1712)

Nef, J. U. *The Rise of the British Coal Industry* (Routledge 1932)

Plot, Robert *The Natural History of Oxfordshire* (1705)

Throsby, John *The History and Antiquities of the Ancient Town of Leicester* (1791)

Willan, T. S. (ed.) 'The Navigation of the Great Ouse between St. Ives and Bedford in the Seventeenth Century' *Bedfordshire Record Society* **24** (1946)

Willis, Browne *The History and Antiquities of Buckingham* (1755)

Wright, J. *The History and Antiquities of Rutland* (1684)

CHAPTER 7

Arkell, W. J. *Oxford Stone* (Faber and Faber 1947)

Barley, M. W. *The English Farmhouse and Cottage* (Routledge and Kegan Paul 1961)

Batsford, H. and Fry, C. *The English Cottage* (Batsford 1938)

Beresford, M. W. and St Joseph, J. K.   *Medieval England, an Aerial Survey* (Cambridge University Press 1958)

Dickinson, R. E.   *The West European City* (Routledge and Kegan Paul 1951)

Hussey, C.   *English Country Houses, Early Georgian* (Country Life 1955)
— *English Country Houses, Mid-Georgian 1760–1800* (Country Life 1956)
— *English Country Houses, Late Georgian 1800–1840* (Country Life 1958)

Keating, H. M.   ' Village types and their distribution in the plain of Nottingham ' *Geog.* **20** (1935), 282–96

Paget, E.   ' Settlements [of the Oxford region] ', in *Oxford B.A. Handbook* (1954), 158–64

Pevsner, Nikolaus.   *An Outline of European Architecture* (John Murray 1948)
— *The buildings of England* (County Volumes, Penguin Books)

Radig, W.   *Die Siedlungtypen in Deutschland* (Henschelverlag 1955)

Summerson, J.   *Architecture in Britain 1530–1830* (3rd ed., History of Art Series, Penguin Books 1958)

Tipping, H. A.   English Homes series (Country Life)
Period I, vol. i, *Norman and Plantagenet, 1066–1485* (1921)
Period II, vol. i, *Early Tudor, 1485–1558* (1929)
Periods I and II, vol. ii, *Medieval and Early Tudor, 1066–1558* (1936)
Period III, vol. i, *Late Tudor and Early Stuart, 1558–1649* (2nd ed. 1929)
Period III, vol. ii, *Late Tudor and Early Stuart, 1558–1649* (1927)
Period IV, vol. i, *Late Stuart, 1649–1714* (1920)
— and Christopher Hussey
Period IV, vol. ii, *The Work of Sir John Vanbrugh and his School, 1699–1736* (1938)
Period V, vol. i, *Early Georgian, 1714–1760* (1921)
Period VI, vol. i, *Late Georgian, 1760–1820* (1926)

Wickham, A. K.   *The Villages of England* (Batsford 1933)

Yates, E. M.   ' Map of Ashbourne, Derbyshire ' *Geog. Journ.* **126** (1960), 479–81

County maps, and other similar maps, of the later eighteenth century, and Sanderson's Survey of the Mansfield District

Armstrong, A.   Rutland (surveyed and published 1780)
Burdett, P. P.   Derbyshire (surveyed 1762–7, published 1767)
Chapman, J.   Nottinghamshire (surveyed 1774, published 1776)
Eyre, T. and Jefferys, T.   Northamptonshire (surveyed before 1775, published 1779)
Jefferys, T.   Bedfordshire (surveyed and published 1765)
— Buckinghamshire (surveyed 1766–8, published 1770)
— Huntingdonshire (surveyed 1766, published 1768)
— Oxfordshire (surveyed 1766–7, published 1767)
King, W.   Belvoir district (surveyed 1804–6, published 1806)
Prior, J.   Leicestershire (surveyed 1775–7, published 1779)
Sanderson, G.   Twenty miles round Mansfield (surveyed and published 1835)

CHAPTER 8

Reports to the Board of Agriculture

Batchelor, T.   *General View of the Agriculture of the County of Bedford* (1813)
Brown, T.   *General View of the Agriculture of the County of Derby* (1794)
Crutchley, J.   *General View of the Agriculture of the County of Rutland* (1794)
Davis, R.   *General View of the Agriculture of the County of Oxford* (1794)
Donaldson, J.   *General View of the Agriculture of the County of Northampton* (1794)
Farey, J.   *General View of the Agriculture and Minerals of Derbyshire* (3 vols. 1811)
James, W. and Malcolm, J.   *General View of the Agriculture of the County of Buckingham* (1794)

Lowe, R. *General View of the Agriculture of the County of Nottingham* (1794, reprinted 1813)
Monk, J. *General View of the Agriculture of the County of Leicester* (1794)
Parkinson, R. *General View of the Agriculture of the County of Rutland* (1808)
— *General View of the Agriculture of the County of Huntingdon* (1811)
Pitt, W. *General View of the Agriculture of the County of Leicester* (1809)
— *General View of the Agriculture of the County of Northampton* (1813)
Priest, the Rev. St John *General View of the Agriculture of Buckinghamshire* (1810)
Stone, T. *General View of the Agriculture of the County of Huntingdon* (1793)
— *General View of the Agriculture of the County of Bedford* (1794)
Young, A. *General View of the Agriculture of Oxfordshire* (1813)

Other references

Beresford, M. W. ' Revisions in economic history xi : ridge and furrow and the open fields ' *Econ. Hist. Review* **1-2**, Second Series (1950), 34–45
Chandler, T. J. ' The canals of Leicestershire, their development and trade ' *East Mid. Geog.* **10** (1958), 27–40
Fitton, R. S. and Wadsworth, A. P. *The Strutts and the Arkwrights* (Manchester University Press 1958)
Macpherson, D. *Annals of Commerce*, vol. iii (1805)
Marshall, W. *Rural Economy of the Midland Counties* (Nicol 1790)
— *A Review of Reports to the Board of Agriculture from the Northern Department of England* (Longmans, Hurst, Rees, and Orme 1808)
Mead, W. R. ' Ridge and furrow in Buckinghamshire ' *Geog. Journ.* **120** (1954), 34–42
Pilkington, James *A View of the Present State of Derbyshire* (2 vols. 1789)

CHAPTERS 9–10

General references

Hammond, J. L. and Hammond, Barbara *The Skilled Labourer 1760–1832* (Longmans, Green 1920)
Hoskins, W. G. *Leicestershire* (Hodder and Stoughton 1957)
Houston, J. M. ' Industry [of the Oxford Region] ', in *Oxford B.A. Handbook* (1954), 141–51
Porter, G. R. *The Progress of the Nation* (Methuen 1912)
Smith, Wilfred *An Economic Geography of Great Britain* (Methuen 1949)
Stamp, L. D. and Beaver, S. H. *The British Isles* (4th ed., Longmans, Green 1959)

Directories, mid-nineteenth century

Gardner, R. *History, Gazetteer, and Directory of the County of Oxford* (subscription, 1852)
Glover, S. *History and Directory of the Borough of Derby* (Glover and Son 1843)
— *History, Gazetteer, and Directory of the County of Derby* (Glover 1829)
Rusher, J. G. *Banbury List and Directory* (J. G. Rusher and successors, 1795–1896)
Slater's Directory of Bedfordshire, Buckinghamshire, Cambridgeshire, Huntingdonshire, Leicestershire, Lincolnshire, Norfolk, Northamptonshire, Nottinghamshire, Oxfordshire, Rutland, and Suffolk (Isaac Slater 1851)
History, Directory, and Gazetteer of Nottinghamshire (F. and J. White 1844)
History, Gazetteer, and Directory of the County of Derby (Francis White 1957)
History, Gazetteer, and Directory of Northamptonshire (W. Whelan 1849)
History, Gazetteer, and Directory of Nottinghamshire (William White 1832)
History, Gazetteer, and Directory of Leicestershire and the Small County of Rutland (William White 1846)

History, Gazetteer, and Directory of the Counties of Leicester and Rutland (Simpkin, Marshall 1863)
Post Office Directory of Derbyshire, Leicestershire, Nottinghamshire, Rutland, Bedfordshire, Buckinghamshire, Huntingdonshire, Berkshire, Northamptonshire, and Oxfordshire (W. Kelly 1845)

Agriculture

Auty, R. M.   *Leicestershire* (Land Utilisation Survey 1943)
Barnes, F. A.   'The evolution of the salient patterns of milk production and distribution in England and Wales ' *Trans. Inst. Brit. Geographers*, Publication No. 25 (1958), 167–95
Beaver, S. H. and Allen, D. M.   *Northamptonshire and the Soke of Peterborough* (Land Utilisation Survey 1943)
Broughton, M. E.   *Rutland* (Land Utilisation Survey 1937)
Caird, J.   *English Agriculture in 1850–51* (Longmans, Brown, Green, and Longmans 1852)
Clarke, J. I., Orrell, K. and Taylor, S. A.   ' Edale, a south Pennine valley ' *Occasional Papers, Department of Geography, University of Durham*, No. 1 (1957)
Chew, H. C.   'The post-war land use pattern of the former grasslands of eastern Leicestershire ' *Geography* **38** (1953), 286–95
— ' Fifteen years of agricultural change ' *Geography* **43** (1958), 177–90
Coppock, T. J.   ' Crop and livestock changes in the Chilterns ' *Trans. Inst. Brit. Geographers*, Publication No. 28 (1960), 179–98
Edwards, K. C.   *Nottinghamshire* (Land Utilisation Survey 1944)
Fitchett, C. E.   *Bedfordshire* (Land Utilisation Survey 1943)
Fleming, R. J.   ' Farming in Leicestershire ' *Journ. Roy. Agric. Soc.* **115** (1954), 14–16
Fryer, D. W.   *Huntingdonshire* (Land Utilisation Survey 1941)
Harris, A. H. and Henderson, H. C. K. H.   *Derbyshire* (Land Utilisation Survey 1941)
Hopkins, J. S.   ' Farming in Nottinghamshire ' *Journ. Roy. Agric. Soc.* **115** (1954), 9–11
Leay, P.   ' The market garden industry of the Melbourne district ' *East Mid. Geog.* **1** (1954), 33–40
Marshall, Mary   *Oxfordshire* (Land Utilisation Survey 1943)
Moscrop, W. J.   ' A report on the farming of Leicestershire ' *Journ. Roy. Agric. Soc.*, Second Series, **2** (1966), 289–337
Orr, J.   *Agriculture in Oxfordshire* (Clarendon Press 1916)
Waud, L. M.   ' Farming in Derbyshire ' *Journ. Roy. Agric. Soc.* **115** (1954), 11–14

Hosiery and other textile-working

Commissioners . . . [on] the Condition of the Frame-work Knitters.   Report (H.M.S.O. 1845)
Erickson, Charlotte   *British Industrialists : Steel and Hosiery 1850–1950* (Cambridge University Press 1959)
Felkin, W.   *An Account of the Machine-wrought Hosiery Trade* (Strange 1845)
Henson, G.   *The Civil, Political, and Mechanical History of the Framework Knitters* (1831)
Patterson, A. T.   *Radical Leicester* (University College Leicester 1954)
Plummer, A.   *The Witney Blanket Industry* (Routledge 1934)
Rawstron, E. M.   ' Some aspects of the location of hosiery and lace manufacture in Great Britain ' *East Mid. Geog.* **9** (1958), 16–28
Wells, F. A.   ' The hosiery trade ', in *Britain in Depression* (British Association, Pitman 1935)
— *The British Hosiery Trade* (Allen and Unwin 1935)

Coal

Colliery Yearbook
Edwards, K. C. ' East Midlands coal production in relation to Britain's fuel and power problem ' *East Mid. Geog.* **6** (1956), 26–34
Estall, R. C. ' The distribution of coal from the East Midland division ' *East Mid. Geog.* **8** (1957), 11–21
Gibson, W. *The Concealed Coalfield of Yorkshire and Nottinghamshire* (Memoir of the Geological Survey 1913)
Holmes, W. D. ' The Leicestershire and South Derbyshire coalfield I the coal mining industry ' *East Mid. Geog.* **10** (1958), 16–26
Royal Commission on Coal Supplies. *Report* (H.M.S.O. 1871)
Royal Commission on Coal Supplies. *Report* (H.M.S.O. 1903–5)

Iron and steel

Beaver, S. H. ' The development of the Northamptonshire iron ore industry, 1851–1930 ', in *London Essays in Geography*, ed. L. D. Stamp and S. W. Wooldridge (Longmans, Green 1951)
British Iron and Steel Federation. *Annual Statistics*
Burn, D. L. *The Economic History of Steelmaking* (Cambridge University Press 1940)
Clapham, J. H. *An Economic History of Modern Britain : Free Trade and Steel 1850–1886* (Cambridge University Press 1932)
Development in the Iron and Steel Industry. Special report published by the Iron and Steel Board (1961)
Pocock, D. C. D. ' Iron and steel at Corby ' *East Mid. Geog.* **15** (1961), 3–10
Roepke, Howard G. ' Movements of the British iron and steel industry 1720 to 1951 ' *Illinois Studies in the Social Sciences* **36** (University of Illinois Press, Urbana 1956)

Other references

Advisory Committee on Sand and Gravel, Report : Part 3, Trent Valley (H.M.S.O. 1950)
British Stone Federation. *Quarry Directory*
Carruthers, R. G. and Strahan, Sir Aubrey Special Reports on the Mineral Resources of Great Britain, vol. xxvi : *Lead and Zinc Ores of Durham, Yorkshire, and Derbyshire* (Memoir of the Geological Survey 1923)
Carter, E. *An Historical Geography of the Railways of the British Isles* (Cassell 1959)
Hadfield, C. *British Canals, An Illustrated History* (Phoenix House 1950)
Healey, P. R. and Rawstron, E. M. ' The brickworks of the Oxford Clay vale ' *East Mid. Geog.* **4** (1955), 42–8
Holmes, W. D. ' The Leicestershire and South Derbyshire coalfield ; 2, the clay industry ' *East Mid. Geog.* **12** (1960), 9–17
— ' The Leicestershire and South Derbyshire coalfield ; 3, light industry ' *East Mid. Geog.* **13** (1960), 16–21
Houston, J. M. ' Industries [of the Oxford region] ', in *Oxford B.A. Handbook* (1954), 141–6
Hoyle, B. S. ' The production and refining of indigenous oil in Britain ' *Geography* **46** (1961), 315–21
Johnston, W. B. ' The East Midlands and postwar development in manufacturing ' *East Mid. Geog.* **4** (1955), 3–18
Lewin, H. G. *Early British Railways 1801–1844* (Locomotive Publishing Co. 1925)
Rawstron, E. M. ' Power production and the river Trent ' *East Mid. Geog.* **2** (1954), 23–9
— ' Power stations on the river Trent : a note on further developments ' *East Mid. Geog.* **14** (1960), 27–32
Smith, J. ' Geographical conditions affecting grain milling in the Nene basin ' *East Mid. Geog.* **1** (1954), 24–32

Brown, P. A. ' Centres of retail distribution in the East Midlands ' *East Mid. Geog.* **6** (1956), 3–9
— ' The local accessibility of Nottingham ' *East Mid. Geog.* **11** (1959), 37–48
Census Reports (H.M.S.O. 1801 onwards)
Chambers, J. D. ' Population Change in a Provincial Town : Nottingham 1700–1800 ', in *Studies in the Industrial Revolution,* ed. L. S. Pressnell (University of London, Athlone Press 1960)
Chambers, J. D. and others *Nottingham : a Century of Nottingham History 1851–1951* (University of Nottingham 1952)
City of Nottingham Official Handbook
Constant, A. ' The geographical background of inter-village population movements in Northamptonshire and Huntingdonshire ' *Geography* **33** (1948), 78–88
Couzens, F. C. ' Distribution of population in the mid-Derwent basin since the industrial revolution ' *Geography* **26**, 31–8
Edwards, K. C. ' The East Midlands : some general considerations ' *East Mid. Geog.* **1** (1949), 3–11
— and Wells, F. A. *A Survey of the Chesterfield Region* (Chesterfield Regional Planning Committee 1949)
Geographia Ltd. Marketing Areas Handbook (1955)
Gilbert, E. W. ' The Growth of the City of Oxford ', in *Oxford B.A. Handbook* (1954), 165–73
— ' The idea of the region ' *Geography* **45** (1960), 157–75
Gray, D. Nottingham, *Settlement to City* (Nottingham Co-operative Society 1953)
Holford, W. and Wright, H. M. *Corby New Town* (Corby Development Corporation 1952)
Hunt, A. J. ' The urban centres [of the Sheffield region] ', in *Sheffield B. A. Handbook* (1956), 303–13
Kimble, G. H. T. ' The Inadequacy of the Regional Concept ', in *London Essays in Geography,* ed. L. D. Stamp and S. W. Wooldridge (Longmans, Green 1951)
Large, D. C. ' Nottingham : its urban pattern ' *East Mid. Geog.* **6** (1956), 35–41
Morley, C. D. ' Population of Northampton and the Ise Valley, 1801–1951 ' *East Mid. Geog.* **11** (1959), 20–9
Moser, C. A. and Scott, W. *British Towns* (Oliver and Boyd 1961)
Odell, P. R. ' Urban spheres of influence in Leicestershire in the mid-nineteenth century ' *Geographical Studies* **4** (1957), 30–45
Osborne, R. H. ' Population concentration and conurban tendencies in the Middle Trent counties ' *East Mid. Geog.* **2** (1954), 30–7
Peel, R. F. ' Local intermarriage and the stability of rural population in the English Midlands ' *Geography* **27** (1942), 22–30
Philip, I. G. ' The Growth of the University [of Oxford] ', in *Oxford B.A. Handbook* (1954), 174–80
Pocock, D. C. D. ' The urban field of Corby ' *East Mid. Geog.* **13** (1960), 3–15
Powell, A. G. ' The 1951 census : an analysis of population changes in Derbyshire ' *East Mid. Geog.* **2** (1954), 13–22
— ' The 1951 census (2) : an analysis of population changes in Leicestershire ' *East Mid. Geog.* **3** (1955), 3–15
— ' The 1951 census (3) : an analysis of population changes in Nottinghamshire ' *East Mid. Geog* **4** (1955), 29–42
Redford, A. *Labour Migration in England 1800–50* (Manchester University Press 1926)
Smith, D. M. ' The employment structure of the counties of Derbyshire, Leicestershire, and Nottinghamshire ' *East Mid. Geog.* **12** (1959), 26–37
— ' Beeston : an industrial satellite of Nottingham ' *East Mid. Geog.* **14** (1960), 41–57

Schöller, P. ' Aufgaben und Probleme der Stadtgeographie ' *Erdkunde* 7 (1953),
    161–84
Turton, B. J. ' Industry and transport in Derby ' *East Mid. Geog.* 14 (1960),
    3–10
Vollans, E. C. ' Derby, a railway town and regional centre ' *Trans. Inst. Brit.
    Geographers* (1949), 93–112
Weekley, I. G. ' Service centres in Nottingham ' *East Mid. Geog.* 6 (1956), 41–5
— ' Industry in the small country towns of Lincolnshire, Northamptonshire,
    and Rutland ' *East Mid. Geog.* 7 (1957), 21–30

Town plans (historical)

J. Speed's *Atlas of England and Wales* (1610) includes town plans of Buckingham, Derby, Huntingdon, Leicester, Nottingham, Northampton, Oakham,
Oxford, and Peterborough. The *British Atlas* of 1810 has plans of Bedford,
Derby, Northampton, and Oxford. The county maps of Bedfordshire,
Buckinghamshire, Derbyshire, Leicestershire, and Northamptonshire,
listed in the references for Chapter 7, include plans of the county towns.
Among other relevant plans are those of Oxford by Guil[ielmus] Williams
(1733), Oxford by J. Rocque (in his map of Berkshire, 1762), and Nottingham by J. Badder and T. Peat (1744).

Planning and regionalism

Development plans and progress reports made under the Town and Country
Planning Act of 1947 are issued principally for county capitals, and for
remainders of counties ; certain towns other than county capitals are treated
individually. Among the particularly full and geographically informative
material come the Bedfordshire County Development Plan (1952) which lists
villages by form and site, indicating possible future developments for each,
and the Amendments to the Development Plan for the County of Derby, for
example Amendment No. 2 (1958), Chesterfield Town Map, Analysis of
Survey.

The following items possess little more than historical interest.

Fawcett, C. B. *Provinces of England* (Williams and Norgate 1919) ; revised by
    W. G. East and S. W. Wooldridge (Hutchinson 1960)
Gilbert, E. W. ' Practical regionalism in England and Wales ' *Geog. Journ.* 94
    (1939), 29–44

Proposals for reorganisation of local government appear in reports for specified
areas, for example the Local Government Commission for England and Wales,
Report No. 3 [on] East Midlands General Review Area (H.M.S.O. 1961).

INDEX

INDEX

Figures in bold type indicate where the main information on the subject will be found.

administrative structure, 227
afforestation, 60, 64, 85
agriculture, 91, 94–7, **124-34, 145-59**
—, employment in, 207
Akeman Street, 78–9
Alchester, 78–9
Alfreton, 163, 178–9
Althorp, 109
aluminium, 186
Amber (river), 26, 32–3, 168
Ancaster Gap, 34, 36
Antepenultimate Glacial, 38, 74
anthills, 126–7, 133
arable, *see* tillage
Arkwright, 136
Arnold, 136, 210, 221, 227
artificial fibres, 164, 206
Ashbourne, 205, 211
Ashby Canal, 142, 168
Ashby de la Zouch, 88, 211
Ashop (river), 25, 51
Ashover anticline, 9, 26
ashwood, 25, 64–5, 69, 71
Atlantic Phase, 64
automobile manufacture, 186, 205–6, 215–16
Aylesbury, 79–80, 95, 97, 135, 209, 224
Aynho Park, 109–10

back lanes, 111–13, 118–19
Badby, 118
Banbury, 95, 134, 167, 186, 211
Banbury orefield, 13–14, 180–1
barley, 91, 124, 130, 153, 157
barns, 108
barrows, 75
Barton in the Clay, 118
basement, 9, 12, 41–2
Bedford, 97, 167, 186, 203, 209, 215, 225
beechwood, 69
Beeston, 206, 210, 222
Beeston Terrace, 36
Belper, 44, 130, 141, 162, 178, 204
Belvoir Castle, 110
Belvoir country, 81, 125, 131
Bernwood, 85, 95
bevel, on Jurassic backslope, 24, 37–8
—, on Magnesian Limestone, 34
Bingham, 84, 119
birchwood, 64, 67, 73
Birmingham, 96, 98, 126, 225
Black Death, 90, 93

blast furnaces, 138, 141, 170–1, **177-8, 180-3**
Bleaklow, 25, 48, 63
Blenheim Palace, 109
Bletchley, 186, 225
bloomeries, 141
Boreal Phase, 63–4
boroughs, 80, 84, 88
Boston, 97, 90
boulder-clay, 28, **36-9**, 69, 70–2
Brackley, 95, 118
Braunston, 113, 118
brewing, 98, 129
bricks, 97, 104–5, 140, **184-5**
brickwork, in buildings, 104–7
Bronze Age, 75–6
brownearth, 65–7, 70
brownstone, 103–6
Buckingham, 80, 97, 205, 209–11, **216-18**, 227
building stone, 95, **102-8**
Bunter Sandstone, 26–7, 66–7
Burford, 89
bus services, 211
butter, 127, 132–3, 146
Buxton, 44, 168, 184

canals, 128, 131, **141-4,** 166–9
Carboniferous rocks, 4–9
Carboniferous Limestone, **4-5, 20, 25, 64-5,** 102–3
Carlton, 210, 221, 227
carpets, 137
carriers, 97, 127, 132, **211**
carrland, 72
Cartwright family, 110
cash crops, 94, **152-3**
cast iron, 141, 182
Castle Donington, 88
Castleton, 25, 140
cattle, 97, **124-34, 149-57**
causewayed camps, 75
caverns, 21
cement, 13, 185, 204
ceramic industries, 184–5
Chalk, 16–17, 70, 75
Chalk Rock, 17
Chalky Boulder-Clay, 38, 40, 70
chamber tombs, 75
Chapel-en-le-Frith, 121, 211
charcoal, 96, 141
Charnian rocks, **11,** 105
Charnwood Forest, 11, 28, 69, 81, 95, 130–1

293

Charnwood Forest Canal, 142
Chater (river), 30
Chatsworth House, 109
cheese, 124, 126, 129, 146, 150
chemicals, 184, 222
Cherwell (river), 29, 41
Cherwell valley, 84, 167
Chesterfield, 88, 136, 141, 179, 214, 216, **218-19**, 225
Chesterfield Canal, 142, 218
Chilterns, 1–2, 17, 30, 41, 69, 128
Chipping Norton, 89
Civil War, 67
Clay Cross, 214
clearing of woodland, 64, 67, 69, 86
climate, **43-55**
climates, local, 47
—, urban, 47
climatic change, 50, 62, 76
Clipstone Forest, 66–7
cloth-making, 88–9, 95
clothing industry, 165
coal, 98, 138, 140, 142, 169, **170-6**
coalfields, 94, 98, 187, 203–4, 206, 211
Coal Measures, **7-9**, 26, 33, 65–6 ; iron ores in, 140–1, 177–8
coal seams, **7-9**, 171, 175
Coalville, 165
coke (coking coal), 139, 141, 171, **174-5**
cold-air drainage, 47
collieries, 174–5
colliery villages, 176, 204
Collyweston Slate, 15, 103, 106
commons, 96, 127–8, 221
concrete, 185
conifers, 25
convertible land, 91, 149, 157
Coombe Terrace, 40
coppice, 96
Corallian rocks, **15-16**, 30
Corby, 175, 180, **182-3**, 205–6, **214-16**
corn, 87, 91, 94, 126, 145
Cornbrash, 15, 70
cotton, 130, 135–6, 161–2
cotton-grass, 63
Cotswolds, 14, 75
county boundaries, 1, 227
Coventry Canal, 142
Cowley, 167, 186
Creswell, 74–5
Cromford Canal, 142
cuvettes, 4, 9–12

dairying, 124–34, 145–52
dales, 65–6
Danes, 80
Dark Age settlement, 79–80
Daventry, 225
Dean, 113

Defoe, 97–8
density of population, 81, 84, 93, **187-205**
depopulation, **90-4**, 96, 204
Derby, 80, 88, 136, 141–2, 161–3, 168, 179, 186, 203, 206, **209-10**, 216
Derbyshire Dome, 4, 18, 20, 25, 27, 31
Derwent (river), 25, 26, 31–2, **56**, 136, 142
Derwent Reservoir, 58–9
Derwent valley, 25, 166, 168
Derwent Valley Water Supply Scheme, 58–60
Devon (river), 28
discharge of rivers, 55–6
disforestation, 69
dispersion of rainfall, 50–1, 53–6
— of temperature, 45–6
dissolution of monasteries, 91
distraint, 88
Doe Lea (river), 26, 33
dolomitisation, 11
Domesday towns, 84
— population, 81, 83–4
— vills, 81–2
dormitory settlement, 203–4, 206
Dorn (river), 29
Dove (river), 25, 27, 32
drainage, artificial, 133, 145
—, natural, 21
—, reconstruction of, 24, 31
Dronfield, 88
droving, 97–8
dry valleys, 42
Duchess of Rutland, 110
Duckmanton, 141
Duke of Bedford, 128, 145
— Devonshire, 109
— Newcastle, 125
— Norfolk, 95, 125
— Portland, 125, 145
— Rutland, 131
Dukeries, 145
dumbles, 27, 59
dyeing, 88, 222

earth movements, 5–7, 9, 12
earthquakes, 9
earthworks, 76
East Haddon, 113
East Moor, 81
Edale, 25, 47
Edale Shales, 7, 25
Edge Hill, 13, 29
employment structure, 98, 134–5, 159, 163–5, **206-9**
enclosure, 91, 94, 124–7, 131–3
engineering, 165, 167, 182, **186**, 204, 207, 216, 222
epidemics, 90, 93, 99
Epwell Rift, 15, 19
Erewash (river), 26, 33

Erewash Canal, 142, 168–70
Erewash valley, 166, 169, 171, 179, 203
Ermine Street, 78–9
erosion of peat, 63
erosional benches, 32–3
evapotranspiration, 51, 56–7
extension of boundaries, 221, 227
Evenlode (river), 29, 41
Eydon, 115

facies, 4–5, 9–10, 13–15
fairs, **87-9**, 130, 132, 211
fallow, 125–6, 130–1, 133
farming-combinations, 150–2
faults, 5, 11, 15
fenland, 30, 73, 81, 96, 169
Fenny Compton Gap, 34
fescue, 65–6
firewood, 127
floods, 51, 58–9, 127
floodplains, 72–3, 127
flour mills, 84, **169-70**
fluorite, 7, 184
fodder crops, 153
fog, 48
folds, **9**, 31
Foolow, 118
foothills of Derbyshire, 27, 81
forest, *see* woodland
forest, depletion of, 64, 67, 69, 80–1, 86
Forestry Commission, 25, 67
forges, 98, 139, 141
Fosse Way, 78
foundries, 141, 166–7
framework knitting, 98, 137, **159-61**, 207
Freeland Terrace, 40
frost, 45–6
frost-free period, 45–6
frozen ground, 40
fulling, 88
functions of towns, 87–8, 214–16
furnaces, 98, **138-40**, 141, **177-83**

ganister, 7, 140
gaps, Chiltern, 30, 41
—, Pennine, 31
—, plugged, 37
Gault, 16, 69–70
geological structure, 4–6, 9, 11, 14, 16, 41–2
geology, solid, 4–17
geophysical survey, 10, 12, 41–2
gilds, 88
glacial deposits, 28–30, 36–40
glaciation, 36–40
gley, 73
Glossop, 162
gloves, 135
Glyme (river), 29
Goring Gap, 41

Gotham, 113
grain, 94, 97, **124-33, 157-8,** 169
grain-milling, 169–70
Grand Junction Canal, 167–8
Grand Union Canal, 169
Grantham Canal, 131, 143
grassing-down, 90, 126, 130, **147-50**
grassland, calcareous, 65, 69–70
grassland, siliceous, 64
grassland farming, *see* grazing
gravity anomalies, 10, 12
grazing, 84, 90–1, 96, **124-34, 145-57**
great houses, 108–110
Great Oolite, 15, 29–30
Great Ouse (river), 38, **55-6,** 60, 97, 167
grips, 26, 66
Grits, 7, 25, 26
gritstone, 25, 102–4
groundwater, 56–7, 60–1
growing season, 46–7
Gwash (river), 30

Haddenham, 118
Haddon Hall, 109
half-timbering, 104, 107
hamlets, 119–23
Hardwick Hall, 109
Hargreaves, 136
hay, 126–7, 129, 131
Heanor, 162–3
heath, 64, 67, 70, 73, 96
heather moor, 64
Hellidon, 115–17
Helmdon, 113
hemp, 131
henge monuments, 75
Hickling, 113
Higham Ferrers, 97, 163, 211
High Peak, 2, 168, 187, 205
High Peak Railway, 168
Hilton Terrace, 35–6
Hinckley, 88, 135, 159, 164, 211
hinterlands of towns, 211–15
Hipper valley, 218–19
Hiz-Ivel (river), 30
Holwell, 180–1, 183
Homo neanderthalensis, 74–5
Hope Dale, 25
Hope Forest, 64
horses, 97, 124, 126
Horsley Woodhouse, 162
hosiery, 137, 159, **163-5,** 204, 207, 222
Howden Reservoir, 58–9
Hucknall, 136, 222
Huntingdon, 84, 88, 209–10, 216
Hydraulic Limestone Series, 13

Ibstock, 113
Icknield Way, 76

Idle (river), 26–7, 141
igneous activity (igneous rocks), 4, 7, 9, 11, 69
Ilkeston, 162–3, 165, 203
incision, 25, 40, 42
Inferior Oolite, 14–15, 29–30
inselbergs, 11
intakes of land, 64
inversion of temperature, 44, 47
iron (iron manufacture, iron smelting), 78, 98, **141,** 166, 170–1, **177-84,** 218
iron ore (ironstone), 13–15, 78, 98, 140–1, 166, **177-84**
iron ore, reserves of, 183
ironworks, 166, 218
irrigation, **60-1,** 158
Ise (river), 30
Ise valley, 203
isohyets, 48–9

Jurassic rocks, **13-16,** 28–30, 69–70
Jurassic Way, 76–8

Kettering, 135, 163, 167, 180, 183
Keuper Marl, 11, 27, 67, 125, 206
Keuper Sandstone, 27–8
Kimmeridge Clay, 16, 69
Kinderscout, 25, 48, 63
King's Lynn, 97
Kirtlington, 118
knitting, 98

labour force, 98, 127, **206-9**
lace, 134–5, 137, 161, 163, 222
Ladybower Reservoir, 58–9, 204
Lake Harrison, 28, 34–5, 37
land-use, 94, 96–7, **124-34, 145-58,** 225
— in sample areas, **157-8**
landforms, 22–42
Last Glacial, 40, 74–5
Last Interglacial, 74
lath-and-plaster, 103, 107–8
lead (lead ore), 7, 78, 98, **137-40,** 184
Leafield, 118
Leafield Forest, 71
leases, 87, 133, 145
leather, 97, 134, **163-4,** 166, 203, 207, 222
Leen (river), 26–7, 33
Leen valley, 222
Leicester, 80, 84, 88, 95, 136, 159, 161, **163-5, 167-8,** 186–7, 203, 205–6, 209–10, 216, 227
Leicester Abbey, 87, 93
Leicester Forest, 95
Leicestershire orefield, 180–1
Leicestershire Wolds, 28, 187
Leighton Buzzard, 227
Leland, 94–5
Liddington, 113
lime, 129, 184

limestone, 4–5, 13–15, 25, **32,** 69–70, 81, 102–4, 106–7, 142, 184
Lincoln, 80
local climates, 47
Long Eaton, 163
London, 2, 126–8, 130, 132–3, 137, 150, 206, 225
London and Birmingham Railway, 167
London to Birmingham motorway, 225
lost villages, 90–3, 96
Loughborough, 142, 159, 167, 211
Loughborough Navigation, 168
Lower Greensand, 16, 30, 61, 76
Lower Lias, 13, 27–8, 69
Ludgershall, 118
Luton, 95, 161, 186, 203, 205–6, 209, 216, 224, **227**
Lutterworth, 88, 204, 211

Magnesian Limestone, 11, 26, 34, 66, 102
malting, 141
Manifold (river), 32
Mansfield, 44, 136, 165, 176
Mansfield Woodhouse, 119
Market Bosworth, 211
Market Harborough, 204–5, 211
market gardens, 125, 134, 150, 153, 157
markets, 97, 211
market-places, 118–19, 216, 218, 220
Marl Rock, 16–17
Marlstone, 13, 29, 105–6
Marlstone ore, 180–1
Maun (river), 26
Matlock, 184, 204
Matlock Forest, 64
mechanisation of agriculture, 158–9
— of coal-mining, 175
— of ore-working, 181, 183
— of leather industry, 164
— of textile industries, 135, 139, 160, 163
Mede (river), 26
megaliths, 75
Melbourn Rock, 17, 30
Melbourne, 150
Melton Canal, 143
Melton Mowbray, 98, 181, 183, 211
Mercia, 80
meres, 73
Mesolithic occupance, 75
metal manufactures, 204, 207, 216
Middle Lias, 13–14, 28–9, 106
Midland Railway, 167
migration, 76, **99,** 134, 145, 187, **203-4, 209,** 211, 220–1
milk, 129, 146, **150**
Millstone Grit, 7, 25, 26, 63–4, 102–3, 140
monasteries, 87, 91
Monyash, 115
moorland, 25, 26, 64, 129

morphological development, 25–42
Morton, 96–7
Morton Pinkney, 115
moss, 64
motorway, 225
Mountsorrel, 11, 105
mud walls, 108

navigation, 97–8, 105
Nene (river), 29, 38, 40, **55-7**, 79
Nene valley, 81, 167, 169–70
Neolithic occupance, 75–6
Newark, 84, 88, 95
Newnham, 118
Newport Pagnell, 84, 135
Noe (river), 31, 59
Northampton, 84, 87–9, 95, **163-4,** 186, **203,** 206, 209, 215–16, 227
Northampton Sand, 14, 105–6
Northampton Sand ore, 180–4
Northern Drift, 38, 40
Nottingham, 80, 88–9, 95, 98–9, 136, 142, 159–61, **163,** 186–7, 203–6, 209–10, 216, **219-23**
Nottingham Canal, 142, 222
Nottinghamshire Wolds, 28, 125

Oadby, 210, 227
Oakham, 143, 209–10
oakwood, 64, 66–7, 69, 91
oats, 91, 124, 131, 146, 153, 157
occupations, 98, 134–5, 159, 163–5, **206-9**
ores, *see* iron, lead, zinc
Olney, 119, 135
open fields, 124–6, 129, 131, 133, 146
opencast coal, 153, 174
orchards, 125, 150
Otmoor, 127–8, 132
Oundle, 95
Ouse (river), *see* Great Ouse
Ouse valley, 81, 169–70
outwash, 28–30, 72, 185
outworking, 164
Ouzel (river), 30, 167
overspill schemes, 225
Oxford, 44, 80, 84, 88–9, 167, 186–7, 205–6, 209–10, **215-16,** 224–5
Oxford Canal, 167–9
Oxford Clay, 15, 69

palaeoliths, 74
pantiles, 102–3, 108
parks, 94–5, 125
Peak District, 7, 75–6, 80, 85, 121
Peak Forest Canal, 142, 168
peasants, 93–6
peat, 25, 63, 73
Pennines, 4, 7, 78
Penultimate Glacial, 40, 74

Penultimate Interglacial, 40–**1**
periglacial conditions, 40
permanent grass, *see* grazing
Permo-Trias, **9-12,** 31, 81
personal service, 207
Peterborough, 215
Peterborough Abbey, 87
pig iron, 141, 179–82
pigs, 124, 127, 133
place-names, 80–1, 86, 120–3
planning, 221, 225–7
planting, 67, 70, 125, 128
Plot, 97
plough-teams, 81, 85
Podington, 113
podsols (podsolic soils), 63, 65–6, 70, 128
population, 76, 81–6, 90, 93–4, 98–9, 126, **187-206**
Portland and Purbeck Beds, 16, 30
portway, 89
potatoes, 146
pottery, 78, 97, 140
Poulter (river), 26
power stations, 176
precipitation, 48–55
prehistoric implements, 74
prices, 87, 91, 95
proglacial lakes, 36, 38
proto-Trent, 34, 36
purlieu woods, 127
pyroclastic rocks, 11, 69

Quainton, 118
quarries (quarrying), 142, 168, 181–2, 184–5, 203

Radcliffe, 115
railways, 144, 166–8, 170, 203, **211**
rain-days, 48
rainfall, 50–5
Rainworth Water, 26–7
Ramsey Abbey, 85–6
Ratby, 118
Ravensthorpe, 113
Ray (river), 30, 41
reclamation, 64, 120
red beds, 7, 104–5
reef limestones, 4–5, 15, 32
regional boundary, 1–2
rejuvenation, 31, 32, 40, 41
relief, 18–42
rendzinas, 65–6, 69–70
Renishaw, 141
rents, 85, 133, 145
re-seeding, 129
reserves of coal, 175
— of iron ore, 183
— of labour, 165
reservoirs, 28, 58–9, 60–1

Retford, 88, 95, 136, 141
Rhaetic rocks, 13, 108
ridge-and-furrow, 126, 130, 134
Ripley, 178–9
river capture, 31–2, 36–7, 41
roads, 76–8, 88–9, 144, 225–7
Rockingham, 115, 118
Rockingham Forest, 71, 85, 127, 163
Roman occupance, 76–9
rotation grass, 152, 157
rotation of crops, 125–7, 131, 133–4, 146
Rother river, 26, 33
Rother valley, **141**, 166, 168, **178**, **218-19**
Rothley Plain, 130–1
rough grazing, 150
royal forests, 85
Rufford Forest, 66–7
runoff, 51, 55–6
rural domestic architecture, 94, **101**
rural settlement, fabric of, 101–9
—, form of, 110–9
—, pattern of, 120–3
rye, 91, 127
Ryton (river), 26

St Ives, 87–8
Salcey Forest, 71, 85, 127
saltways, 89
sand and gravel, 185
sandstone, 7, 15, 26, 104
Savile family, 125
Sence (river), 28
settlement, Anglian, 79–80
—, dispersion of, 101, 123
—, pioneering, 79–80
—, rural, **101-23**
—, Scandinavian, 80
—, secondary, 86
Sewestern Lane, 76, 78
shale, 7, 65, 104, 140
sheep, 89–90, 95–6, **124-34**, **146-56**
Sheepbridge, 182–3
Sheffield, 2, 59–60, 225
Sherwood Forest, **67-8**, 80–1, 85, 95, **125**, 187, 206
Shillington, 118
silk, 136, 161, 164
silver, 7
sinkholes, 11, 31–2
slag-milling, 140
sludge deposits, 40, 70
smelting, **138-9**, **141**, 170–1, **177-84**, 203, 205
Smite (river), 27
Smite valley, 130
snow, 48, 50
snowmelt, 58
Soar (river), 27, 35, 79
Soar Navigation, 142
Soar valley, 81, 168, 203, 206

soil erosion, 66–7
— moisture, 56–7
— texture, 66–7, 70–2
soils, **62-73**, 97
sokemen, 80
Somercotes, 141–2
soughs, 136, 137
Southampton, 89
Spencer family, 109, 145
Stamford, 80, 88
Stanton, 179, 182–3
Stanton Moor, 75
Stanwick, 113
Staverton, 118
steam power, 137, 159, 163
steel, 182–3, 205
stockbreeding, 128, 130, 132
stock-farming (stock-fattening), 97–8, **124-34**, **146-58**
stocking-frame, 137
stone circles, 75
stone-slab roofing, 103, 106–7
Stonesfield Slate, 15, 103, 106
Stony Stratford, 119
straw plaiting, 161, 207
Strutt, 136
sub-Boreal Phase, 64
sub-drift contours, 35
sub-infeudation, 85
suburbs, 95, 216, 218, 221
Summertown-Radley Terrace, 40, 74–6
Summit Surface, 31
sunshine, 47–8
superficial structures, 14, 40–1
superimposed drainage, 31, 34
Sutton-in-Ashfield, 159, 165, 183
Swadlincote, 177

tallage, 88
tanneries, 163, 166–7
temperature, 43–7
temperature gradients, 44–5
tenure, 85, 93–4, 134, 145
terra rossa, 65–6
terrace housing, 176, 218, 220
terraces of rivers, 27, 30, **36**, **40**, 74, 81, 125, 185
terrain, 18–42
Tertiary drainage, 30–1, 34–5
textiles, 94, 96, **134-7**, **159-63**, 166, 207, 216, 222
Thame, 118
Thame (river), 41, 79
Thames (river), 30, 41, 79, 97, 167
thatch, 105–6, 108
thunder, 50, 58
Tideswell, 88, 121
tiles, 105, 107–8
tillage, 2, 84, 90–3, 96, **124-34**, **147-58**

timber, used in building, 95
Tingewick, 113
Tissington, 118
Totternhoe Stone, 17
Tove (river), 29–30
Towcester, 80
towns, 84, 87–8, 118–19, **209-16**
—, morphology of, 118–19, **216-33**
—, walls of, 95, 216, 220
trackways, 78
Trent (river), 27, 34, 42, 98, 141–2
Trent and Mersey Canal, 142
Trent valley, **99,** 168, 187, 203, 206
turbary, 64, 125
turnips, 125–7, 130, 146
Turnpike Trusts, 144
Twin (river), 29

underfit streams, 42
underground drainage, 32
Upland Surface, 31
Upper Dean, 113
Upper Greensand, 16
Upper Lias, 14, 29
urban climates, 47
— fields, 211–5
— functions, 87–8, 214–16

Vale of Aylesbury, 153
Vale of Belvoir, 81, 125, 131
Vale of Moreton, 14, 34
Vale of Trent, 99
verges, 115, 118
village greens, 115, 118
villages, forms of, 111–16, 118–19
—, lost, 90–3, 96
—, populations of, 93

wages, 145
war, effects of, 150, 152, 181
water balances, 57

water loss, 56–8
— supply, 58–61
waterways, 129, 131, 141–4, 166–9
Watford Gap, 34–5
Watling Street, 78, 80, 89
weaving, 88
Welland (river), 29, 38
Wellingborough, 135, 167, 180, 183
West Bridgford, 210, 221
Whaddon Chase, 71
wheat, 91, 124, 146, 153, 157–8
Whittlebury Forest, 81, 85, 127
Whittlewood, 71
Wigston, 210, 227
Windrush (river), 29
Witney, 89, 97, 134–5
Wirksworth, 140
woad-growing, 130
Wollaston, 113
Wolvercote Channel, 40, 74
Wolvercote Terrace, 40
Wolverton, 167, 186
woodland, 78, 81, 95, 127–8
woodland, clearance of, 64, 67, 69, 80–1, **86**
Woodnewton, 113
Woodstock, 135
wool, 97–8, 91, 127, 130
woollens, 97, 134–6
wool tax, 90
Wootton, 118
Worksop, 95, 136, 176
worsted, 136
Wreake (river), 28–9
Wreake valley, 81
Wychwood, 70, 81, 85, 132
Wye (river), 25, 31

Yardley Chase, 71, 81, 127
Yelden, 118

zinc (zinc ore), 7, 140

Plate 1 (*top*) THE HIGH PEAK : KINDERSCOUT AND BLEAKLOW. Nearly all the ground shown here lies above 1,650 feet, constituting part of the Summit Surface (p. 31) ; small areas exceed 2,000 feet. The plateau is formed on thick, well-cemented gritstone, in which lying snow reveals the gentle dips and some of the planes of bedding. Patchy snow in the foreground occupies hollows in eroded peat.

Plate 2 (*bottom*) UPPER VALLEY OF THE DERWENT : view near Kingsterndale village, looking upstream. Gritstone edges appear on the skyline, centre, with treeless moor behind. Timber on the valley walls is mainly ash ; a belt of trees hides the river itself. The small fields are all in pasture, or in hay, chiefly for dairying.

Plate 3 (*left*) DEEPDALE, a sharply incised valley of the upper Derwent system, now almost perennially dry. Steep upper valley walls are cut through thick, well-cemented, flat-lying beds of Carboniferous Limestone of the massif facies. Scree lies banked against the lower valley wall, centre. Vegetation includes ashwood, calcareous grassland, and hawthorn scrub. The windings of this and of nearby similar valleys correspond to the valley meanders of the cuestas in the south of the region. Compare with the dry valley shown in Plate 9.

Plate 4 (*bottom*) VALLEY OF THE ASHOP AT ABBEY BANK. Peat moor on the summits is developed on intact cappings of Millstone Grit ; valley walls, cut through the cappings and in the underlying Edale Shales, are partly clothed with planted conifers. The apparent width of the main stream is due to impounding by Howden Dam (see Fig. 27). Small lateral streams descend the main valley walls in sharply cut lateral valleys known locally as cloughs ; see right and left centre distance, and the head of a clough in the left foreground.

Plate 5 (*right*) PART OF CHARNWOOD FOREST. Charnian rocks, considerably dissected beneath the Trias, are being revealed by stripping. Mixed farmland in the sub-rectangular fields of parliamentary enclosure, underlain by Trias or by boulder-clay of Triassic provenance, gives way at the margins of the low hills to blocks of planted timber, or to the rough grazing which mantles slopes leading down from the outcrops. Trackways in the rough grazing, made by walkers, relate to the use of the Forest as resort area.

Plate 6 (*bottom*) CHANNEL OF THE LOWER TRENT, looking downstream. Very faint levees which occur on either bank are largely artificial: the Trent is not a great levee-builder, and this reach has moreover been subject to much regularisation over the years. The gravel in the left foreground relates to scour through a bridge, but the rubble lining farther along the left bank is defensive (see Plate 10 for the influence on flooding of alterations in the channel). Pasture on the floodplain is replaced by arable farther out, where low terraces rise.

Plate 7 (*left*) SCARP OF THE MIDDLE LIAS near Long Clawson, Leicestershire ; view towards the northeast, beds dipping gently towards the right of the view. Deciduous wood outlines the upper scarp, cut in Marlstone ; tabular summits above are widely in arable. Lower slopes cut across Middle Lias silts, and vale country developed on Lower Lias and glacial drift, are in mixed farmland, with ridge-and-furrow in the left foreground indicating old-established permanent pasture.

Plate 8 (*bottom*) SCARP OF THE CHILTERNS : view from Sharpenhoe Clapper, Bedfordshire, looking northeast. The scarp-face is in calcareous grassland, scrub, and beechwood, parts of it preserved by the National Trust. A subdued rise in the centre of the view is Pulloxhill, a low watershed in the Gault, while the Greensand cuesta near Ampthill forms the skyline. Contrast with this unbroken piece of Chalk scarp the re-entrants in Plate 9 and the sub-scarps in Plate 48.

Plate 9 (*top*) THE PEGSDON DRY VALLEYS. This group of dry valleys cuts into the Chiltern scarp. Springs are known to have flowed here, at least as late as the Atlantic Phase of postglacial time. Apparent flatness in cross-section of floor is due chiefly to ploughing. Plateau benches are cut in Middle Chalk.

Plate 10 (*bottom*) VALLEY OF THE MIDDLE TRENT, IN TIME OF FLOOD. Incidence of flooding on this reach is affected by local improvements to the main channel (cf. Plate 6), but also by drainage works in upstream catchments (see pp. 58–9). Scalloped edge of floodplain marks the curves of former large meanders.

Plate 11 (*top*) OLNEY, BUCKINGHAMSHIRE, AND THE GREAT OUSE RIVER. The mill exemplifies the former significance of modest resources of water-power : it is now, however, powered by electricity. Clay-based slopes descending toward the river sustain permanent grass, here grazed by beefstock.

Plate 12 (*bottom*) LADYBOWER RESERVOIR (cf. Fig. 27). Skyline runs across fairly intact Millstone Grit ; advanced dissection in the middle distance leaves grit cappings on hills of Edale Shales. The main arm of the reservoir extends up the Derwent valley, centre right ; the Ashop valley enters from the left of the view. Woodland is remnantal or improved hardwood timber, or else planted conifers. Farmland is almost exclusively pasture.

Plate 13 (*top*) BOROUGH HILL, Leicestershire : a defended hilltop site of unproven date. Fosse-and-vallum layout, roughly rectangular plan, and defended gateway at the far side are visible either in the form of the ground or in crop-markings. Land-use includes partly regenerating, or coppiced, deciduous woodland, and old-established permanent pasture where ridge-and-furrow is preserved (cf. Pl. 17). There has been some recent ploughing, however (left distance, centre-right distance).

Plate 14 (*right*) FOSSE WAY near High Cross, Leicestershire ; view towards the northeast. In this general area the course of the trunk Roman road is marked by metalled roads, dirt roads, or even merely by footpaths : through traffic at the present day is directed mainly across the line of Fosse Way. Nevertheless the ancient line is well preserved in some form or other, despite numerous displacements in detail, such as those which appear in the photograph as offsetting.

Plate 15 (*top*) BUCKWORTH, HUNTINGDONSHIRE : A DEPOPULATED LAY SITE (cf. Pl. 16 and Fig. 34). The church (centre) is disproportionately large for the present village, which has been reduced by deliberate depeopling. Depressions alongside the cross-connecting road show sites of former dwellings and former ways.

Plate 16 (*bottom*) WARDEN ABBEY, BEDFORDSHIRE : A DESPOILED ECCLESIASTICAL SITE. Isolated portions of the Abbey remain standing, or are incorporated in later building ; much of the original fabric has gone to build the mansion and the farm. Sites of the Abbey fishponds appear in the left centre-foreground. As in the case of Welbeck and Woburn Abbeys, this site retains its ecclesiastical name.

Plate 17 (*top*) RIDGE-AND-FURROW, brought into strong relief by oblique air photography under a low sun. Hedgerows of parliamentary enclosure coincide only in part with lines of ridges or with breaks in the ridge-and-furrow systems. Variations in the width of ridges appear to left of centre. For the most part this piece of country is in old-established permanent pasture, but some blocks of ridges have been ploughed down.

Plate 18 (*right*) ALCONBURY, HUNTINGDONSHIRE. A mainly linear village, strung out alongside a small lateral of the Great Ouse ; some compaction of form occurs at the far (northwest) end, near the church. Note the incomplete building-up of the frontage on the main street. An extension of the village lies in the centre distance, left. The trunk road near by is part of the improved Great North Road system. The settlement in the right distance is Alconbury Weston.

Plate 19 (*left*) RURAL HOUSING AT BAKEWELL, DERBYSHIRE. The house walls are of Carboniferous Limestone ; the coping of the garden walls is of Millstone Grit, which, to some extent, can be shaped. Note also stone slabs used in gateway and to edge the flower-border. Contrast the thin thatch of one house with the thatch in Plates 22, 25, and 28. Other roofs are of flat tile. The small-paned, white-painted casements are typical of the locality.

Plate 20 (*bottom*) BRICK AND PANTILE WORK AT LOUND, NOTTINGHAMSHIRE. Lound is deep within the area of predominant brick-and-pantile building in the northeast of the region (see Fig. 35). Farmhouses occur within the village, massed against cottages in the main street, which runs across the end of the white-faced house on the right, and past the wide-doored barn. Minor walling is also of brick, with coping of curved tiles. Even in this homogenous district, however, corrugated iron roofs appear on barns.

Plate 21 (*right*) STONE-WORK WITH STONE-SLAB ROOFING at Wansford, where Ermine Street crosses the Nene. Walls are built of ashlar from the Great Oolite, roofs are of Collyweston Slate (cf. Fig. 35). As is typical of the principal districts of stone building, chimneys are of faced stone. Contrast the form of dormer windows here with the forms in Plates 22, 25, and 28. For slab in the Stonesfield Slate belt, see Plate 23.

Plate 22 (*above*) THATCH AND ASHLAR AT SHARNBROOK, BEDFORDSHIRE. This portion of Sharnbrook is an early extension beyond the centre of the village. Roofs exhibit the high pitch characteristic of thatch in this part of the region ; contrast Plates 19, 24, 26. Dormer windows are exposed by means of trimming-back the thatch. Where eaves descend below floor-level of the upper storey, upstairs rooms are lit by windows at floor-level, and considerably reduced in size by the sloping ceilings. Here again walls are of Great Oolite, but windows are enclosed by worked freestone blocks of Inferior Oolite.

Plate 23 (*left*) STONEWORK WITH STONE-SLAB ROOFING at Filkins, Oxfordshire, in the main Cotswold belt of stone building (cf. Fig. 35, and compare also Pl. 21). The Stonesfield Slate outcrop has produced slabs of considerable size, numbers of which are used at Filkins and in neighbouring villages for minor walling (foreground); this is unusual for the East Midland region. Some slabs have even been used as tombstones ; but they are not satisfactory for this purpose, because they lose their inscriptions under weathering. Nor are they wholly satisfactory as flooring material, for which the well-bedded and evenly-splitting Rhaetic limestone is better.

Plate 24 (top) HOUSES AT RAMSEY, Huntingdonshire. These single-storeyed dwellings, of yellow brick with thatched roofs of moderate pitch, and with tall brick chimneys and shuttered windows, represent an antique and apparently an indigenous style of construction. Access to attics is provided by hatches in the gable ends.

Plate 25 (right) THATCH AND COB AT EVERTON, Bedfordshire. Chalk Marl and sludge deposits from the Chalk supplied cob in parts of the southeast, while minor outcrops of Upper Jurassic rocks were used elsewhere. The houses are probably walled with rammed Chalk Marl. Thatch is moderately ornate, with the ridge-ends finished and raised, and with binders fastened along all edges.

Plate 26 (bottom) COTTAGES AT WINWICK, Northamptonshire. Located in a boundary zone of building styles, these decrepit structures include thatch, brick, and stone. The nearer house was perhaps once stone-built, but its rotting fabric has been much repaired with brick. These houses, like those in Plates 21 and 22, open directly on to the roadway.

Plate 27 (*top*) BIRDLEYS FARM, STAGSDEN, north Bedfordshire. Walls, including most barn walls, are of stone, but roofing material varies from flat tile on the farmhouse and its extension to pantile on a small cottage and on barns (cf. p. 108).

Plate 28 (*bottom*) CADDINGTON, BEDFORDSHIRE, showing part of the green in the centre of the village. Walls are principally of stone, but include some plasterwork ; houses are tiled or thatched ; barns are tiled. The central green is traversed by the through road ; it carries the disused village pump, and the wooden bench which, here as in many other villages, constitutes the single outdoor feature of amenity.

Plate 29 (*top*) HADDON HALL, near Bakewell, Derbyshire. Parts of the stout towers on the right date from the twelfth century, while the main face on the left of this view belongs to the sixteenth. Mullioned windows, castellated parapet, and formal gardens with stone balustrade are all highly effective of their kind.

Plate 30 (*bottom*) AYNHO PARK, Northamptonshire, exemplifying the architectural rigour of the late eighteenth century and the beginning of the nineteenth. Walls are of oolitic limestone, roofs of Stonesfield Slate. Frontage, wings, court, and gateway combine in a single harmonious vista, while a second vista opens from the park side. From within the house the orangery appears to be part of the interior. The great house adjoins the village churchyard (left).

Plate 31 (*top*) BLENHEIM PALACE, Oxfordshire. A major production of Sir John Vanbrugh. Mature parkland trees help to indicate the great scale of the Palace and of the adjoining formal gardens. In the extreme right foreground appears part of one of the ornamental lakes formed by impounding of the river Glyme.

Plate 32 (*bottom*) BELVOIR CASTLE, Leicestershire. An early result of nineteenth-century romanticism. Early medieval and Tudor architecture combine to inspire a structure which, if it were less bulky, might have been classed with Scottish baronial. Neither in close view, nor in distant perspective from the Vale of Belvoir, however, is it possible to dismiss the qualities of the Castle out of hand. Whatever else, it forms an imposing edifice.

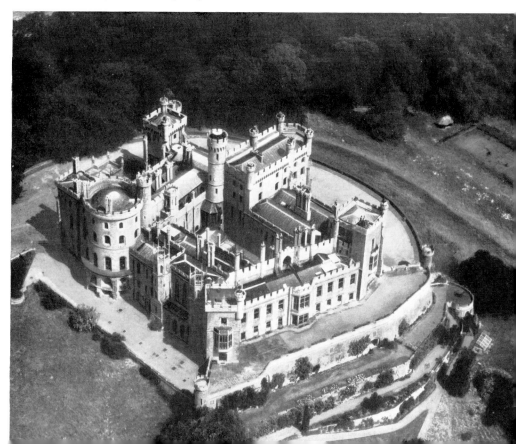

Plate 33 (*top*) FARMLAND IN THE WREAKE VALLEY : panorama near Burrough on the Hill, Leicestershire, looking northeast. The steep slope of pasturage in the centre foreground is developed across the Middle Lias, but most of the expanse shown is underlain by soils developed on Lower Lias or on boulder-clay. By long tradition this is grazing country, but light tones reveal a sizable fraction of arable, which increased in extent in this part of the region during and after the Second World War.

Plate 34 (*bottom*) MARKET GARDENS NEAR MELBOURNE, Derbyshire. The outskirts of Melbourne appear in the left distance. Treeless fences and hedgerows replicate the aspect of the more extensive market-garden belt of Bedfordshire and contrast with the tree-scattered landscape in Plate 33.

Plate 35 (*top*) COMBINE HARVESTER reaping wheat, near Newnham, Northamptonshire. Stout hedgerows with elm and ash, which characterise this part of the region, relate to the former dominance of stock-farming and especially to the grazing of beefstock. Most of the fields visible are however under the plough, with their 8-foot gateways widened to admit farm machinery.

Plate 36 (*bottom*) SPRAY IRRIGATION OF SUGAR-BEET, near Cuckney, Nottinghamshire, on the Bunter Sandstone belt. The woodland at the rear belongs to Welbeck Park. Sugar-beet is extensively planted on the arable of this belt, where coarse soils warm rapidly, but where in many situations they require considerable fertilising and abundant irrigation. Rotary sprinklers, of the type shown, are widely used throughout the valley of the lower Trent.

Plate 37 (*top*) OLLERTON COLLIERY, Nottinghamshire. This large modern colliery lies about 12 miles east of the eastward limit of exposed Coal Measures, working seams below sea level. Barley in the foreground exemplifies grain growing in the Bunter Sandstone belt.

Plate 38 (*bottom*) OPENCAST IRONSTONE WORKING near Kirby Hall, Northamptonshire. These are the extremities of the large-scale ridges and furrows of opencast working, where overburden is stripped from above the working face (line tone in the photograph) and dumped on the site already worked over. The working face itself, with rail tracks running parallel, is in the left foreground. Since the photograph was taken, working has been further extended and the Hall demolished.

Plate 39 LIMESTONE QUARRIES IN THE PEAK DISTRICT. This complex of quarries near Buxton, on the limestone plateau of Derbyshire, is rail-served but depends increasingly on road transport. Increasingly specialised demands from consumers lead to increasing specialisation in the working of the purer limestones, here obtained from beds of the massif facies where shale partings are very thin or absent altogether. Vegetated dumps of spoil, left of centre, indicate lengthy operation. The surrounding gentle slopes of the plateau are in grass throughout ; field boundaries consist in a net of limestone walls. Some of the wooded rises in the centre distance are based on igneous outcrops.

Plate 40 (*top*) THAME, OXFORDSHIRE : a small market town, with cigar-shaped axial market-place partly built over. Back lane on left of view is incorporated in outgoing road, beside which stands recent semi-detached housing.

Plate 41 (*bottom*) HUNTINGDON IN THE EARLY SEVENTEENTH CENTURY : Speed's plan of 1610. Very little building appears, except fronting the axial street and the central square. Ermine Street enters from the southeast and leaves to the northwest ; the road marked G, Germans Street, leads to Ramsey and Ely, while D, St Georges, branches outside the town to Kettering and Bedford. Huntingdon grew little beyond the size mapped here until very recent years, and the extent recorded by Speed is easily recognisable today by the closeness of its buildings.

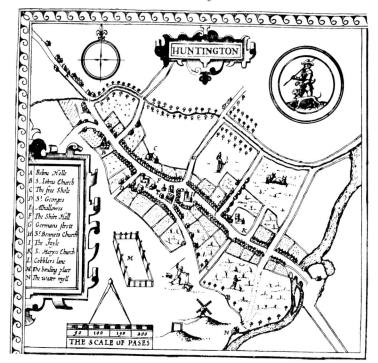

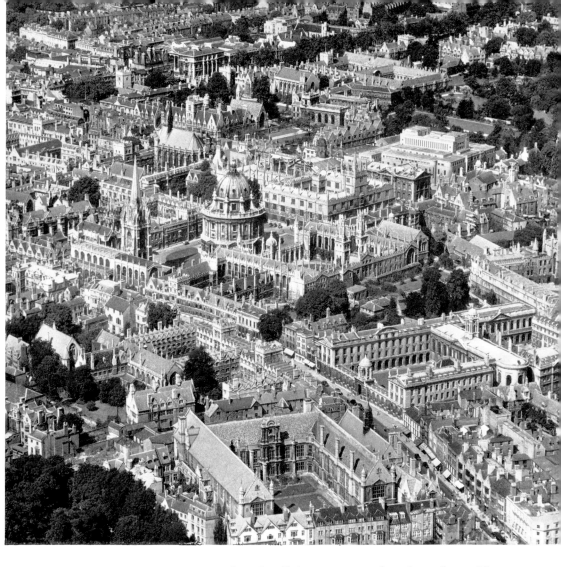

Plate 42   PART OF CENTRAL OXFORD : the main collegiate quarter, seen from the southeast.   All this portion of the town produces a highly turreted effect in views from a height.   The large dome, left of centre, is that of Radcliffe Library.   High Street runs across the view from bottom right to left middle distance.   Quadrangular layout is well shown in places, for instance by Queen's College, which fronts on the far side of the High Street in the foreground and possesses a cupola over its main entrance.   All Souls College is on the near side of the Radcliffe, with the Bodleian Library immediately behind and almost in the centre of the view.   The oblique belt of trees in the background marks St Giles's Street.

Plate 43 (*top*) URBAN RENEWAL AT BEDFORD. Multiple-storey blocks of flats, a shopping plaza, a multi-floored car park, and a new bus station replace run-down terraced housing. Note the location of the developed site apart from the through road to the left. Shops and associated services in this new development are additional to those provided by the main shopping-centre at Bedford, which continues in full operation. A completely new neighbourhood is being produced, on a scale which would be difficult in the town centre itself.

Plate 44 (*right*) PART OF CENTRAL NOTTINGHAM : view towards the north. The railway tunnels under the extreme western limit of the enclosed Anglo-Saxon site; much of the foreground lies in this, or in the former Norman town. The main concentration of lace factories occurs to right of centre. Large covered buildings beyond the Anglo-Saxon enclosure, and right of the station, belong to the market.

Plate 47 (*top*) STAYTHORPE POWER STATION on the lower Trent. Coal is delivered by rail (see branch track at left rear of station). Because a station of this size uses large quantities of water, it poses considerable problems of design and operation, e.g. of preventing heated water from backing upstream.

Plate 48 (*bottom*) THE LONDON TO BIRMINGHAM MOTORWAY, just beneath the Chiltern scarp at Sundon. The Chilterns form the high ground in the distance and on the left. The broad bench at an intermediate level, also on the left, is sustained by resistant beds within the Chalk (see pp. 16–17, 30, and contrast Pl. 8). The cement works in the middle distance uses Chalk and Chalky sludge.